Advances in Physical Organic Chemistry

Advances in Physical Organic Chemistry

Volume 36

Edited by

T. T. TIDWELL

Department of Chemistry
University of Toronto
Toronto
Ontario M5S 3H6, Canada

J. P. RICHARD

Department of Chemistry
University of Buffalo, SUNY
Buffalo NY 14260-3000, USA

ACADEMIC PRESS
A Division of Harcourt, Inc.

San Diego San Francisco New York
Boston London Sydney Tokyo

Academic Press
A Division of Harcourt Inc.
Harcourt Place, 32 Jamestown Road, London NW1 7BY, UK
http://www.academicpress.com

Academic Press
A Division of Harcourt Inc.
525 B Street, Suite 1900, San Diego, California 92101-4495, USA
http://www.academicpress.com

ISBN 0-12-033536-0

A catalogue record for this book is available from the British Library

This serial is covered by the *Science Citation Index*.

Typeset by Keyset Composition, Colchester, Essex
Printed and bound in Great Britain by
MPG Books Ltd, Bodmin, Cornwall

01 02 03 04 05 06 MP 9 8 7 6 5 4 3 2 1

Contents

Editor's preface

This year there is a new co-editor of the series, Professor John Richard of the State University of New York at Buffalo. With two editors, there is a wider range of expertise available, thus providing more opportunity for soliciting manuscripts that cover the full breadth of topics included within the field of Physical Organic Chemistry. It is planned to expand the Board of Editors as well, as these individuals help to ensure that the subject matter covered includes a wide range of topics. We intend to continue to solicit contributors not only from around the world, but from the increasingly diversified group of laboratories at which modern aspects of the subject are pursued.

In 2001 the new millennium officially begins, and the current volume includes a retrospective of one of the major topics in Physical Organic Chemistry in the 20th Century, namely free radical reactivity. There is a fascinating report by the late Lennart Eberson, who was a valued member of the Board of Editors, concerning the reasons that the many nominations of Moses Gomberg for the Nobel Prize in Chemistry were not successful. In 1900 Gomberg made the bold claim that he had prepared a stable free radical, namely triphenylmethyl, and this proposal was shown, after great discussion, to be correct, and sparked an outpouring of chemical creativity that continues unabated into the 21st Century. Eberson reveals why the Nobel Prize Committee on Chemistry missed the opportunity to recognize Gomberg's great insight, through a combination of a lack of appreciation on the part of the Committee, and unfortunate timing. This essay was Eberson's last major contribution, and was sent to the Editor shortly before his untimely death. We wish to acknowledge the assistance of Anne Wiktorsson at the Center for History of Science, The Royal Academy of Sciences, Stockholm, in the editing of this manuscript. The Nobel prizes exert a profound influence on the conduct of science, and it is helpful for the scientific community to be aware of how these are decided. Eberson was uniquely suited for this task, as he was Chair of the Nobel Committee on Chemistry, a free radical chemist himself who could easily read the Nobel archives in his native Swedish, and he possessed a lucid style of writing.

Accompanying this article, Tidwell has contributed a summary of the development of free radical chemistry from the work of Gomberg through the year 2000. Free radicals have been featured in *Advances in Physical Organic Chemistry* since Volume 1, and all of the chapters in the current volume deal with this topic to some degree.

The other chapters in Volume 36 include a report on the kinetics and mechanism of reductive bond dissociations, by Maran, Wayner, and

Workentin. This complements other chapters in Volume 35 that dealt with electron transfer processes, and also highlights the work of Eberson.

The two other Chapters deal with reactive intermediates, specifically N-arylnitrenium ions by Novak and Rajagopal, and phenylnitrenes by Gritsan and Platz. These species have long been known, and nitrenium ions and arylnitrenes are interconvertible by proton transfer. These nitrogen analogs of the more familiar carbocations and carbenes share the property of existing as singlets or triplets, but have not received the attention of their carbon-centered cousins. Particularly in the case of arylnitrenes, their study is a challenging problem, while arylnitrenium ions may be formed under surprisingly mild conditions. With the realization that nitrenium ions are active carcinogens, and that nitrenium ions can form from nitrenes, these species are receiving increasing attention. Because of the different spin states of nitrenes and the rapidity of their interconversion, it is only with the availability of very fast spectroscopic techniques that these species may be studied in detail. These chapters, by leading practitioners in the areas, provide an up-to-date summary of the investigations of these species.

The editors will continue to strive to highlight important areas of the field in a timely fashion at reasonable cost. Suggestions for further topics for coverage are always welcome.

J. P. Richard, T. T. Tidwell

Contributors to Volume 36

Lennart Eberson Department of Chemistry, Lund University, Lund, Sweden

Nina Gritsan Institute of Chemical Kinetics and Combustion, 630090, Novosibirsk, Russia

Flavio Maran Dipartimento di Chimica Fisica, Universita di Padova, via Loredan 2, 35131, Padova, Italy

Michael Novak Department of Chemistry and Biochemistry, Miami University, Oxford, Ohio 45056, USA

Matthew S. Platz Department of Chemistry, Newman & Wolfrom Lab. of Chemistry, Ohio State University, 100 West 18th Avenue, Columbus, Ohio 43210 1173, USA

Sridharan Rajagopal Department of Chemistry and Biochemistry, Miami University, Oxford, Ohio 45056, USA

Thomas Tidwell Department of Chemistry, University of Toronto, Ontario, M5S 3H6, Canada

Daniel D.M. Wayner Molecular Interfaces Program, Steacie Institute for Molecular Sciences, National Research Council, Ottawa, Ontario, K1A 0R6, Canada

Mark S. Workentin Department of Chemistry, The University of Western Ontario, London, Ontario, N6A 5B7

The Gomberg Century: Free Radicals 1900–2000

Thomas T. Tidwell

Department of Chemistry, University of Toronto, Toronto, Ontario, Canada

1

ADVANCES IN PHYSICAL ORGANIC CHEMISTRY
VOLUME 36 ISBN 0-12-033536-0

1 Introduction

MOSES GOMBERG AND THE TRIPHENYLMETHYL RADICAL

The proposal[1] by Moses Gomberg in 1900 of the formation of the stable and persistent free radical triphenylmethyl was a major landmark that set the stage for the rapid development of free radical chemistry in the 20th Century. Prior to Gomberg's proposal, the theory of free radicals had risen to prominence and then fallen into disrepute, but his work immediately attracted the attention of the world chemical community, and led to the ultimate acceptance of this once controversial concept.

Gomberg treated triphenylmethyl chloride with silver or zinc metal and obtained a colored solution which reacted with oxygen to yield a peroxide.[1] The species in solution was confidently identified by Gomberg as the triphenylmethyl radical **1**, and he published his discovery in both German and English, which ensured its wide exposure to chemists worldwide. Upon removal of the solvent, a solid dimer was formed, for which the symmetrical structure **2** and the unsymmetrical structure **3** were given serious consideration over the next decade, while the peroxide was assigned as **4**. Wilhelm Schlenk and co-workers in 1910 obtained tris(4-biphenylyl)methyl (**5**) as a deeply colored solid which was almost completely dissociated in solution, and thus removed all doubt as to the existence of **1**.[2] As recounted by McBride,[3] the wrong structure for the dimer, namely the head-to-head structure **2**, became accepted for half a century, before this was corrected to the unsymmetrical structure **3** based on spectroscopic data.[4] Techniques were widely available that would have permitted correction of this structure well before 1967.

$$Ph_3CCl \xrightarrow[-AgCl]{Ag} Ph_3C \bullet \xrightarrow{O_2} Ph_3COOCPh_3 \tag{1}$$

1   **4**

Ph_3CCPh_3

2   **3** 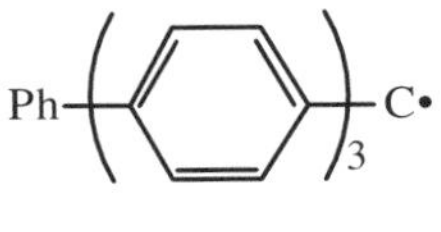   **5**

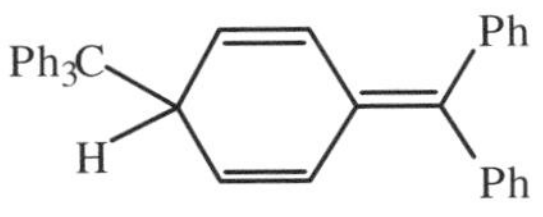

OVERVIEW OF FREE RADICALS IN THE 20TH CENTURY

On the occasion of the centennial of Gomberg's discovery it is appropriate to look back over the subsequent development of the field, highlighting some of the advances that have been made. Such a survey must of necessity be cursory, as a comprehensive review would occupy many volumes. The goal of this essay is to note the more prominent original contributions, and for some examples to cite recent advances of these themes. It is also of interest to note missed opportunities, or errant interpretations. This is not to belittle the pioneers involved, but to illustrate that science is a human activity, and progress is based on individual decisions that may favor certain areas rather than others. The discussion is roughly chronological, and is intended to show the evolution of new ideas. Much has been excluded, either by design or oversight, and the author is responsible if important topics or contributors have been unfairly neglected.

The history of the radical concept prior to Gomberg in the 19th Century has been described by Ihde,[5,6] who recounted how the existence of free radicals had gained strong support from the work of Kolbe[7] in 1849, who reported the electrolytic decarboxylation of carboxylic acids which apparently gave free radicals such as $CH_3 \cdot$. However, the development of valence theory shortly thereafter, particularly the concept of the tetravalency of carbon, led to the recognition that these "radicals" were dimers, and caused the general abandonment of free radicals as organic intermediates. However, in 1891 Walker and Crum Brown reintroduced the idea of electrolysis as involving radicals (equation 2),[8] and Nef in 1897[9] formulated a theory of organic reactivity with a major role for divalent carbon. Thus there were premonitions of the revival of the free radical concept.

$$RCO_2H \xrightarrow{-e^-, -H^+} RCO_2\cdot \xrightarrow{-CO_2} R\cdot \longrightarrow RR \qquad (2)$$

The history of free radicals in the 20th Century may be conveniently divided into thirds, with the dividing points being the General Discussion of the Faraday Society held at the University of Cambridge from 28–30 September, 1933, and published in 1934,[10] and the 1966 International Free Radical Conference in Ann Arbor, Michigan.[11] At the close of the century, from 25–29 June, 2000, there was another conference in Ann Arbor marking the Centennial of Gomberg's original discovery, which was designated as an International Chemical Landmark.[12] Brief summaaries of this development have appeared.[13,14]

The Cambridge meeting had a distinctly physical orientation, and those in attendance included Gomberg and many pioneers of the subject and other prominent figures, including F. Paneth, K. Ziegler, M. Polanyi, E. Rabinowitch, C.P. Snow, E. Hückel, and C.K. Ingold. Besides the discovery of triphenylmethyl, other developments at that time included the elucidation of the free radical chain reaction of H_2 with Br_2, the demonstration of nitrogen, oxygen, and sulfur-centered organic radicals, the discovery of ketyl and nitroxyl radicals, the elucidation of free radical mechanisms for thermal and photochemical reactions of the halogens, the generation of free alkyl radicals by Paneth, free radical polymerization, and the formation of free radicals from azoalkane thermolysis and ketone photolysis. Later, Faraday Discussions on free radicals were held in London, in 1947,[15] on "The Labile Molecule", and then in Toronto in 1952.[16] The latter meeting was notable for the participation of five future Nobel laureates (R.G.W. Norrish, G. Porter, J. Polanyi, Linus Pauling, and Gerhard Herzberg).

At the Conference on Free Radicals in Ann Arbor in 1966, plenary lecturers included C. Walling, P.D. Bartlett, K.U. Ingold, S. Hunig, and Glen Russell.[12] Further advances up to this time included a thorough understanding of the reactivity of many free radical initiators, the examination of phenyl radicals and radical aromatic substitution, the study of free radical halogenation of alkanes which revealed the loss of stereochemistry of alkyl radicals, the widespread utilization of free radical polymerization, and the elucidation of polar effects in radical reactions. The epochal monograph on free radicals by Walling had appeared in 1957,[17] and while this was by no means the first book on free radicals it was the most influential. In the final third of the Century, advances have emphasized the utilization of ESR spectroscopy and CIDNP, spin trapping and spin labeling, further examination of the cage effect, rate measurements of free radical reactions including cyclizations and ring openings, the elucidation of the role of free radicals in biological systems, and the systematic utilization of radicals in organic synthesis.

2   Free radicals: The first generation

DELOCALIZED PERSISTENT RADICALS

Following Gomberg's discovery, a variety of related persistent radicals were prepared. Schlenk and Hermann Mark reported the pentaphenylethyl radical **6**,[18] and Karl Ziegler and co-workers prepared the tetraphenylallyl radical (**7**)[19] and the pentaphenylcyclopentadienyl radical (**8**).[20] Ziegler did extensive work on free radicals and also in the 1920s began work on organometallic compounds, which led to his discovery of organoaluminum catalysts for ethylene polymerization, for which he won the Nobel Prize in Chemistry in 1963. However, even in 1931 the idea of stable radicals met some resistance, as Koelsch prepared and submitted for publication a report of the long-lived radical **9**, but the complete unreactivity of the radical towards oxygen seemed improbable, and the manuscript was rejected. In 1957, ESR spectroscopy of the same sample confirmed the identification, and the original manuscript was resubmitted and published.[21] The radical **10** was reported by Löwenbein: it reversibly forms a dimer, and reacts with oxygen to give the peroxide.[22] Ballester also prepared the perchlorotriphenylmethyl radical **10a**, which is almost completely inert.[23]

$Ph_3C\overset{\bullet}{C}Ph_2$

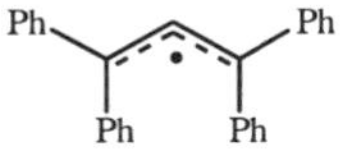

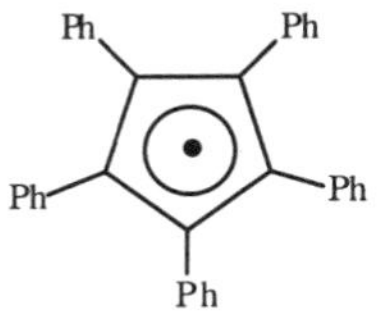

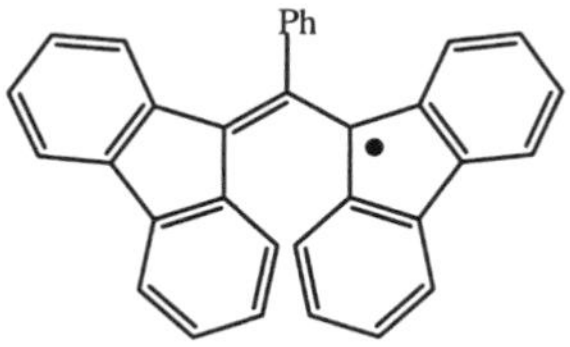

6

7

8

9

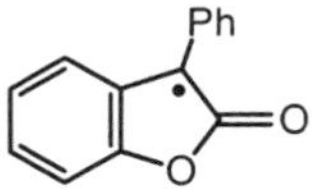

10 $(C_6Cl_5)_3C\cdot$

10a

DIRADICALS

Even before the report of the stable triphenylmethyl radical, Tanatar discovered in 1896 the cyclopropane to propene rearrangement (equation 3),[24] which eventually led to the recognition of diradicals and radical rearrangements in aliphatic systems. Chambers and Kistiakowsky[25] measured the kinetics of this reaction in 1934, and suggested the diradical pathway (equation 3) that is now generally accepted. The study of this reaction is still being pursued, and the suggestion has been made that a concerted path is almost competitive with the diradical route.[26,27] The stable diradical **11** analogous to triphenylmethyl was reported by Schlenk in 1915 (Schlenk diradical),[28] and the analogous trisradical by Leo in 1937.[29] This marked the beginning of the study of "high-spin" molecules, and these are gaining increasing attention.[30]

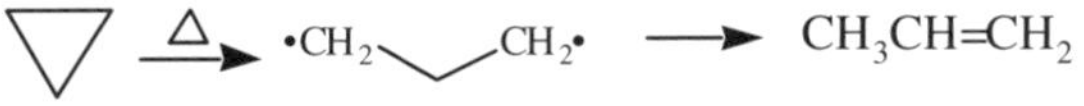

$$ \triangle \quad \overset{\Delta}{\longrightarrow} \quad \cdot CH_2 \diagdown CH_2\cdot \quad \longrightarrow \quad CH_3CH{=}CH_2 \qquad (3) $$

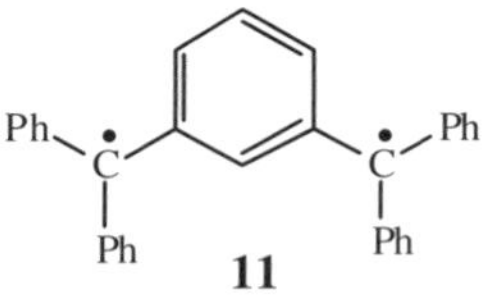

11

FREE RADICAL REARRANGEMENTS

Wieland observed, in 1911, that the Gomberg peroxide **4** rearranged upon heating to the pinacol ether **14** and attributed this to initial dissociation forming an intermediate alkoxy radical **12**. This rearranged forming the radical **13** (equation 4), which dimerized forming **14** (equation 5).[31] The kinetics of this rearrangement were later measured by Schuster et al.[32] In 1944 Urry and Kharasch reported the analogous rearrangement of phenyl to carbon, the neophyl rearrangement (equation 6),[33] and phenyl migration in $PhCOCH_2 \cdot$ was discovered by McBay *et al.*[34,35]

$$\underset{4}{\underset{|}{\overset{Ph}{\underset{|}{\overset{|}{PhC}}}}} O{-}O{-}\underset{|}{\overset{Ph}{\underset{|}{\overset{|}{CPh}}}} \longrightarrow \underset{12}{\underset{|}{\overset{Ph}{\underset{|}{\overset{|}{PhC}{-}O\cdot}}}} \longrightarrow \underset{13}{Ph{-}\overset{\cdot}{C}\underset{Ph}{\overset{OPh}{\diagdown}}} \quad (4)$$

$$13 \longrightarrow \underset{14}{\underset{Ph\ \ Ph}{\overset{PhO\ \ OPh}{\underset{|\ \ \ |}{\overset{|\ \ \ |}{PhC{-}CPh}}}}} \quad (5)$$

$$Ph_3CCH_2Br \xrightarrow{\ Mg\ } Ph_3C\overset{\cdot}{C}H_2 \longrightarrow Ph_2\overset{\cdot}{C}CH_2Ph \quad (6)$$

NITROGEN-CENTERED RADICALS.

The reversible dissociation of colorless tetraphenylhydrazine into the green diphenylaminyl (**15**) at $100°C$ was discovered by Wieland in 1911 (equation 7), and extended the free radical concept to nitrogen.[36-38] These radicals are trapped by nitric oxide to give diphenylnitrosoamine (**16**), and the rate of this reaction was used to show the rate of dissociation of the hydrazine.[39]

$$Ph_2NNPh_2 \rightleftharpoons \underset{15}{2Ph_2N\cdot} \xrightarrow{\ NO\ } \underset{16}{Ph_2NN{=}O} \quad (7)$$

NITROXYL RADICALS

Nitric oxide, NO, may be represented as either a nitrogen- or oxygen-centered radical, as can aminoxyl, H_2NO. Arylaminoxyls $Ar_2NO\cdot$ were reported by Wieland *et al.*,[40-42] and others of these have been prepared. The electronic structure as represented by **17** was proposed by Banfield and Kenyon in 1926.[43] Aminoxyls substituted with aliphatic groups bearing alpha hydrogens are subject to disproportionation and are often not isolable. In 1959, preparation of tetramethylpiperidinyloxy (TEMPO, **18**) was reported as a material that is quite stable, but this was initially in a provincial journal that was little noticed.[44,45] Then in 1961 the preparation of di-*tert*-butylnitroxyl **19** appeared,[46] and aliphatic aminoxyls have been widely used ever since. Important physiological roles of NO were found later, and discoveries in this area were recognized by the award of the 1998 Nobel Prize in Medicine.

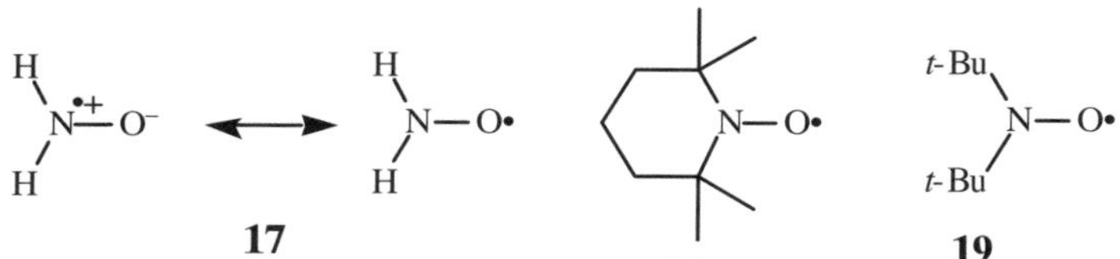

17   **18**   **19**

Because nitroxyl radicals do not react with most organic functional groups, they have found wide application as radical traps, and in "living" free radical polymerizations. Nitroxyl radicals are also used as spin labels, and are formed in spin trapping by nitroso compounds and nitrones (*vide infra*).

ARYLOXYL RADICALS

The oxidation of phenols forming aryloxyl radicals was first recognized by Pummerer and Frankfurter in 1914,[47] who reacted 2,2′-dihydroxy-1,1′-binaphthyl with ferricyanide, and isolated dimers and trimers of the radical **20** (equation 8), which was later observed by ESR.[48] Many further examples were studied by Goldschmidt, Müller, and others,[49–51] and an X-ray crystal structure confirmed dimer formation with C—O bonding at the 4-position for 3-bromo-2,4,6-triphenylphenoxyl.[51]

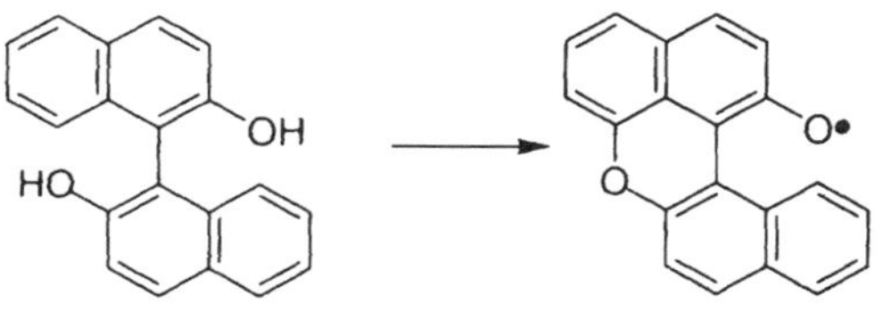

(8)

20

SULFUR-CENTERED RADICALS

The effect of air and the acceleration by light of the addition of PhSH to styrene was observed in 1928,[52] and in 1934 the formation of the PhS· radical from dissociation of PhSSPh (equation 9) and from reactions of PhSH was proposed.[53,54] The use of peroxides to catalyze the reaction was reported by Jones and Reid in 1938,[55] and in the same year the radical chain mechanism for this process was proposed (equation 10).[56]

$$PhSSPh \rightleftharpoons 2PhS\bullet \tag{9}$$

$$PhS\bullet + CH_2{=}\overset{|}{\underset{Ph}{CH}} \longrightarrow PhSCH_2\overset{\bullet}{\underset{\underset{Ph}{|}}{CH}} \xrightarrow[{-PhS\bullet}]{PhSH} PhSCH_2CH_2Ph \tag{10}$$

KETYL RADICALS

As first observed by Beckmann and Paul in 1891,[57] the reaction of sodium metal with benzophenone in ether gives rise to a blue color. From the fact that reaction of this species with iodine or oxygen reforms benzophenone, Schlenk and Weickel proposed in 1911 that this species was the ketyl radical **21** (equation 11).[58] Further experiments showed this was in equilibrium with the dimer **22** which gives benzpinacol upon hydrolysis.[59] Magnetic susceptibility measurements suggested **21** was largely associated to **22**,[59,60] while the potassium derivative was largely dissociated.[60] Later these radicals were investigated by ESR, and finally the structure of **21** was determined by X-ray crystallography (Fig. 1).[61] In 1934 Favorsky and Nazarov proposed the formation of a ketyl radical anion from the aliphatic ketone $t\text{-}Bu_2C{=}O$,[62] and the ESR spectrum of this radical was first observed in 1961 (Fig. 2).[63] Studies of reduction of ketones by metals were extended to α,β-unsaturated ketones in 1926 by Conant and Cutter.[64]

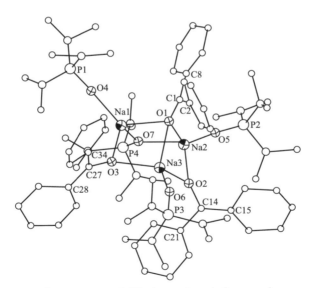

Fig. 1 X-ray crystal structure of **21** (reproduced from reference 61 with the permission of Wiley-VCH).

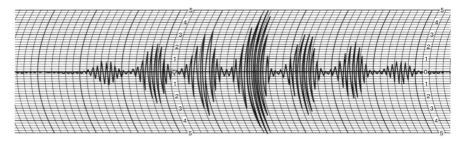

Fig. 2 ESR spectrum of $t\text{-}Bu_2\dot{C}-O^-Na^+$ (reproduced from reference 63 with the permission of the American Chemical Society).

$$\underset{\underset{Ph}{\overset{O}{\underset{\|}{}}}{\overset{}{C}}\underset{Ph}{} + Na \longrightarrow \underset{21}{\underset{Ph}{\overset{O^-Na^+}{\underset{\bullet}{C}}}Ph} \rightleftharpoons \underset{22}{\underset{\underset{Ph\ \ Ph}{}}{\overset{NaO\ \ \ ONa}{PhC-CPh}}} \qquad (11)$$

RADICAL CATIONS AND ANIONS

Wurster in 1879 had already prepared crystalline salts containing radical cation **23** (equation 12).[65] Subsequently, radical cations of many different structural types have been found, especially by E. Weitz[66] and S. Hünig,[67] and recently these include a cyclophane structure **24** containing two radical cations (Figure 3).[68] Leonor Michaelis made extensive studies of oxidations in biological systems,[69–74] and reported in 1931 the formation of the radical cation species **25**, which he designated as a "semiquinone."[69,70] Michaelis also studied the oxidation of quinones, and demonstrated the formation of semiquinone radical anions such as **26** (equation 13).[71,72] Dimroth established quantitative linear free energy correlations of the effects of oxidants on the rates of formation of these species.[75]

$$\underset{\underset{Me_2N}{}}{\overset{Me_2N}{\bigcirc}} \xrightarrow{[O]} \underset{\underset{Me_2N}{}}{\overset{Me_2N+\bullet}{\bigcirc}} \qquad (12)$$

23

24

25

(13)

26

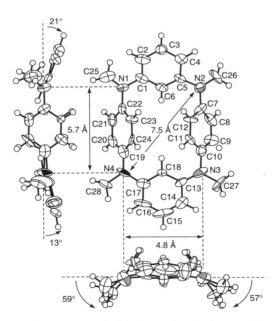

Fig. 3 X-ray crystal structure of **24** (reproduced from reference 68 with the permission of Wiley-VCH).

3 Non-delocalized and aliphatic radicals

FREE RADICAL CHAIN REACTIONS

The study of the reactions of the simple free radicals begun by Bodenstein and Lind in 1906[76] on the kinetics of gas phase reactions showed that the reactions of H_2 with Cl_2 and Br_2 were complex processes,[77] and a radical chain mechanism for these reactions (equations 14–18) was proposed in 1919 by Christiansen, Herzfeld, and Polanyi.[78–80] The theoretical basis for understanding these reactions in terms of free radicals was presented by G.N. Lewis in 1916, with the theory of the electron pair bond, and free radicals, or "odd molecules".[81,82] Further studies on chain reactions including the extension to explosions in gaseous systems were made by Hinshelwood and by Semenov,[83–85] who shared the Nobel Prize in 1956.

$$Br_2 \longrightarrow 2Br\bullet \qquad \text{(initiation)} \qquad (14)$$

$$Br\bullet + H_2 \longrightarrow HBr + H\bullet \qquad \text{(propagation)} \qquad (15)$$

$$H\bullet + Br_2 \longrightarrow HBr + Br\bullet \qquad \text{(propagation)} \qquad (16)$$

$$H\bullet + HBr \longrightarrow H_2 + Br\bullet \qquad \text{(propagation)} \qquad (17)$$

$$2Br\bullet \longrightarrow Br_2 \qquad \text{(chain breaking)} \qquad (18)$$

In 1924 Bonhoeffer demonstrated the formation of atomic hydrogen by an electric discharge (equation 19). The presence of atomic hydrogen was shown by its ability to reduce metal salts (equation 20).[86]

$$H_2 \longrightarrow 2H\bullet \qquad (19)$$

$$2H\bullet + PbCl_2 \longrightarrow 2HCl + Pb^\circ \qquad (20)$$

ALIPHATIC FREE RADICALS

Although the work of Gomberg and those who followed provided good evidence for the existence of arylmethyl radicals, there was still skepticism regarding simple aliphatic radicals such as methyl and ethyl. As noted above, the modern history of these species began with the suggestions of Crum Brown (equation 2).[8]

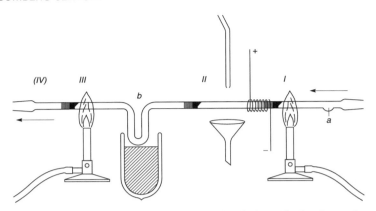

Fig. 4 Paneth apparatus for generation of alkyl radicals (reproduced from reference 87 with the permission of Wiley-VCH).

Convincing evidence for these species was, however, provided by Paneth and his co-workers beginning in 1929.[87–89] Their classic experiments were inspired by the method pioneered by Bonhoeffer[86] for showing the existence of atomic hydrogen. An organometallic compound such as tetramethyllead when passed through a hot zone in a glass tube was found to deposit a metallic mirror. When the gases from such a decomposition were allowed to pass over the metal mirror in a cold section of the tube, the mirror was removed and tetramethyllead was reformed (Fig. 4). This demonstrated the formation of methyl radicals in the hot zone where the mirror was laid down, and then regeneration of the organometallic compound by reaction of the methyl radicals with the cold mirror (equation 21).

$$(CH_3)_4Pb \longrightarrow 4CH_3{}^\bullet + Pb^o \qquad (21)$$

This technique was quickly adopted by others and it was soon found by F.O. Rice and co-workers that the pyrolysis of many organic compounds at 800 to 1000°C removed metallic mirrors, implicating the formation of free radicals.[90] The cleavage of larger free radicals into smaller radicals and olefins under these conditions, was also proposed (equation 22),[91,92] as well as chain reactions in which radicals abstract hydrogen from alkanes. Reactions of alkyl halides with metal atoms in the gas phase were also found by M. Polanyi and co-workers to yield alkyl radicals (equation 23).[93,94]

$$CH_3CH_2CH_2{}^\bullet \xrightarrow{\Delta} CH_3{}^\bullet + CH_2{=}CH_2 \qquad (22)$$

$$CH_3Cl + Na \longrightarrow CH_3{}^\bullet + NaCl \qquad (23)$$

4 Radical reactions and processes

FREE RADICAL FORMATION IN GRIGNARD REACTIONS

The formation of coupling and reduction products in the Grignard reactions of alkyl halides with magnesium led to the suggestion by Gomberg and Bachmann that free radicals are formed in these processes (equation 24),[95] and this has been generally accepted.[96] However, there has been a long and contentious debate as to the extent that the reactions of these radicals occur while adsorbed on the metal surface as opposed to freely diffusing through the solution and back to the metal surface.[97–99] The reactions of Grignard reagents with carbonyl compounds have also been found to proceed by single electron transfer processes in some cases (equation 25).[100,101]

$$RHal + Mg \longrightarrow R\bullet + MgHal \tag{24}$$

$$Ph_2C{=}O + RMgHal \longrightarrow Ph_2\overset{\bullet}{C}{-}O^- + RMgHal^+ \tag{25}$$

FREE RADICAL ADDITION OF HALOGEN TO ALKENES

Michael Faraday reported in 1821 that chlorine addition to alkenes is stimulated by sunlight[102] and today this is taken to indicate the involvement of a free radical process (equation 26). Free radical chain mechanisms were proposed in 1927 by Berthoud and Béraneck[103] for the isomerization of stilbene catalyzed by Br_2 (equation 27), and by Wachholtz for bromine addition to ethyl maleate (equation 28).[104] Later studies showed inhibition of halogen addition by reaction of the intermediate radicals with oxygen,[105,106] and a free radical chain mechanism for solution and gas phase halogenations as in equation (26) was shown (equation 29).[107] Kinetic and mechanistic studies of free radical addition of Cl_2 to benzene were also reported,[108] as well as Br_2 addition to phenanthrene.[109]

$$CCl_2{=}CCl_2 + Cl_2 \xrightarrow{h\nu} CCl_3CCl_3 \tag{26}$$

$$\tag{27}$$

$$\tag{28}$$

$$CCl_2{=}CCl_2 \xrightarrow{Cl\bullet} CCl_3\overset{\bullet}{C}Cl_2 \xrightarrow[-Cl\bullet]{Cl_2} CCl_3CCl_3 \tag{29}$$

THE PEROXIDE EFFECT. FREE RADICAL ADDITION OF HBr TO ALKENES

Kharasch and Mayo in 1933,[110] in the first of many papers on the subject, showed that the addition of HBr to allyl bromide in the presence of light and air occurs rapidly to yield 1,3-dibromopropane, whereas in the absence of air and with purified reagents, the reaction is slow and 1,2-dibromopropane is formed. The latter reaction is the normal addition occurring by an ionic pathway giving the Markovnikov orientation. In 1933 the mechanism of the abnormal process ("anti-Markovnikov" addition) was not discussed, and it was only in 1937 that the free radical chain mechanism for this process was proposed by Kharasch and his co-workers.[111,112] The mechanism was extended to propene, for which the role of peroxides in promoting the reaction was demonstrated (equations 30, 31). This mechanism was also proposed independently in 1937 by Hey and Waters.[113] This paper [113] also popularized the use of the dot to represent an unpaired electron, as introduced by Lewis in 1916.[82]

$$CH_3CH{=}CH_2 \ + \ Br{\bullet} \ \longrightarrow \ CH_3\overset{\bullet}{C}HCH_2Br \tag{30}$$

$$CH_3\overset{\bullet}{C}HCH_2Br \ + \ Br_2 \ \longrightarrow \ CH_3CHBrCH_2Br \ + \ Br{\bullet} \tag{31}$$

Interestingly, in 1935 Rice and Rice had incorrectly proposed[92] a free radical chain mechanism for the normal Markovnikov addition (equations 32, 33). They suggested the anti-Markovnikov product arose from a different process, which was yet to be elucidated. In retrospect, it is surprising that Kharasch was so slow to recognize the peroxide effect as resulting from free radical reactions, given the large body of precedent from other studies, particularly from his contemporaries Taylor and Rice. However, Kharasch approached these studies from a completely different perspective, and his work originated from a desire to develop a theory for polar reactions.[114] Once he recognized the role of free radicals he devoted the rest of his career to their study, and with his great talent and energy, developed many of the modern concepts of these intermediates.

$$CH_3CH{=}CH_2 \ + \ Br{\bullet} \ \longrightarrow \ CH_3CHBrCH_2{\bullet} \tag{32}$$

$$CH_3CHBrCH_2{\bullet} \ + \ HBr \ \longrightarrow \ CH_3CHBr\overset{.}{C}H_3 \ + \ Br{\bullet} \tag{33}$$

Independently, at Oxford, Yoshiyuki Urushibara ın the laboratory of Robert Robinson had been studying the addition of HBr to fatty acids, and had noticed the direction of addition was reversed upon exposure to the air, as reported in 1933.[115,116] Initially, these authors supposed water possibly caused the effect. Urushibara became Professor at Tokyo, and continued studies of the peroxide effect,[117] but it was not until 1939 with his student Osamu Simamura that these investigators proposed that free radicals were responsible.[118] Simamura later also became Professor in Tokyo, and played a major role in the promotion of the study of free radicals in Japan.

OXYGEN ADDITION TO FREE RADICALS

The conversion of benzaldehyde in the presence of air to benzoic acid was reported in 1832 by Wohler and Liebig,[119] and in 1900 Baeyer and Villiger proposed perbenzoic acid as an intermediate in the reaction.[120] The currently accepted free radical chain mechanism for the process was proposed by Bäckström in 1934 (equation 34).[121] Bates and Spence already in 1931 had proposed that photolysis of CH_3I forming $CH_3\cdot$ in the presence of O_2 led to peroxyl radicals $CH_3OO\cdot$.[122]

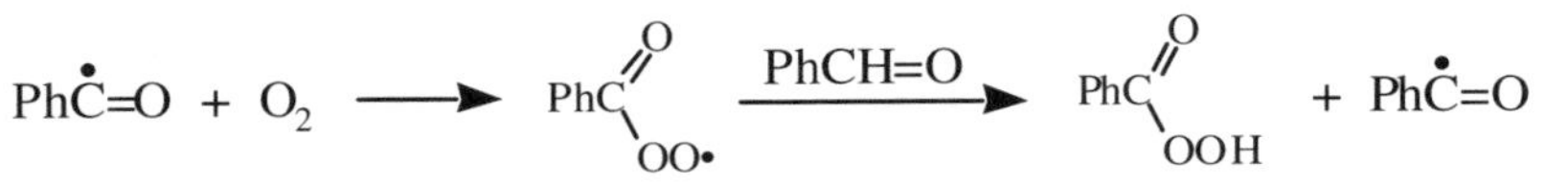

$$\text{Ph}\overset{\bullet}{\text{C}}\text{=O} + O_2 \longrightarrow \text{PhC}\overset{O}{\underset{OO\cdot}{\big/\!\!\big/}} \xrightarrow{\text{PhCH=O}} \text{PhC}\overset{O}{\underset{OOH}{\big/\!\!\big/}} + \text{Ph}\overset{\bullet}{\text{C}}\text{=O} \quad (34)$$

The reaction of the triphenylmethyl radical with oxygen to form the peroxide discovered by Gomberg in 1900 (equation 1) was a strong piece of evidence for the radical structure **1**, and the affinity of carbon centered radicals for oxygen remains one of their defining characteristics. Willstätter and Haber in 1931[123] also proposed a general role for free radicals in oxygen reactions in chemistry, which further stimulated interest in this field.

The known reaction product of the oxidation of cyclohexene was assigned as the hydroperoxide **27** by Criegee in 1936.[124] The oxidation of cumene to the hydroperoxide **28** proceeds by a chain mechanism (equations 35, 36), and the conversion of the hydroperoxide by acid to phenol and acetone, in what has become a commercially important process, was reported by Hock and Lang in 1944.[125]

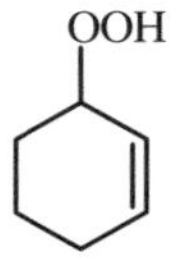

OOH

27

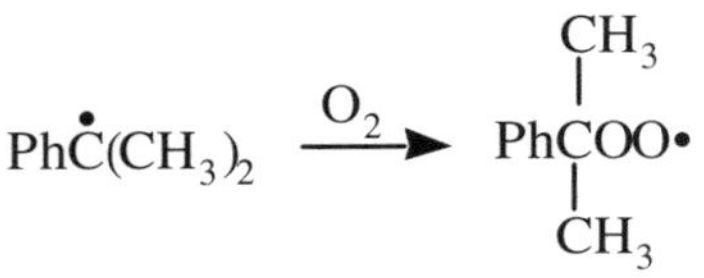

(35)

$$\text{Ph}\overset{\bullet}{\text{C}}(CH_3)_2 \xrightarrow{O_2} \text{Ph}\underset{\underset{CH_3}{|}}{\overset{\overset{CH_3}{|}}{C}}\text{OO}\cdot$$

$$\underset{\underset{CH_3}{|}}{\overset{\overset{CH_3}{|}}{PhCOO\bullet}} + PhCH(CH_3)_2 \longrightarrow \underset{\underset{CH_3}{|}}{\overset{\overset{CH_3}{|}}{PhCOOH}} + Ph\dot{C}(CH_3)_2 \quad (36)$$

28

FREE RADICAL POLYMERIZATION

Taylor[126] in 1925 demonstrated that hydrogen atoms generated by the mercury sensitized photodecomposition of hydrogen gas add to ethylene to form ethyl radicals, which were proposed to react with H_2 to give the observed ethane and another hydrogen atom. Evidence that polymerization could occur by free radical reactions was found by Taylor and Jones in 1930, by the observation that ethyl radicals formed by the gas phase pyrolysis of diethylmercury or tetraethyllead initiated the polymerization of ethylene,[127] and this process was extended to the solution phase by Cramer.[128] The mechanism of equation (37) (with participation by a third body) was presented for the reaction,[126,127] which is in accord with current views, and the mechanism of equation (38) was shown for disproportionation. Staudinger in 1932 wrote a mechanism for free radical polymerization of styrene,[129] but just as did Rice and Rice (equation 32),[92] showed the radical attack on the most substituted carbon (anti-Markovnikov attack). The correct orientation was shown by Flory in 1937.[130] In 1935, O.K. Rice and Sickman reported that ethylene polymerization was also induced by methyl radicals generated from thermolysis of azomethane.[131]

$$H\bullet + CH_2{=}CH_2 \longrightarrow CH_3\dot{C}H_2 \xrightarrow{CH_2{=}CH_2} CH_3CH_2CH_2CH_2\bullet \quad (37)$$

$$CH_3(CH_2)_4CH_2\bullet + CH_3CH_2\bullet \longrightarrow CH_3(CH_2)_3CH{=}CH_2 + CH_3CH_3 \quad (38)$$

FREE RADICAL AROMATIC SUBSTITUTION

The formation of phenyl radicals by the thermolysis of diacyl peroxides and other sources was proposed by Hey, Waters, and co-workers,[113,132,133] and these were suggested to give free radical aromatic substitution via intermediate **29** (equation 39). This mechanism was also applied[113] to the formation of biaryls from diazonium ions in benzene,[134] a reaction now known as the Gomberg–Bachmann reaction. Initially, such free radical substitutions on aromatic rings were suggested by Hey and Waters[113,132] to involve displacement of hydrogen atoms, but it is currently accepted that these reactions are much more likely to involve intermediates from which hydrogen is abstracted by another radical (equation 39). Free radical addition of halogens to aromatics are noted above.[108,109]

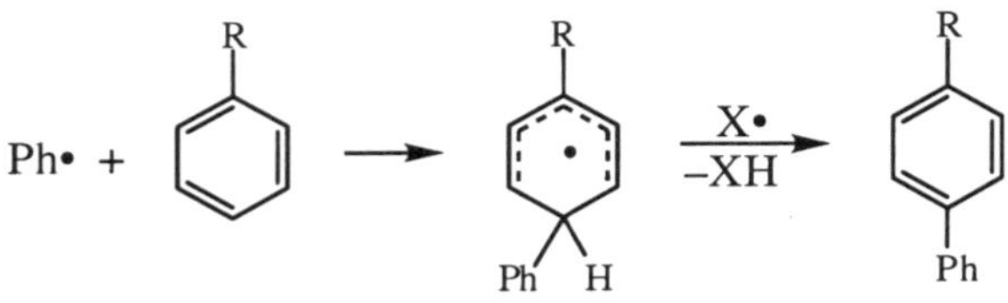

$$Ph\bullet + \quad \longrightarrow \quad \xrightarrow[-XH]{X\bullet} \quad \tag{39}$$

29

FREE RADICAL HALOGENATION OF ALKANES

Halogenation of alkanes had long been known, and in 1930 the kinetics of the chlorination of chloroform to carbon tetrachloride were reported by Schwab and Heyde (equation 40),[135] while the kinetics of the chlorination of methane were described by Pease and Walz in 1931.[136] Both of these studies showed the currently accepted mechanism, which was extended to reactions in solution by Hass *et al.* in 1936.[137] The free radical halogenation mechanism of other alkanes was described by Kharasch and co-workers,[138–140] including side chain halogenation of toluene.[140]

$$CHCl_3 \xrightarrow[-HCl]{Cl\bullet} \bullet CCl_3 \xrightarrow{Cl_2} CCl_4 + Cl\bullet \tag{40}$$

N-BROMOSUCCINIMIDE

Wohl in 1919 reported that *N*-bromoacetamide ($CH_3CONHBr$) induced allylic bromination.[141] Then *N*-bromosuccinimide (**30**) was described in 1942 by Ziegler and co-workers to be useful in such free radical bromination reactions (equation 41),[142] and this widely utilized procedure is known as the Wohl–Ziegler reaction. In 1963 the mechanism of the reaction was proposed to involve halogen atoms in the hydrogen abstraction step[143,144] instead of succinimidyl radicals as had been commonly supposed. The halogen atom mechanism had previously been proposed by Gosselain *et al.* for reactions of *N*-chlorosuccinimide.[144(a)]

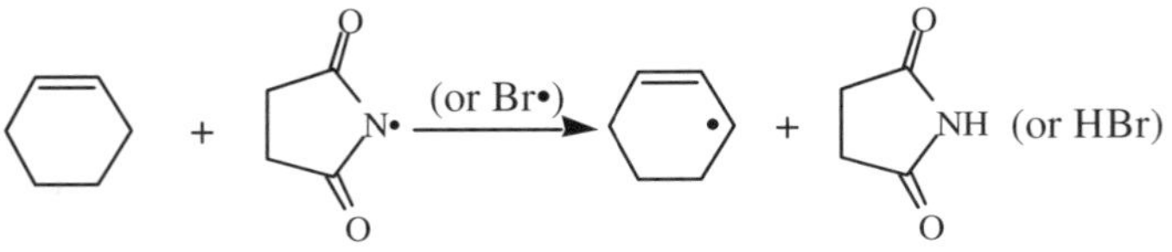

$$\tag{41}$$

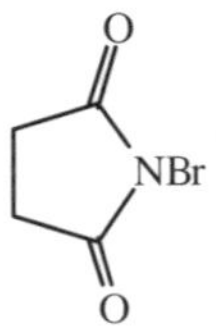

30

5 Free radical initiators

AZO COMPOUNDS (DIAZENES) AS SOURCES OF FREE RADICALS

Gomberg[146] used phenylazotriphenylmethane (PAT, **31**) in the classic preparation of tetraphenylmethane. Wieland *et al.*, in 1922,[147] showed that $Ph_3C \cdot$ (**1**) was formed in this reaction, and proposed phenyl radicals were formed as well (equation 42). In the 1920s, kinetic studies by Ramsperger[148] of substituent effects on the reactions of azoalkanes were interpreted as showing that these reacted in one step to form two alkyl radicals and N_2 (equation 43). In 1933 Leermakers[149] used the Paneth mirror technique to demonstrate that methyl radicals were generated upon pyrolysis of azomethane, and from the work of Ramsperger[148] it was known that substituent effects on both sides of the molecule could affect the ease of decomposition, implying concerted reaction if suitably stable radicals could be formed. In 1934 it was shown that methyl radicals from azomethane abstract hydrogen from CH_3CHO,[150] and in 1938 it was found that essentially all of the methyl radicals could be trapped by nitric oxide (equation 44).[151] Extensive further work on substituent effects in diazene reactions has continued, and includes examination of polar, conjugative, and steric substituent effects.[152] In 1998, the sequence of bond breaking in this reaction was studied by Zewail and co-workers using femtosecond spectroscopy.[153] For applications of this technique, Zewail was awarded the 1999 Nobel Prize in Chemistry.

$$Ph_3CN=NPh \longrightarrow Ph_3C\bullet + Ph\bullet \longrightarrow Ph_4C \qquad (42)$$

$$\mathbf{31}$$

$$RN=NR \longrightarrow 2R\bullet + N_2 \qquad (43)$$

$$CH_3\bullet + NO\bullet \longrightarrow (CH_3)_2NO\bullet \qquad (44)$$

Photochemical denitrogenation of the stereolabeled diazabicyclo[2.2.1]-heptene **DBH-1** leads to both inverted and retained bicyclo[2.1.0]pentane (housane) products, and the effect of solvent viscosity in this reaction has been examined by Adam *et al.*[154]

DBH-1

DIACYL PEROXIDES AS RADICAL SOURCES

The thermal reactions of diacyl peroxides (**32**), were initially studied by
Hermans et al.[155–157] and by Wieland,[158,159] but only gradually were these
recognized as forming free radicals. Thus Wieland and Razuvaev[158] considered radical formation in these reactions, but excluded this possibility. The
kinetics of benzoyl peroxide decomposition reactions were first studied by
D.J. Brown,[160] and were interpreted as showing the formation of benzoyloxy
radicals (equation 45), which could form phenyl radicals by decarboxylation.
Polar effects on rates of these reactions were found by Swain et al.,[161] who
found a linear correlation of the rates with Hammett σ values, with
$\rho = -0.38$. This was interpreted as resulting from the enhancement of the
reactivity by electron donor substituents because of increased repulsion
between the oxygens in the peroxy group in **32**.

$$R-\!\!\left\langle\bigcirc\right\rangle\!\!-\!\overset{O}{\underset{\underset{O-O}{}}{C}}\!\overset{O}{\underset{}{C}}\!\!-\!\!\left\langle\bigcirc\right\rangle\!\!-R \longrightarrow R-\!\!\left\langle\bigcirc\right\rangle\!\!-\!\overset{O}{\underset{\underset{O}{}}{C}}\!\overset{O}{\underset{O}{C}}\!\!-\!\!\left\langle\bigcirc\right\rangle\!\!-R \quad (45)$$

32

PEROXY ESTERS

Ethyl peracetate was the first ester of a peroxy acid, and was characterized by
Baeyer and Villiger in 1901.[162] Kinetic studies of perester decomposition
were reported by Blomquist and Ferris in 1951,[163] and in 1958 Bartlett and
Hiatt[164] proposed that concerted multiple bond scission of peresters could
occur when stabilized radicals were formed (equation 46). As noted below
(equation 57), polar effects in perester decomposition are also significant.

$$RC\!\!\overset{O}{\underset{O-OBu\text{-}t}{\Big\backslash}} \longrightarrow R\text{-}\text{-}C\!\!\overset{O}{\underset{O\text{-}\text{-}OBu\text{-}t}{\Big\backslash}} \xrightarrow[-t\text{-}BuO\bullet]{-CO_2} R\bullet \quad (46)$$

PHOTOCHEMICAL GENERATION OF FREE RADICALS FROM KETONES

The photolysis of ketones was suggested by Norrish et al.[165,166] to involve the
formation of free radicals, and this was confirmed by experiments in which
metallic mirrors were removed.[167] In the Type I reaction, an initial cleavage
of the C—C bond to the carbonyl was suggested to occur upon photoexcitation (equation 47), and this can be followed by the loss of carbon monoxide

giving a further alkyl or aryl radical. The Type II cleavage involves initial formation of a biradical intermediate **33** (equation 48).[167,168] Bond breaking in the transition state of the Norrish Type I reaction has been directly observed by Zewail and co-workers.[169]

$$\underset{R \quad R^1}{\overset{O}{\|}} \xrightarrow{h\nu} \quad R\bullet \quad O=\overset{\bullet}{C}R^1 \tag{47}$$

$$\text{(structure)} \xrightarrow{h\nu} \underset{33}{\text{(structure)}} \longrightarrow \text{(structure)} + \text{(structure)} \tag{48}$$

Triplet benzophenone

The assignment of the excited state of benzophenone as a triplet which could act as a sensitizer was made by Hammond and Moore in 1959 (equation 49),[170] and this led to a great surge in radical study using photochemical techniques. The role of photoexcited benzophenone as a diradical initiator for benzaldehyde oxidation was previously shown explicitly by Bäckström in 1934 (equation 34).[121]

$$Ph_2C=O \xrightarrow{h\nu} Ph_2C=O^{1*} \longrightarrow Ph_2C=O^3 \xrightarrow{RH} Ph_2\overset{\bullet}{C}OH + R\bullet \tag{49}$$

ESTER PHOTOLYSIS AND THE META EFFECT

The pre*h*νference for solvolysis of *meta* substituted esters such as *m*-nitrophenyl phosphate and *m*-methoxybenzyl acetate was discovered by Havinga *et al.*[171] and studied further by Zimmerman (equation 50).[172,173] Radicals can be formed in these reactions, and there is some dispute as to whether radical pairs also lead to ion pairs (equation 50).[174]

$$ArCH_2O_2CR \longrightarrow ArCH_2\bullet \quad \bullet O_2CR \longrightarrow ArCH_2^+ \quad {}^-O_2CR \tag{50}$$

INDUCED DECOMPOSITION OF RADICAL INITIATORS

The phenomenon of induced decomposition, in which radicals derived from reaction of the solvent with the initiator benzoyl peroxide consume some of the initiator in a chain process, was first elucidated by Bartlett and Nozaki (equation 51),[175,176] and by Cass.[177]

$$R\bullet + PhCO_2O_2CPh \longrightarrow PhCO_2R + PhCO_2\bullet \tag{51}$$

MOLECULE-INDUCED HOMOLYSIS

The direct reaction of free radical initiators with non-radical substrates resulting in the formation of free radicals[178–180] has been termed molecule-induced homolysis.[181] An example is the reaction of a diacyl peroxide with an alkene (equation 52).[181]

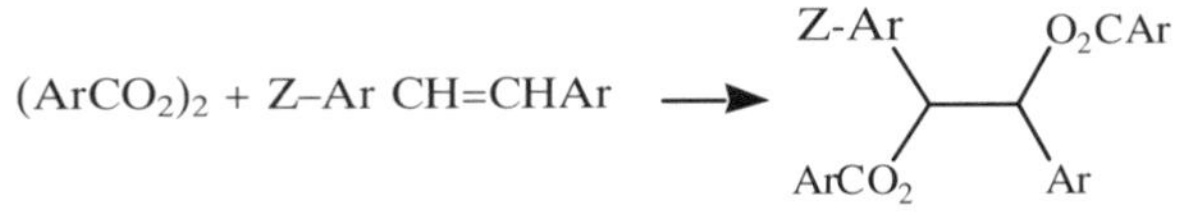

$$(ArCO_2)_2 + Z\text{–}Ar\ CH=CHAr \longrightarrow \quad \overset{Z\text{-}Ar}{\underset{ArCO_2}{\bigg\rangle}}\!\!\overset{O_2CAr}{\underset{Ar}{\bigg\langle}} \qquad (52)$$

6 Properties of radicals

STERIC EFFECTS AND PERSISTENT RADICALS

It was recognized by Gomberg[1] in his initial paper that the stability of the triphenylmethyl radical is due partly to steric factors, and Conant and Bigelow[183] reported in 1928 the reversible dissociation at 50°C of 1,2-di-*tert*-butyltetraphenylethane (later shown to have the head-to-tail structure)[183(a)] to the yellow colored radical (equation 53), which reacts rapidly with O_2. In 1973, Ingold and co-workers[184,185] showed that purely aliphatic free radicals including di-*tert*-butylmethyl (**34**) and tri-*tert*-butylmethyl (**35**) could be observed by ESR spectroscopy and were not only long lived, but showed no noticeable tendency to dimerize. Studies by Rüchardt *et al.* have provided a detailed analysis of steric factors on the tendency of crowded aliphatic hydrocarbons to undergo dissociation.[186] A stable crystalline carbon-centered radical without resonance stabilization has been prepared, and the X-ray structure reported.[187]

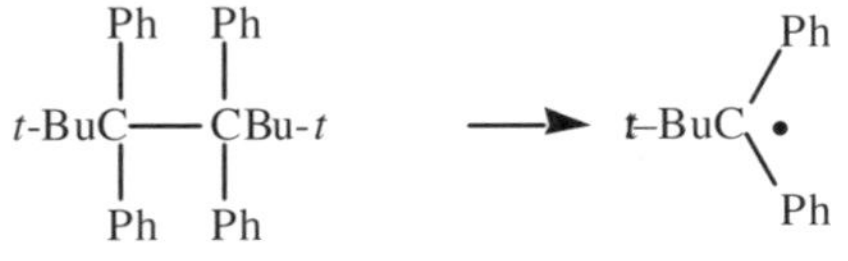

$$
\begin{array}{c}
\overset{Ph}{\underset{Ph}{\overset{|}{t\text{-}BuC}}}\!\!-\!\!\overset{Ph}{\underset{Ph}{\overset{|}{CBu\text{-}t}}}
\end{array}
\longrightarrow
t\text{-}BuC\overset{Ph}{\underset{Ph}{\Big\backslash}}\!\!\bullet
\qquad
\underset{\mathbf{34}}{t\text{-}Bu_2CH\bullet}
\qquad
\underset{\mathbf{35}}{t\text{-}Bu_3C\bullet} \quad (53)
$$

CAGE EFFECTS

The cage effect, or the enhanced probability for recombination of two radicals formed in close proximity, was discussed by Franck and Rabinowitch in 1934,[188] and Rabinowitch and Wood[189] used a "pinball" illustration of this process (Fig. 5). The theory of this reaction was further developed by Noyes.[190]

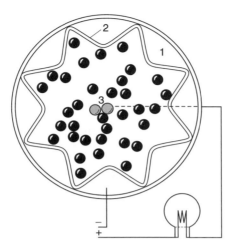

Fig. 5 Rabinowitch and Wood apparatus for demonstrating the radical cage effect (reproduced from reference 189 with the permission of the Royal Society of Chemistry).

In 1967 Kiefer and Traylor demonstrated the effect of solvent viscosity on cage effects in solution (equation 54).[191] Thus the viscosity of the solvent had a major effect on the yield of di-*tert*-butyl peroxide formed from cage recombination of the *tert*-butoxyl radical pair formed from thermolysis of di-*tert*-butyl peroxyoxalate (**36**). The efficiency of cage combination was also affected by the initial separation in the radical pairs formed from different precursors. The effect of mass on cage recombination has also been shown, using organometallic radicals.[192] Generation of radical pairs constrained in zeolites involve "supercages".[193,194]

$$t\text{--BuOOCCOOBu--}t \xrightarrow{-2CO_2} t\text{--BuO} \bullet \qquad \bullet \text{OBu--}t \longrightarrow t\text{--BuOOBu--}t \quad (54)$$

36

THEORETICAL STUDY OF FREE RADICALS

The theoretical basis for the understanding of free radicals was first provided by G.N. Lewis in 1916.[81,82] His clear recognition of the electron pair bond and the possibility of odd electron systems was heavily influenced by the work of pioneers such as Gomberg, Schlenk, and Wieland, who had showed remarkable prescience in formulating free radical structures without, however, using the principles of electron pair bonding. The theoretical study of the triphenylmethyl radical was introduced by Erich Hückel at the 1933 Faraday conference.[195]

STEREOCHEMISTRY OF ALIPHATIC FREE RADICALS

It was shown in 1940 by Brown, Kharasch, and Chao that, during free radical chlorination of optically active 2-methyl-1-chlorobutane chloride, the product 1,2-dichloro-2-methylbutane was racemic, implying that the intermediate radical was either planar or rapidly inverting (equation 55).[138] However, radical formation at the bridgehead center constrained to maintain non-planarity in bicyclic system **37** was also demonstrated (equation 56).[139]

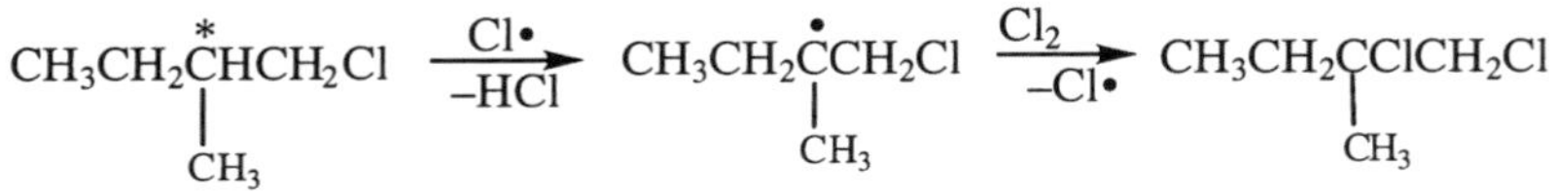
CH3CH2CHCH2Cl
CH3
Cl•
-HCl
CH3CH2CCH2Cl
CH3
Cl2
-Cl•
CH3CH2CClCH2Cl
CH3

(55)

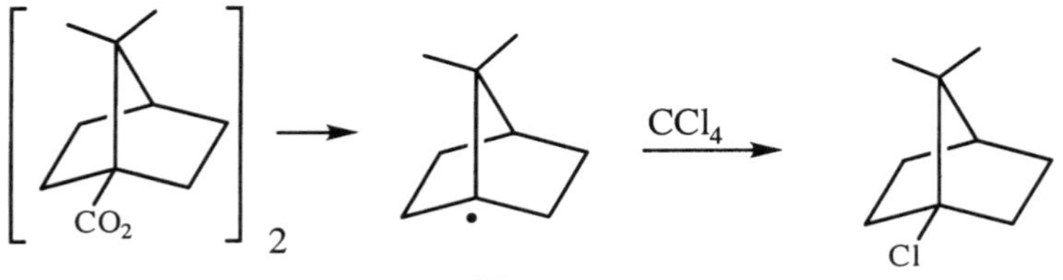
CO2
2
CCl4
Cl

37

(56)

POLAR EFFECTS ON FREE RADICAL REACTIONS

The understanding of polar effects on free radical reactions arose from studies of free radical polymerization where transition state effects were emphasized.[196–198] Further studies involved diacyl peroxide reactions (equation 45),[161] hydrogen abstraction from ring-substituted toluenes,[199] and reactions of peresters involving transition state **38** (equation 57).[200]

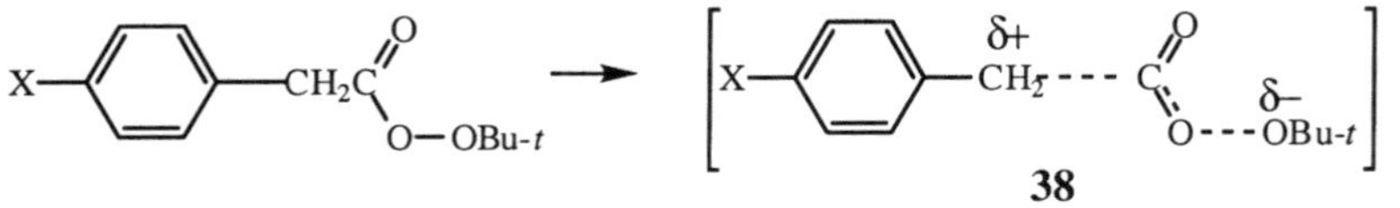
X
CH2C
O
O—OBu-t
X
δ+
CH2
C
O
δ−
O---OBu-t

38

(57)

SUBSTITUENT EFFECTS ON FREE RADICALS. CAPTODATIVE EFFECTS

Because radicals are known to be stabilized by electron donor and by electron acceptor substituents, it has been proposed that radicals "enjoy particular stabilization when they are substituted simultaneously by a donor and an acceptor group."[201] Such stabilization is said to be due to captodative effects. Many scales of radical substituent constants have been devised,[202–204] but while these have some utility they have not achieved the same success as has the use of Hammett constants for polar reactions, as is not surprising, considering the amphoteric nature of free radicals.

7 Techniques for radical study

ROTATING SECTOR

One of the early specialized techniques used for the study of radical reactions was the rotating sector method. The use of this technique (Fig. 6) for determining reaction kinetics was demonstrated by Melville[205] for the gas phase polymerization of methyl methacrylate, and later by Bartlett and Swain[206] for the liquid phase reaction, and by Carlsson and Ingold for tin hydride reductions.[207]

ELECTRON SPIN RESONANCE

Electron spin resonance spectroscopy permits the direct observation of free radicals, and provides a powerful stimulus to studies of these species.[208] When this phenomenon was first demonstrated it was used for studies of persistent organic radicals in solution, and for more reactive species trapped in solid matrices.[209] Then in 1963, using the power of an electron beam from a van de Graaf generator, Fessenden and Schuler first recorded, in static liquid solution, spectra of reactive radicals which underwent self-reaction at the diffusion-limited rate.[210] A much less costly procedure for recording spectra of reactive radicals was reported by Dixon and Norman in 1962,[211–213] and depended on flowing together aqueous solutions of acidified hydrogen peroxide and a titanium(III) salt, each of which contained an organic substrate which reacted with the hydroxyl radicals generated by reduction of the hydrogen peroxide (equation 58).[211,212] The solutions were mixed immediately prior to passing through the spectrometer cavity.

$$Ti(III) + H_2O_2 \xrightarrow{-Ti(IV)} \bullet OH \xrightarrow{RH} H_2O + R\bullet \qquad (58)$$

Other flow techniques were developed in subsequent years, but towards the end of the 1960s it was recognized that detectable concentrations of reactive radicals could be obtained in a static sample by ultraviolet photolysis of suitable radical precursors using the focused beam from an inexpensive but intense ultraviolet light source. As for so many discoveries in science, this approach was developed independently in different laboratories.[214,215] The vigorous exploitation of the technique by Kochi and Krusic for the observation of specific radicals provided information on a multitude of interesting and unusual species.[216]

FREE RADICAL INHIBITORS: DPPH AND GALVINOXYL

The stable free radical diphenylpicrylhydrazinyl (**39**) was first prepared by Goldschmidt in 1922,[217] and this[218] and galvinoxyl (**40**)[219] have found application as radical scavengers in kinetic studies.[220] Davies and Roberts used galvinoxyl as a radical inhibitor to show the radical nature of the autoxidation of 1-phenylethylboronic acid.[220(a)]

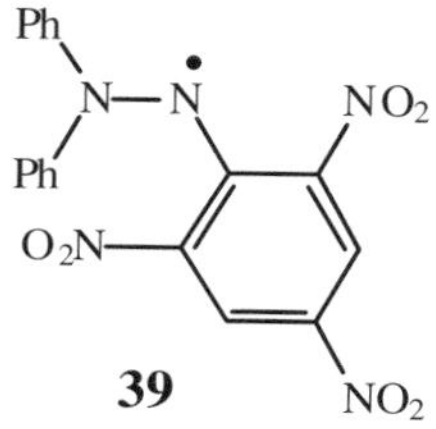

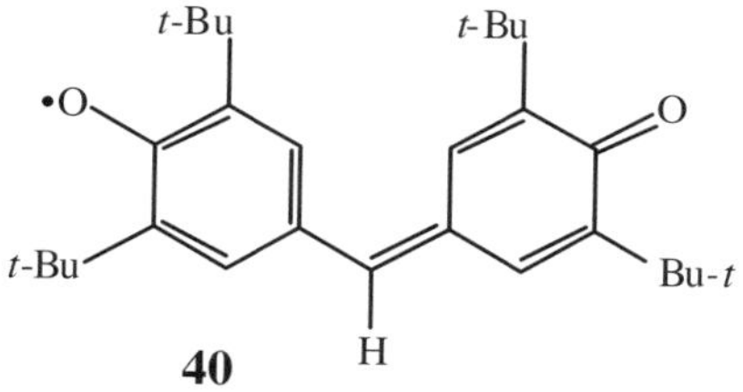

MATRIX ISOLATION OF RADICALS

The generation and spectrosopic observation of radicals in a frozen matrix was first reported by Lewis and Lipkin,[221] who photolyzed tetraphenylhydrazine in EPA (ether/isopentane/EtOH) at 90 K (equation 59). This technique was developed further by Norman and Porter,[222] and the early work was reviewed by Pimentel.[223]

$$Ph_2NNPh_2 \xrightarrow{h\nu} Ph_2N\bullet \ + \ Ph_2N^+ \qquad (59)$$

RADICALS BY FLASH PHOTOLYSIS

The flash photolysis technique for generating radicals with fast spectroscopic observation was pioneered by Porter and Wright,[224] who observed benzyl, anilino, and phenoxyl radicals in the gas phase. Further applications of this technique include diradicals from diazenes,[153,154] nucleoside-derived radicals,[371] and ultrafast radical clocks.[315]

The first observations of the additions of transient radicals to nitroso compounds (equation 60)[225,226] and nitrones (equation 61)[227] to form stable
nitroxyl radicals, which could be conveniently detected by ESR for the
identification of the transient radicals, were reported in the mid-1960s. This
technique has been extensively applied in chemical[228–233] and biological
systems.[234,235]

The name "spin trapping" was coined by Janzen,[228] and derives from
analogy with the use of stable nitroxyls as "spin labels" (or "spin probes")
that provide spectroscopic information regarding their microscopic environment, a procedure pioneered by McConnell *et al.*[235]

$$R\bullet\ +\ R^1N{=}O\ \longrightarrow\ RR^1NO\bullet \tag{60}$$

$$R\bullet\ +\ R^1CH{=}\overset{+}{\underset{R^2}{N}}\overset{O^-}{\diagup}\ \longrightarrow\ RR^1CH\overset{O\bullet}{\underset{R^2}{N}}\diagup \tag{61}$$

Chemically induced dynamic nuclear polarization (CIDNP) was first reported
in 1967 in independent work from three different laboratories.[236–241] The
effects of free radicals on NMR spectra were revealed (Fig. 6) in studies of
radicals from peroxides (equation 62) and azo compounds,[236] as well as
radicals generated from the reaction of alkyl halides and organolithium
compounds.[239]

$$(PhCO_2)_2\ \longrightarrow\ PhCO_2\bullet\ \longrightarrow\ Ph\bullet\ \xrightarrow[-R\bullet]{RH}\ PhH \tag{62}$$

8 New radical types

The generation of silyl radicals, species which have proven to be of great
value in both mechanistic and synthetic studies, was reported independently
in 1947 by Sommer and Whitmore (equation 63),[243] and by Barry *et al.* at
Dow Chemical.[244] These are useful for many purposes, including halide
reductions.[245]

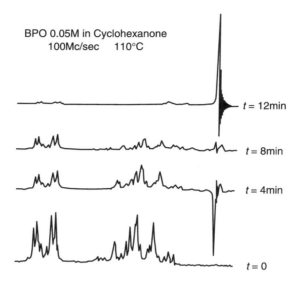

Fig. 6 CIDNP spectrum from benzoyl peroxide (reproduced from reference 237 with the permission of the American Chemical Society).

$$(CH_3CO_2)_2 \xrightarrow{-2CO_2} 2CH_3\cdot \xrightarrow{HSiCl_3} Cl_3Si\cdot + CH_4$$

$$RCH=CH_2 \xrightarrow{Cl_3Si\cdot} R\dot{C}HCH_2SiCl_3 \xrightarrow[-Cl_3Si\cdot]{HSiCl_3} RCH_2CH_2SiCl_3 \qquad (63)$$

TIN RADICALS

Tin radicals were generated by Noltes *et al.* in 1956,[246] and their applications in organic chemistry were pioneered by Kuivila and co-workers.[247,248] These species have proven to be of tremendous utility in organic chemistry, although their toxicity and other unfavorable properties have led to a search for substitutes.[249] Interestingly, in the initial publication[246] it was proposed that the reaction (equation 64) did not involve a free radical mechanism, as no inhibition by hydroquinone was detected.

$$Ph_3SnH + CH_2=CHPh \longrightarrow Ph_3SnCH_2CH_2Ph \qquad (64)$$

HALOGEN AND THIOL MIGRATION, AND RADICAL BRIDGING

Migrations of chlorine, bromine and thiol groups in free radical reactions have been observed,[250,251] and the role of bridging in these species has been a subject of some dispute.[252] The original example (equation 65)[250] involved the bridged radical **41**, which gave optically active products and is a direct analogue to the initial studies showing that racemization occurred in chlorination (equation 55).

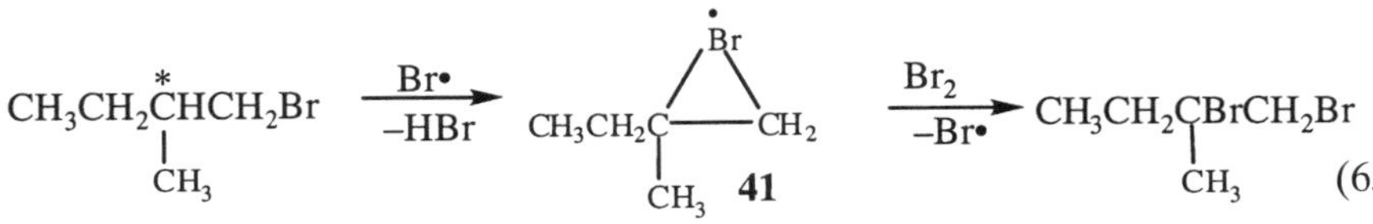

$$CH_3CH_2\overset{*}{\underset{CH_3}{C}}HCH_2Br \xrightarrow[-HBr]{Br\bullet} CH_3CH_2\overset{\overset{\bullet}{Br}}{\underset{CH_3}{C}}\!\!\triangle\!\!CH_2 \quad \mathbf{41} \xrightarrow[-Br\bullet]{Br_2} CH_3CH_2\underset{CH_3}{C}BrCH_2Br \qquad (65)$$

DIRADICALS IN THE VINYLCYCLOPROPANE REARRANGEMENT

This rearrangement (equation 66), discovered independently by several groups, was perhaps the first reaction widely accepted as proceeding through a diradical intermediate.[254–259] Recently, diradical character has also been

$$(66)$$

implicated in the transition state of the Cope rearrangement.[260]

TRIMETHYLENEMETHANE

The diradical species trimethylenemethane (**42**) was first discovered by Dowd in 1966[261] from cleavage of the pyrazoline, and was characterized by its ESR spectrum and the formation of methylenecyclopropane (equation 67). The study of diradicals has a long history (equation 3),[24] and many examples have been studied.[262,263]

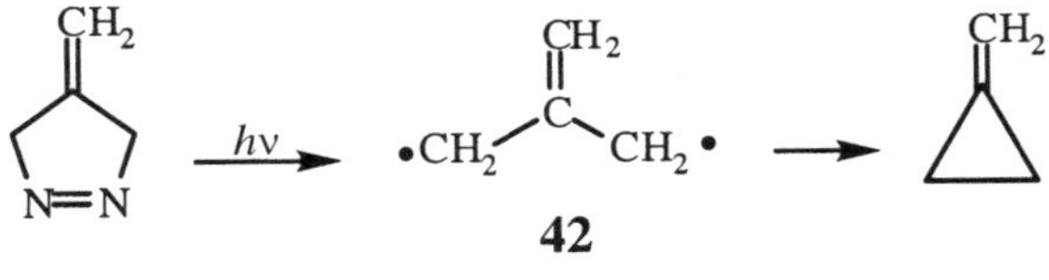

$$(67)$$

42

9 Oxygen-centered radicals

PEROXYL RADICALS

The reaction of carbon-centered free radicals with O_2 is one of the distinguishing features of these intermediates (equations 1, 34, 35). The formation of peroxyl radicals **43** in hydrocarbon oxidation (equation 68) has been of continued interest,[264] including the important role in biological processes. Peroxyl radicals may also be formed by H atom abstraction from hydroperoxides.

$$R\cdot \xrightarrow{\;O_2\;} \underset{\mathbf{43}}{ROO\cdot} \xrightarrow[-R\cdot]{\;RH\;} ROOH \tag{68}$$

TERMINATION IN OXIDATION REACTIONS

This reaction plays an important role in the oxidation of hydrocarbons, as illustrated in Scheme 1.[265–267] The self-reaction of the intermediate peroxyl radicals to form transient tetraoxide intermediates **44** was shown by the direct observation of these intermediates at low temperatures, and isotope scrambling when $^{16}O_2$ and $^{18}O_2$ was used in auto-oxidation with formation of $^{16}O^{18}O$.[265] Tetraoxides with secondary hydrogens (**45**) can undergo disproportionation with formation of singlet oxygen, which can be trapped with added 9,10-diphenylanthracene.[266,267]

$$R_3CH + X\cdot \longrightarrow R_3C\cdot + XH$$

$$R_3C\cdot + O_2 \longrightarrow R_3COO\cdot$$

$$2R_3COO\cdot \longrightarrow \underset{\mathbf{44}}{R_3COOOOCR_3} \longrightarrow R_3CO\cdot + \cdot OCR_3 + O_2$$

$$\underset{\mathbf{45}}{R_2CHOOOOCHR_2} \longrightarrow R_2C{=}O + {}^1O_2 + HOCHR_2$$

Scheme 1

FENTON REACTION

The use of H_2O_2 and Fe(II) for oxidation was reported by Fenton in 1894,[268] and was proposed to involve hydroxyl radicals by Haber and Weiss (equation 69).[269] This reaction was developed by Waters in the 1940s[270] and then by

Walling[271] for the oxidation of organic compounds by hydroxyl radicals. The details of the process still occasion considerable debate.[272]

$$Fe^{2+} + H_2O_2 \longrightarrow Fe^{3+} + HO^- + HO\bullet \qquad (69)$$

GAS PHASE REACTIONS INVOLVING HYDROXYL RADICALS

The study of gas phase free radicals has been of continued interest, for example in recent examples of the analysis of the reactions in equations (70)[273] and (71),[274] which involve vibrationally excited species.

$$D_2 + \bullet OH \rightarrow DOH + D\bullet \qquad (70)$$

$$H\bullet + H_2O \rightarrow H_2 + \bullet OH \qquad (71)$$

GIF CHEMISTRY

In 1983 Barton and co-workers reported the use of iron-based reagents in the functionalization of alkanes (equation 72).[275,276] The elucidation of the mechanisms involved a long dispute, but the role of free radical reactions appears to be well established.[277,278]

$$RH \xrightarrow{\quad Fe^{3+},\ R'OOH \quad} ROH \qquad (72)$$

10 Radical rearrangements

There was a long delay from the observation by Wieland of a radical rearrangement of Gomberg's peroxide (Section 2, equation 4) until the generality of these reactions was recognized. Key advances included the proposals for radical intermediates in the neophyl rearrangement (equation 6),[33] and in halogen migrations (equation 65).[250–253] The McBay rearrangement forming acyl radicals is a more recent example (equation 73).[34,35]

$$\bullet CH_2COPh \longrightarrow PhCH_2\dot{C}{=}O \qquad (73)$$

CYCLOPROPYLMETHYL RADICAL REARRANGEMENT

In 1951 Roberts and Mazur[279] observed that the free radical chlorination of methylcyclopropane gave a mixture of cyclopropylmethyl chloride and 4-chloro-1-butene (equation 74). This reaction was studied further,[280] and in 1969 Kochi, Krusic, and Eaton[281] observed the cyclopropylmethyl radical **46** by ESR and also monitored its rearrangement.

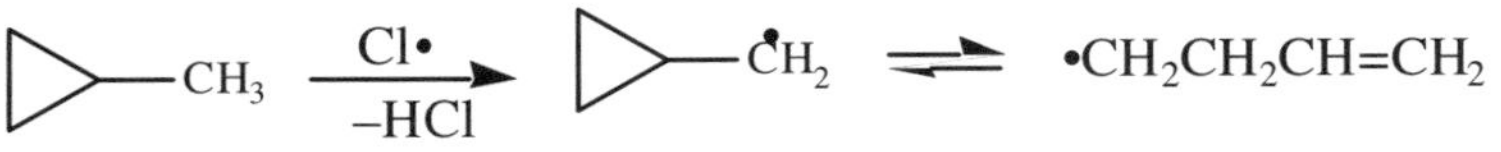

$$\triangleright\!\!-\!\!CH_3 \xrightarrow[-HCl]{Cl\bullet} \triangleright\!\!-\!\!\overset{\bullet}{C}H_2 \rightleftharpoons \bullet CH_2CH_2CH=CH_2 \tag{74}$$

46

HEXENYL RADICAL REARRANGEMENTS

Cyclizations of carbon radicals forming 6-membered rings during polymerizations were reported in 1957 (equation 75)[282,283] and Julia and his co-workers began systematic studies of these reactions in 1960.[284–286]

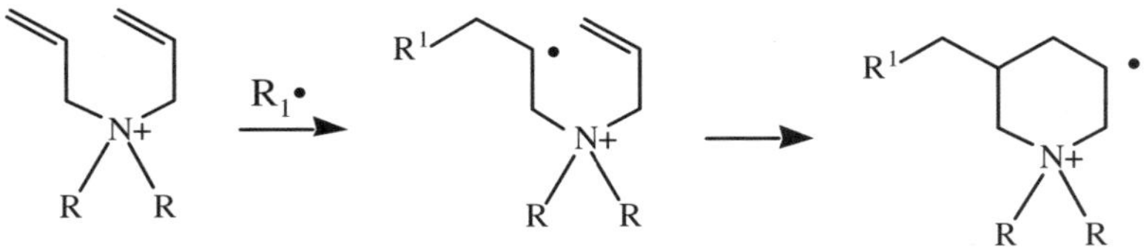

$$\tag{75}$$

The reaction (equation 76) of the hexenyl radical **47** forming cyclopentylmethyl radical was discovered independently in several laboratories and has been of pervasive utility in both synthetic and mechanistic study.[287–290] The competition between formation of cyclopentylcarbinyl and cyclohexyl radicals favors the former even though the latter is more stable, and this kinetic preference is explained by more favourable transition state interaction. The effects of substituents on the double bond, heteroatoms in the chain, and many other factors on the partitioning between these two paths have been examined. In the gas phase above 300°C, methylcyclopentane has been observed to form cyclohexane via isomerization of cyclopentylmethyl radicals into the more stable cyclohexyl radicals.[290(a,b)]

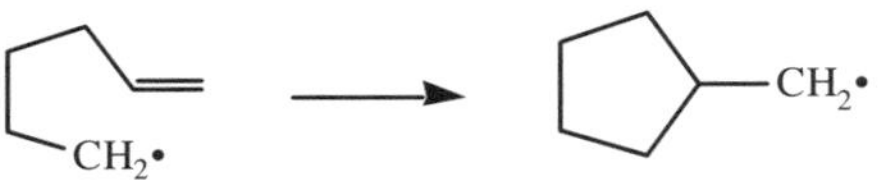

$$\tag{76}$$

47

RING EXPANSION

Ring expansion reactions of free radicals are useful in synthesis (equation 77) and were reported independently in 1987 by the groups of Beckwith[291,292] and Dowd.[293]

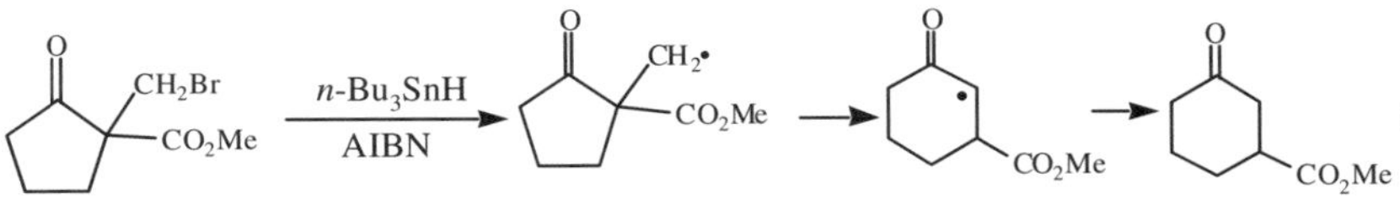

$$(77)$$

ACETOXYL REARRANGEMENTS

The radical rearrangement of acyloxy groups (equation 78), discovered by Surzur and Tessier,[294] and independently by Tanner and Law,[295] and termed the Surzur–Tanner rearrangement, has been the subject of intensive study.[296] It was initially considered to involve a concerted [3,2] acyl migration process of **48** through transition state **A**, but later cleavage to a radical cation/anion pair **B** and a concerted 1,2-migration through transition state **C** have also been considered. Recent calculations support the originally proposed concerted [3,2] acyl shift.[297]

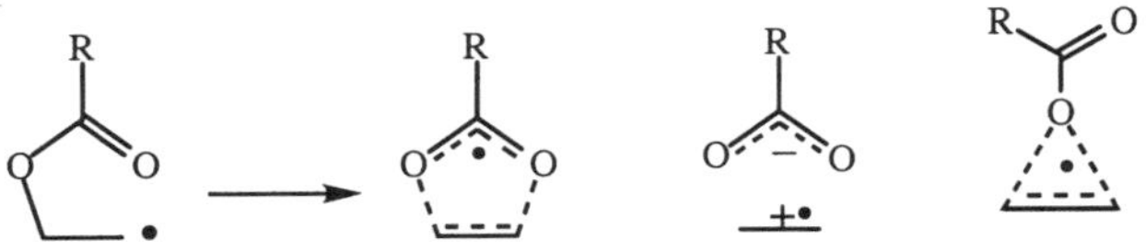

$$(78)$$

48   **A**   **B**   **C**

REARRANGEMENTS OF β-(PHOSPHATOXY)ALKYL RADICALS

The chemistry of radical sites adjacent to phosphatoxy centers elicited interest because of the involvement of such species in DNA degradation processes.[298,299] These species can give rise to rearrangement, elimination, and substitution products, and for some time concerted eliminations and migrations as well as heterolysis to a radical cation and a phosphate anion were considered to be involved (Scheme 2). Recently, experimental studies of the 1,2-dibenzyl-2-(diphenylphosphatoxy)-2-phenylethyl radical and complementary theoretical studies of 1,1-dimethyl-2-(dimethylphosphatoxy)ethyl radical have been interpreted as indicating that a radical cation/anion pathway with initial formation of **49** is favored.[298,299]

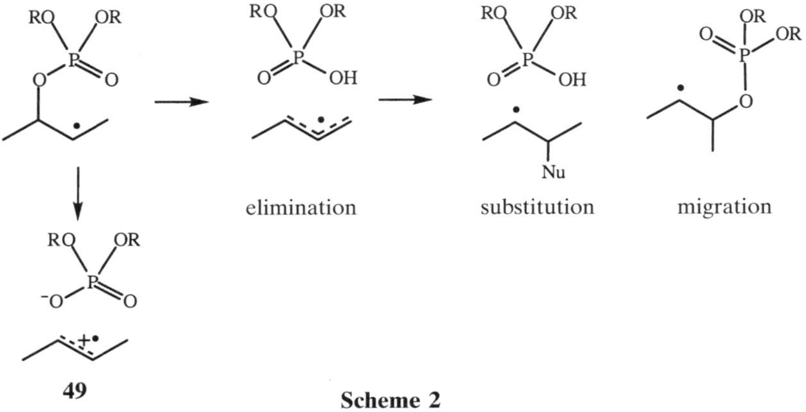

49   **Scheme 2**

REMOTE RADICAL FUNCTIONALIZATION

It was shown by Barton *et al.*[300] that the photolysis of steroidal nitrites **50** proceeding by formation of alkoxy radicals could result in hydrogen abstraction from suitably situated methyl groups forming carbon-centered radicals, which then reacted with the NO generated to give oximes (equation 79). This permitted the functionalization of the unactivated centers.

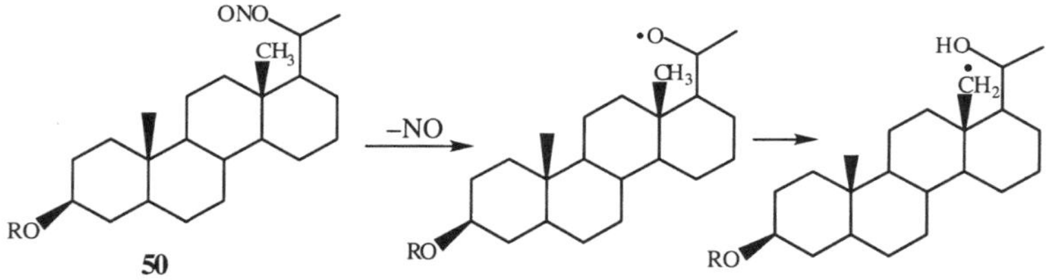

(79)

A comparable functionalization of remote centers was achieved by Breslow and Winnik,[301] in which photolysis of hydrocarbons with a benzophenone moiety attached by a tether of suitable length (**51**) resulted in abstraction of hydrogen by the excited benzophenone from the hydrocarbon chain. This achieved functionalization of the hydrocarbon chain (equation 80).

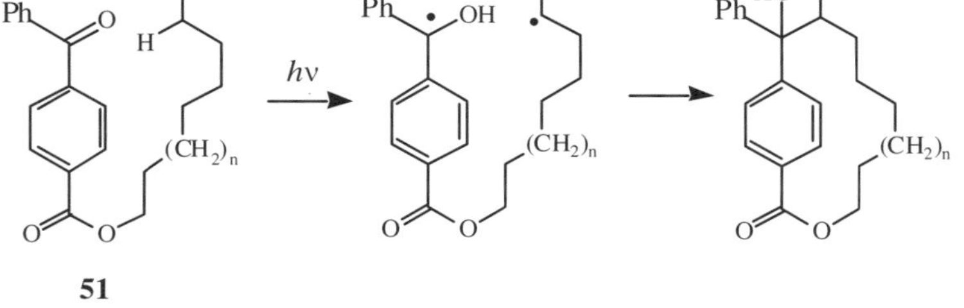

(80)

51

11   New processes

BERGMAN CYCLIZATION

The cyclization of Z-hex-3-en-1,5-diyne (equation 81) forming the diradical intermediate **52** was discovered in 1972 and was initially of largely mechanistic interest.[302,303] Then it was discovered that this reaction occurs in the action of anti-cancer drugs, as with the anti-tumor agent calicheamicin (Fig. 7),[304,305] and this has become a major area of research.

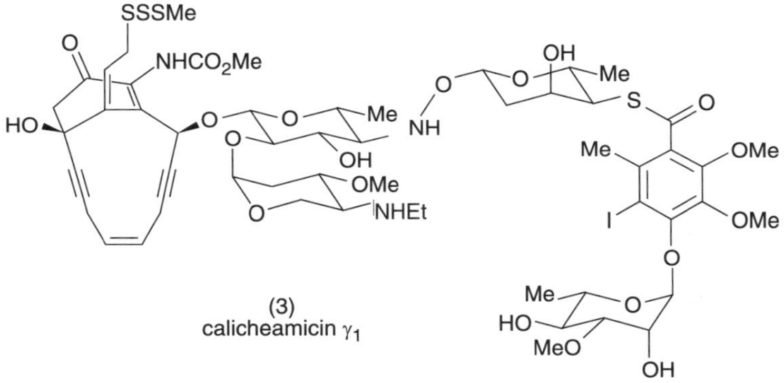

(3)
calicheamicin γ_1

Fig. 7.   Calicheamicin γ_1^1 (reproduced from reference 306 with the permission of the American Chemical Society).

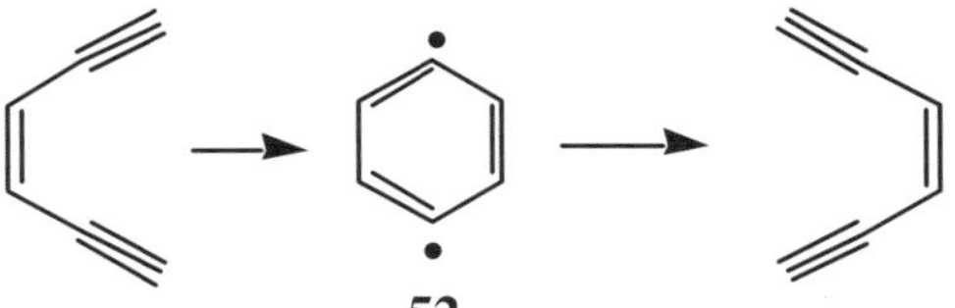

$$(81)$$

52

PTOC ESTERS

Pyridine-2-thione-N-oxycarbonyl (PTOC) derivatives of carboxylic esters **53** were developed by Barton *et al.* and serve as a convenient source of acyloxyl radicals, which upon decarboxylation provide specific routes to free radicals (equation 82).[307] This process can also proceed by a radical addition (equation 83). Acyl selenides (**54**) are a convenient source of acyl radicals, which can undergo decarbonylation also giving specific free radicals (equation 84).[308]

$$\text{(82)}$$

$$\text{(83)}$$

$$\text{(84)}$$

CHLORINATION

As noted previously, free radical substitution of hydrogen by chlorine received early study, and the basic mechanisms of this process were delineated in the period 1930–1936.[135–140] However, in 1957 there was an important new development in this chemistry, when Russell[309] found that the selectivity of the chlorine atom for tertiary versus primary H-atom abstraction from 2,3-dimethylbutane was solvent dependent, and this was ascribed to the formation of π-complexes of the Cl atom with aromatic solvents. These complexes had different selectivities from the uncomplexed chlorine. Then Skell et al.[310,311] made the striking new finding that in inert perhalogenated solvents at very low conversions, for chlorination of hydrocarbons, there were unexpectedly high yields of di- and trichlorinated products. This result was attributed to a cage effect: upon reaction of a hydrocarbon radical with Cl_2 to form a monochlorinated product and a chlorine atom, there was a significant probability of reaction of the two giving a new carbon-centered radical from the already chlorinated product, so that polychlorination could occur (equations 85, 86).[312]

$$c\text{-}C_6H_{12} \xrightarrow[-HCl]{Cl\bullet} c\text{-}C_6H_{11}\bullet \xrightarrow{Cl_2} [c\text{-}C_6H_{11}Cl + Cl\bullet] \quad (85)$$

$$[c\text{-}C_6H_{11}Cl + Cl\bullet] \xrightarrow{-HCl} c\text{-}C_6H_{10}Cl\bullet \xrightarrow{Cl_2} [c\text{-}C_6H_{10}Cl_2 + Cl\bullet] \quad (86)$$

RADICAL CLOCKS

Free radical clocks are reactions with known rate constants such as the cyclization of 5-hexenyl radicals (equation 76) or the ring opening of cyclopropylmethyl radicals **46** (equation 74). Competition reactions of these processes compared to other reactions permit the assignment of rate constants to further processes.[313] These studies were extended by Newcomb and co-workers,[314,315] and include the differentiation between radical and cationic intermediates.

12 Electron transfer processes

RADICAL IONS FROM ARENES: BIRCH REDUCTION AND ARENE OXIDATION

Early examples of electron transfer processes are shown in equations (2), (12), and (13). Birch in 1944[316] followed up the findings of Wooster,[317] and demonstrated that Na metal and ethanol in ammonia reduce benzene, anisole, and other aromatics to 1,4-cyclohexadienes. Birch speculated about the mechanism of this reaction, but did not explicitly describe a radical pathway involving **55** (equation 87) until later, as described in his auto-biography.[318] Electron transfer from arenes was found by Weiss in 1941, who obtained crystalline salts of $C_{14}H_{10}^+$ from oxidation of anthracene.[319]

$$(87)$$

55

ELECTRON TRANSFER IN ALIPHATIC SUBSTITUTION

Reactions occurring by an electron transfer chain reaction in aliphatic systems were reported independently in 1966 by the groups of Kornblum[320,322] and Russell[321] (equations 88, 89). These reactions involve initial transfer of an electron forming a radical anion **56b**, which expels an anionic leaving group forming a neutral free radical, and this radical combines with radical **56a** forming the product.

$$(88)$$

56a   **56b**

$$(89)$$

ELECTRON TRANSFER IN AROMATIC SUBSTITUTION

Kim and Bunnett in 1970 made unexpected observations of reactions occurring by an electron transfer chain mechanism in aromatic systems.[323,324] The selective formation of **60** showed that benzyne intermediates were not formed, and the mechanism of equations (90) and (91) analogous to that found in aliphatic systems (equations 88, 89) was proposed. This process differs in being a chain reaction and not a process in which the product forming step is not a radical–radical combination.

$$\text{57} \xrightarrow{\text{KNH}_2} \text{58} \xrightarrow{-\text{Br}^-} \text{59} \tag{90}$$

$$\text{59} \xrightarrow{\text{KNH}_2} \xrightarrow{\text{57}} \text{60} + \text{58} \tag{91}$$

ELECTROCHEMICAL ELECTRON TRANSFER

The utilization of electrochemistry for electron transfer in organic reactions dates back to Kolbe (equation 2),[7,8] and continues to be a subject of great interest.[325–329] The respective roles of stepwise and concerted dissociative electron transfer (equation 92) have attracted particular attention. As noted above, these reactions were exploited by Michaelis[69–74] in early applications of quantitative biology.

$$\text{R}\bullet + \text{X}^- \xleftarrow{e^-} \text{RX} \xrightarrow{e^-} \text{RX}^{\bullet} \longrightarrow \text{R}\bullet + \text{X}^- \tag{92}$$

13 Radicals in synthesis

SYNTHETIC APPLICATIONS

The utilization of free radical reactions in synthesis, particularly for the formation of carbon–carbon bonds, was given great impetus by initial studies of Stork and Baine (equation 93),[330] and of Hart and co-workers.[330a] A notable early example of a tandem cyclization was the formation of (±)-hirsutene (**61**) in a single process (equation 94).[331,332]

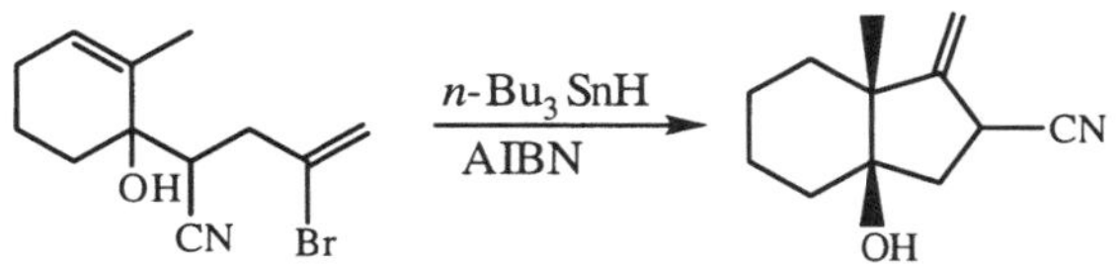

$$n\text{-Bu}_3\text{SnH} \atop \text{AIBN} \tag{93}$$

$$n\text{-Bu}_3\text{Sn}\bullet \atop -n\text{-Bu}_3\text{SnI} \tag{}$$

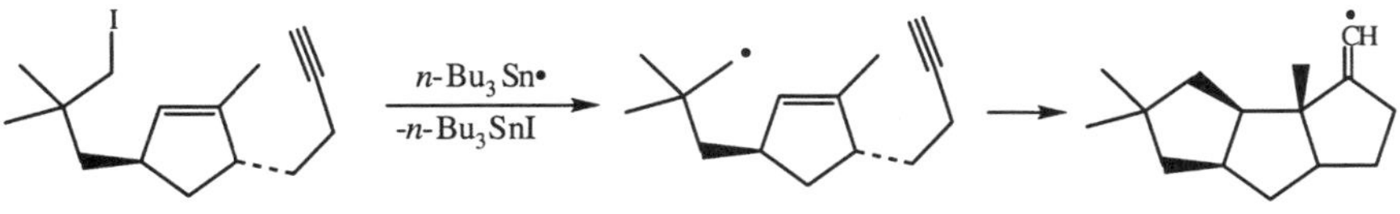

62

$$\textbf{62} \quad \xrightarrow[-n\text{-Bu}_3\text{Sn}\bullet]{\cdot n\text{-Bu}_3\text{S nH}} \tag{94}$$

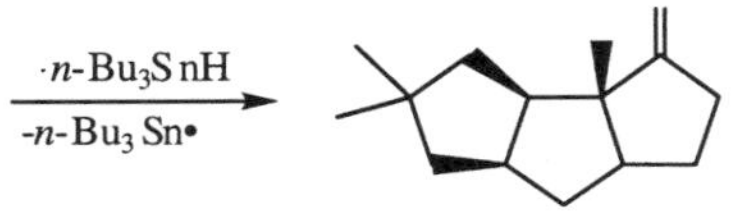

61

ENANTIOSELECTIVE FREE RADICAL REACTIONS

Stereocontrol of free radical reactions has proven to be possible, as in the example shown (equation 95), and is widely exploited.[333-335] The use of chiral auxiliaries as illustrated has proved to have a wide application.

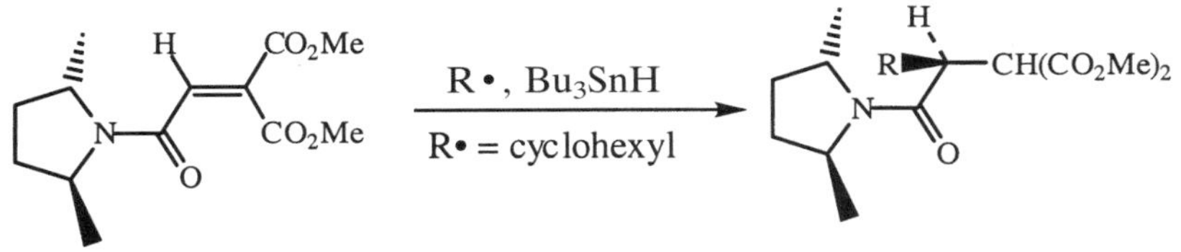

$$\text{R}\bullet, \text{Bu}_3\text{SnH} \atop \text{R}\bullet = \text{cyclohexyl} \tag{95}$$

LIVING FREE RADICAL POLYMERIZATION

The inclusion of stable free radicals such as TEMPO (**18**, TO •) in free radical polymerizations leads to precise control of chain length by restricting the number of polymerizing chains (equation 96).[336-340] This process is known as nitroxyl radical mediated polymerization (NRMP).

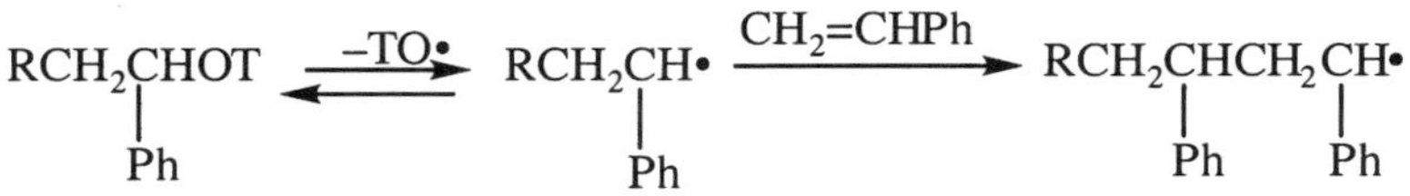

$$RCH_2\underset{\underset{Ph}{|}}{C}HOT \xrightleftharpoons{-TO\bullet} RCH_2\underset{\underset{Ph}{|}}{C}H\bullet \xrightarrow{CH_2=CHPh} RCH_2\underset{\underset{Ph}{|}}{C}HCH_2\underset{\underset{Ph}{|}}{C}H\bullet \qquad (96)$$

Variations on this process include atom transfer polymerization (ATRP),[341] which includes metal catalyzed atom transfer, to give the propagating radical as illustrated in Scheme 3 for Cu(I) catalyzed polymerization of styrene using 1-arylethyl chlorides.

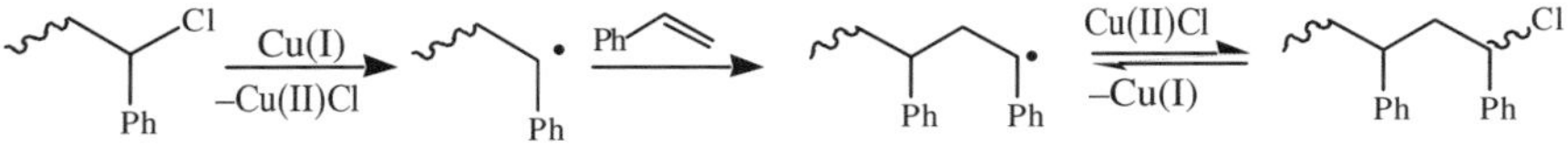

Scheme 3

Reversible addition-fragmentation transfer polymerization (RAFT) typically utilizes a dithioester transfer agent to control the concentration of propagating radicals (equation 97).[342]

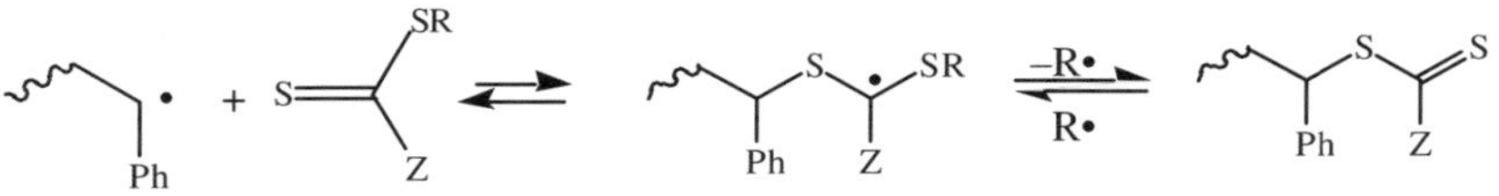

$$(97$$

PERSISTENT-RADICAL EFFECT

The reaction of nitrosoacetanilide, used in Hey's early investigations of aromatic substitution (equation 39),[113,132] revealed it to be one of the more enigmatic sources of phenyl radicals. The essential puzzle was the fact that acetic acid is formed in good yield. The obvious mechanistic analysis (equation 98) was recognized to be unsatisfactory, since acetoxyl radicals invariably decarboxylate far too rapidly to carry through into a high yield product. This led Huisgen and Horeld to advance the "kryptoradical" hypothesis,[343] in which a sort of cage or concerted radical process was proposed wherein the hydrogen is transferred to the acetoxyl radical as it is formed. Another feature which distinguishes this reaction from, e.g., phenylation by benzoyl peroxide, is the absence of products resulting from dimerization of the phenylcyclohexadienyl intermediate. A solution to these puzzles was proposed by Rüchardt in 1964:[344] the acetic acid is the product of a non-radical step, and the absence of dimeric products is attributable to what has become known as the "persistent-radical effect" (sometimes the Fischer–Ingold effect), which was the subject of a detailed kinetic analysis by Fischer in 1986.[345]

$$\underset{\underset{NO}{|}}{\overset{\overset{O}{\|}}{PhNCCH_3}} \xrightarrow{\text{benzene}} \overset{\overset{O}{\|}}{PhN=NOCCH_3} \xrightarrow{-N_2} Ph\bullet + [\bullet O_2CCH_3] \qquad (98)$$

The persistent-radical effect may be illustrated by reference to a reaction of another phenyl radical source, namely phenylazotriphenylmethane (**31**), with tetrachloromethane.[346] This reaction (equations 99, 100) gives excellent yields of chlorobenzene and 1,1,1-trichloro-2,2,2-triphenylethane (**62**). In this case, the azo compound decomposes into phenyl and trityl radicals, together with a molecule of nitrogen. The more reactive phenyl then abstracts chlorine from CCl$_4$ and radical coupling produces **62**. It may at first seem strange that only *unsymmetrical* coupling takes place. No hexachloroethane is found. The explanation is that production of no more than trace amounts of hexachloroethane would, of necessity, be accompanied by equivalent quantities of the dimer **3** of triphenylmethyl *in equilibrium with triphenylmethyl itself*. Therefore, very rapidly the triphenylmethyl concentration far exceeds that of the transient trichloromethyl. Since the rates of reactions of trichloromethyl with itself and with triphenylmethyl are very similar (close to the diffusion limit), unsymmetrical coupling will predominate. Of course, this does not deplete the reservoir of triphenylmethyl since for every trichloromethyl which is formed, another triphenylmethyl is also produced. Consistent with this, examination of the reacting solution by ESR reveals an intense signal from the triphenylmethyl radical.

$$\underset{\mathbf{31}}{Ph_3CN=NPh} \xrightarrow{-N_2} \underset{\mathbf{1}}{Ph_3C\bullet} + Ph\bullet \qquad (99)$$

$$Ph\bullet \xrightarrow[-PhCl]{CCl_4} CCl_3\bullet \xrightarrow{Ph_3C\bullet} \underset{\mathbf{62}}{Ph_3CCCl_3} \qquad (100)$$

In the nitrosoacetanilide system, Binsch and Rüchardt[347] recognized that a relatively high concentration of a persistent radical forms, which efficiently oxidizes the phenylcyclohexadienyl intermediate to biphenyl (equation 39) and produces a second species, from which the radical is regenerated in a catalytic cycle. Two possibilities, **63** and **64**, exist for the identity of the pesistent radical,[348–350] and both of these can reach ESR-detectable concentrations.[350] These concentrations would completely swamp any self-reaction of phenylcyclohexadienyl, and it may be that two competing process are operating.

$$PhN=NO\bullet \qquad\qquad PhNAcN(O\bullet)Ph$$
$$\textbf{63} \qquad\qquad\qquad \textbf{64}$$

Some early examples of a preference for unsymmetrical radical coupling were drawn together in a short paper by Perkins in 1964.[350] Intriguingly, the first correct analysis of an example of this kind of behavior dates from 1936:[351] Bachmann and Wiselogle clearly understood the role of triphenylmethyl in accounting for their observations that, in solution at 100°C, pentaphenylethane dissociates rapidly and reversibly into triphenylmethyl and diphenylmethyl, but dimerization of the diphenylmethyl to form detectable quantities of tetraphenylethane (which is stable under the reaction conditions) occurs only very slowly.

The decomposition of **31** in benzene, like that of nitrosoacetanilide, does not give phenylcyclohexadienyl dimers, since the outcome is again governed by the presence of a persistent radical, in this case triphenylmethyl. A limited kinetic analysis of this system was given by D.F. DeTar in 1967.[352] The Fischer analysis,[346] however, is much more general, and takes account of the effect of less persistent radicals such as t-alkylperoxyls, which do decay irreversibly but only by relatively slow processes. Minisci et al.[353] have shown how hydrogen-bonding solvents can modulate the formation of persistent radicals and direct product formation using tert-butylhydroperoxide. The persistent-radical effect has also been applied to the analysis of homolysis of a benzylcobalt complex.[353]

14 Biological free radicals

The realization that free radicals are involved in biological processes occurred early in the Century, particularly in biological oxidations, as O_2 was known to be a diradical. In 1931 Haber and Willstätter considered the possibility that enzyme-catalyzed reactions, particularly oxidations, occurred by radical chain processes.[123] As noted above, Leonor Michaelis[69–74] pioneered this field, with extensive quantitative studies of oxidation reactions, particularly involving hydroquinones (equations 12, 13), and provided strong evidence for the formation of radicals in such processes and, by implication, in biological reactions as well. In 1939[74] Michaelis made his famous statement "We propound the hypothesis that any oxidation (or reduction) has to proceed in successive univalent steps." Although this bold hypothesis was soon shown to have exceptions, it had a profound effect and the existence of free radicals in biological systems was widely accepted. By 1961 the field had advanced significantly and a review volume was dedicated to Michaelis.[354] This area has continued to grow and more recently even reviews by specialists [355–360] are highly selective "because of the tremendous breadth of that topic".[355] A few recent examples are briefly described below, to illustrate how the principles of free radical chemistry that have been uncovered are finding application in the chemistry of biological systems.

ANTIOXIDANTS

Biological antioxidants such as α-tocopherol (**65**, vitamin E) serve to inhibit free radical chain oxidation, and the mechanisms of their reactions have attracted close attention.[361,362] The chain-breaking reaction of such phenols with peroxyl radicals is by hydrogen transfer (equation 101).

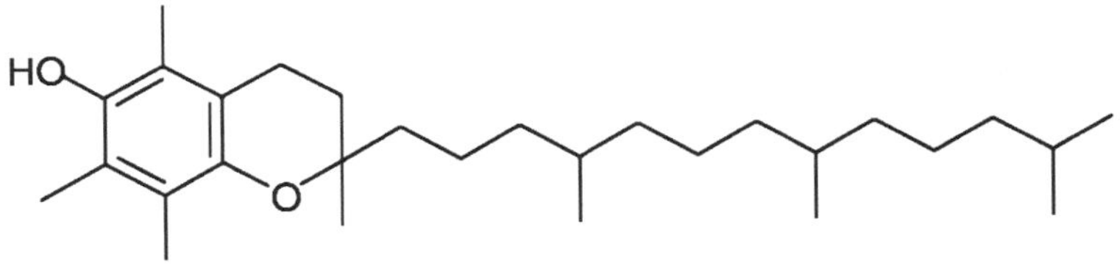

65

$$\text{ArOH} + \text{LOO}\bullet \longrightarrow \text{ArO}\bullet + \text{LOOH}$$

ARACHIDONIC ACID CASCADE

The arachidonic acid cascade is a biological free radical oxidation of unsaturated fatty acids leading to formation of the prostaglandins (equation 102).[363–370] Cyclization of a peroxy radical intermediate **66** leading to endoperoxide **67** was proposed as a pathway for this process, and this was demonstrated in chemical model systems, in which the peroxyl radical **66** was generated by hydrogen abstraction from the hydroperoxide corresponding to **66**.

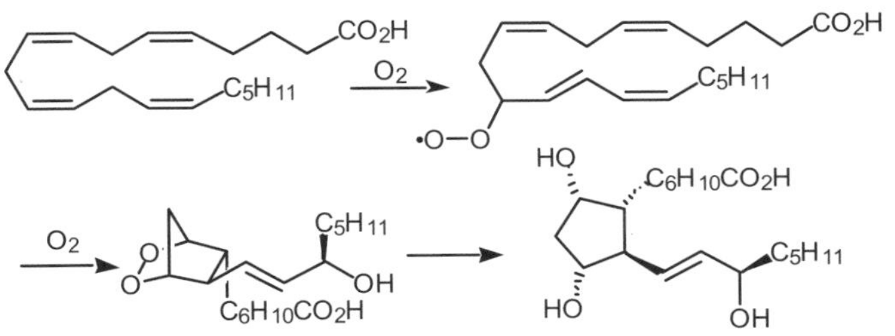

(102)

RADICAL REACTIONS WITH DNA

Because of the susceptibility of DNA to damage by free radical processes, this chemistry has been extensively examined, including studies of the reactions of the primary species generated by radiolysis in water (solvated electrons, H·, and HO·) of purine and pyrimidine bases.[371,372] Investigations of the cleavage of specifically tritium-labeled DNA by oxidants such as bleomycin revealed the site of hydrogen atom abstraction from the deoxyribose.[373] The cyclization of 2'-deoxyadenosin-5'-yl radicals **68** was found to occur as in equation (103).[374] Specific generation of thyminylmethyl and 2'-deoxyuridin-1'-yl radicals (**69, 70**) by laser flash photolysis (equations 104, 105) allowed measurement of their reactivity with various radical traps.[375] The β,α-product ratio from **70** of 64/36 was constant regardless of the precursor stereochemistry. Photolysis of ribose-5-phosphate at 193 nm results in the loss of phosphate and formation of radical sites on the ribose residue by hydrogen atom abstraction.[372]

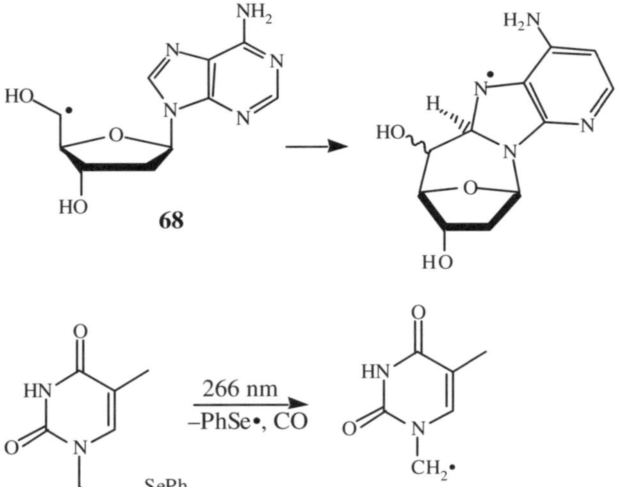

(103)

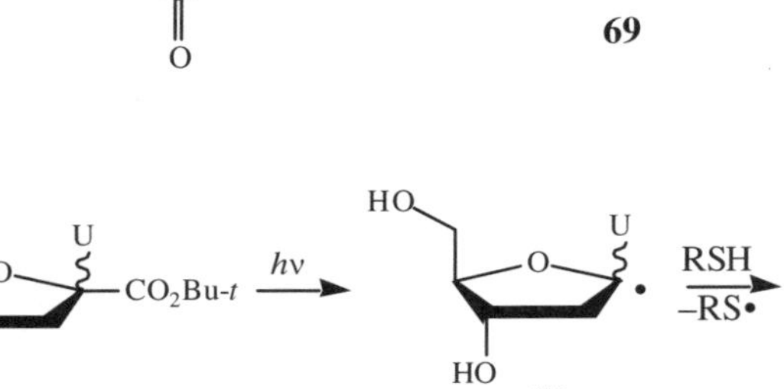

(104)

(105)

Evidence of oxidative damage of DNA forming peroxyl radicals has been identified for the 5,6-dihydrothymidin-5-yl radical numbered *1* (Fig. 8) forming the radical *2*.[376] A mechanism has been proposed whereby *2* forms *9*, but with concomitant formation of superoxide ($O_2^-\cdot$).

RIBONUCLEOTIDE REDUCTASES

Conversion of ribonucleotides to deoxyribonucleotides is an important process that occurs by several pathways, and in one of these, tyrosyl radicals **71** are formed, which serve to generate thiyl radicals from cysteine residues (equation 106).[377–384] A mechanism for this process has been proposed by Stubbe *et al.* (Fig. 9).[377,379] The ESR spectrum of the transient tyrosyl radical from photoactivation of DNA photolyase has been compared to that from other sources.[382] Glycyl based radicals are involved in other reductases,[383] and the free glycyl radical has been identified in the gas phase.[384]

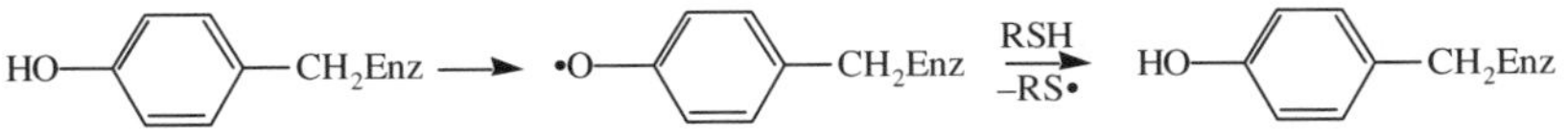

$$\text{HO}-\!\!\!\left\langle\;\right\rangle\!\!\!-\text{CH}_2\text{Enz} \longrightarrow \cdot\text{O}-\!\!\!\left\langle\;\right\rangle\!\!\!-\text{CH}_2\text{Enz} \xrightarrow[-\text{RS}\cdot]{\text{RSH}} \text{HO}-\!\!\!\left\langle\;\right\rangle\!\!\!-\text{CH}_2\text{Enz} \quad (106)$$

71

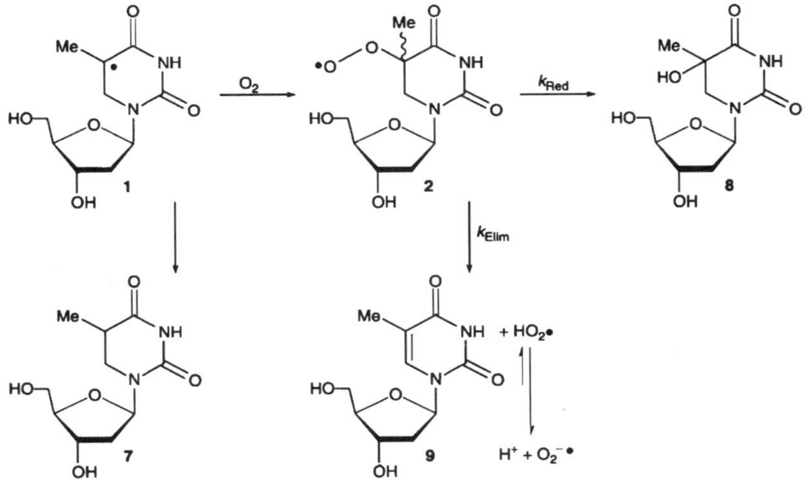

Fig. 8 Model for oxidative damage of DNA (reproduced from reference 376 with the permission of the American Chemical Society).

VITAMIN B_{12}

The chemistry of vitamin B_{12} involves radical generation by cleavage of carbon–cobalt bonds (equation 107), and photoacoustic calorimetry reveals bond strengths of 36 and 37 kcal/mol, respectively, for the Co—CH_3 bonds in methylcobalamin and methylcobinamide.[385] The resultant radicals can generate thiyl radicals that are essential in catalysis (equation 108). However, in some cases, such as the methylmalonyl-CoA to succinyl-CoA rearrangement, the use of cyclopropyl probes provides no evidence for free radical intermediates.[386] Radicals are, however, detected by ESR in B_{12} induced deamination with ethanolamine deaminase.[387] In many cases, enzymes serve to permit selective reaction of free radicals by *negative catalysis*, that is by preventing undesired reactions of the highly active radicals, so that other processes may proceed.[388]

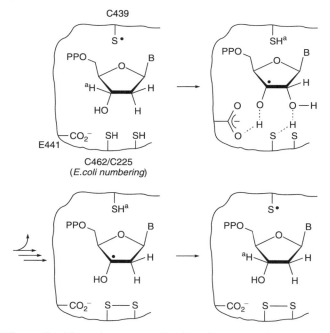

Fig. 9 Ribonucleotide reductase mechanism for conversion of ribonucleotides to 2′-deoxyribonucleotides (reproduced from reference 379 with the permission of the American Chemical Society).

$$RCH_2\text{–}B_{12} \rightleftharpoons RCH_2{\bullet} + {\bullet}B_{12r} \qquad (107)$$

$$RCH_2{\bullet} + HSR^1 \longrightarrow RCH_3 + {\bullet}SR^1 \qquad (108)$$

NITRIC OXIDE

The stable free radical nitric oxide (NO) has an important role as a biological messenger.[389–392] The reaction of NO with superoxide (O_2^- ') forms the powerful oxidant peroxynitrite (ONOO$^-$),[389–392] and a mechanism for the reaction of ONOO$^-$ resulting in the abstraction of H from C—H bonds is shown (equations 109, 110).[389] The formation of HO· from the spontaneous decomposition of peroxynitrite, and of CO_3^- ' radicals from CO_2 catalyzed decomposition of peroxynitrite, have been demonstrated.[392]

$$ONOO^- \underset{}{\overset{H^+}{\rightleftharpoons}} ONOOH \rightleftharpoons [NO_2\bullet \; \bullet OH] \longrightarrow NO_2\bullet + \bullet OH \quad (109)$$

$$ONOOH \xrightarrow{RH} R\bullet + H_2O + NO_2\bullet \qquad (110)$$

CYTOCHROME P-450

There has been a long history of interpretation of the cytochrome P-450-induced hydroxylation of alkenes as involving free radicals by the "oxygen-rebound" mechanism (Fig. 10).[393–396] However, recent experiments cast doubt on this hypothesis, and favor oxygen insertion forming an alcohol, and subsequent carbocation formation resulting in observed rearrangements.[393] Evidence for thiyl-based radicals formed from such iron hemes has appeared.[395]

ACETYLCoA DEHYDROGENASE

These enzymes convert acetylCoA thioesters into E-α,β-enoyl-CoA products. The presence of radicals in this reaction has been investigated in one example by using spiropentylacetyl-CoA as a probe giving the radicals **72–74** (Scheme 4).[397]

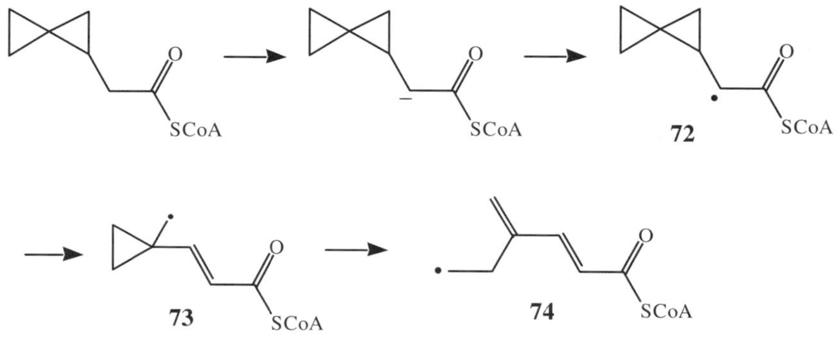

Scheme 4

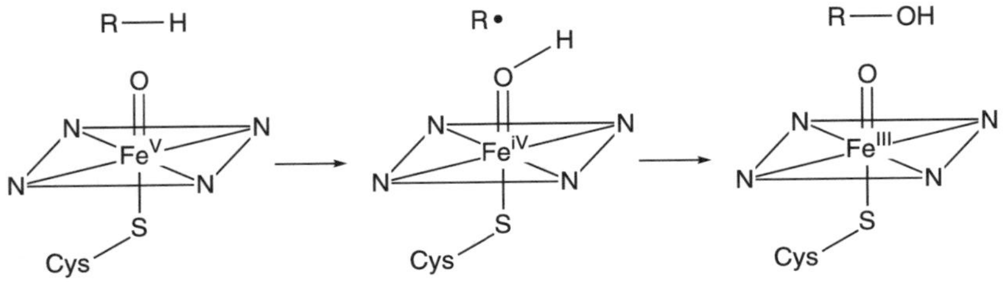

Fig. 10 Oxygen-rebound mechanism for P-450-catalyzed hydroxylation (reproduced from reference 393 with the permission of the American Chemical Society).

15 Summary

In summary, the science of free radical chemistry showed remarkable advancement during the Century following Gomberg's seminal contribution in 1900. The current vigor of the field shows that the impetus provided by the pioneers mentioned in this brief survey is by no means spent. The breadth of the field indicates that any future comprehensive survey will be a major undertaking. However, there are recent concise descriptions of the field that are highly recommended.[398,399]

Acknowledgements

Financial support by The Natural Sciences and Engineering Research Council of Canada is gratefully acknowledged, as is the assistance and encouragement of many individuals. These include Professor John Perkins, who provided much of the text dealing with spin traps and the persistent radical effects, and Professors John Lorand, John Warkentin, Keith Ingold, and Paul Engel.

References

1. Gomberg, M. (1900). *Chem. Ber.* **33**, 3150, *J. Am. Chem. Soc.* **22**, 757
2. Schlenk, W., Weickel, T. and Herzenstein, A. (1910). *Liebigs Ann.* **372**, 1
3. McBride, J.M. (1974). *Tetrahedron* **30**, 2009
4. Lankamp, W., Nauta, W.Th. and MacLean, C. (1968). *Tetrahedron Lett.* 249
5. Ihde, A.J. (1967). *Pure Appl. Chem.* **15**, 1
6. Ihde, A.J. (1966). *Chem. Eng. News*, October 3, 1966, 90
7. Kolbe, H. (1849). *Liebigs Ann.* **69**, 257
8. Crum Brown, A. and Walker, J. (1891). *Liebigs Ann.* **261**, 107
9. Nef, J.U. (1897). *Liebigs Ann.* **298**, 202
10. (1934). *Trans. Faraday Soc.* **30**, 1
11. (1967). *Pure Appl. Chem.* **15**, 1

12. (2000). *Chem. Eng. News*, 17 July, 2000, p 47
13. Rüchardt, C. (1992). *Sitz. Heidelberger Akad. Wiss. Math.-natur. Klasse* 319
14. Tidwell, T.T. (2000). *Chem. Intelligencer* **6(3)**, 33
15. Tidwell, T.T. (1947). *Disc. Faraday Soc.* **2**, 1
16. Tidwell, T.T. (1953). *Disc. Faraday Soc.* **14**, 3
17. Walling, C. (1957). *Free Radicals in Solution*. Wiley, New York
18. Schlenk, W. and Mark, H. (1922). *Chem. Ber.* **55**, 2285
19. Ziegler, K. and Schnell, B. (1925). *Liebigs Ann.* **445**, 266
20. Ziegler, K., Bremer, G., Thiel, F. and Thielmann, F. (1923). *Liebigs Ann.* **434**, 34
21. Koelsch, C.F. (1957). *J. Am. Chem. Soc.* **79**, 4439
22. Löwenbein, A. (1925). *Chem. Ber.* **58**, 601
23. Ballester, M. (1989). *Adv. Phys. Org. Chem.* **25**, 267
24. Tanatar, S. (1896). *Chem. Ber.* **29**, 1297
25. Chambers, T.S. and Kistiakowsky, G.B. (1934). *J. Am. Chem. Soc.* **56**, 399
26. Bettinger, H.F., Rienstra-Kiracofe, J.C., Hoffman, B.C., Schaefer, H.F., III, Baldwin, J.E. and Schleyer, P.v.R. (1999). *J. Chem. Soc., Chem. Commun.* 1515
27. Birladeanu, L. (1998). *J. Chem. Ed.* **75**, 603
28. Schlenk, W. and Brauns, M. (1915). *Chem. Ber.* **48**, 661
29. Leo, M. (1937). *Chem. Ber.* **70**, 1691
30. Iwamura, H. (1990). *Adv. Phys. Org. Chem.* **26**, 179
31. Wieland, H. (1911). *Chem. Ber.* **44**, 2550
32. Falvey, D.E., Khambatta, B.S. and Schuster, G.B. (1990). *J. Phys. Chem.* **94**, 1056
33. Urry, W.H. and Kharasch, M.S. (1944). *J. Am. Chem. Soc.* **66**, 1438
34. Kasai, P.H., McLeod, D., Jr. and McBay, H.C. (1974). *J. Am. Chem. Soc.* **96**, 6864
35. Brunton, G., McBay, H.C. and Ingold, K.U. (1977). *J. Am. Chem. Soc.* **99**, 4447
36. Wieland, H. (1911). *Liebigs Ann.* **381**, 200
37. Wieland, H. and Lecher, H. (1912). *Chem. Ber.* **45**, 2600
38. Wieland, H. (1915). *Chem. Ber.* **48**, 1078
39. Cain, C.K. and Wiselogle, F.Y. (1940). *J. Am. Chem. Soc.* **62**, 1163
40. Wieland, H. and Roth, K. (1920). *Chem. Ber.* **53**, 210
41. Wieland, H. and Kögl, F. (1922). *Chem. Ber.* **55**, 1798
42. Wieland, H. and Offenbächer, M. (1914). *Chem. Ber.* **47**, 2111
43. Banfield, F.H. and Kenyon, J. (1926). *J. Chem. Soc.* 1612
44. Lebedev, O.L. and Kazarnovsky, S.N. (1959). *Treatises on Chemistry and Chemical Technology (Gorky)* **3**, 649
45. Lebedev, O.L., Khidekel, M.L. and Razuvaev, G.A. (1961). *Dokl. Akad. Nauk SSR* **140**, 1327
46. Hoffman, A.K. and Henderson, A.T. (1961). *J. Am. Chem. Soc.* **83**, 4671
47. Pummerer, R. and Frankfurter, F. (1914). *Chem. Ber.* **47**, 1472
48. Forrester, A.R., Hay, J.M. and Thomson, R.H. (1968). *Organic Chemistry of Stable Free Radicals*, Chap. 7, p. 281. Academic Press, London
49. Goldschmidt, S. (1922). *Chem. Ber.* **55**, 3194
50. Müller, E., Ley, K. and Schlechte, G. (1957). *Chem. Ber.* **90**, 2660
51. Allmann, R. and Hellner, E. (1968). *Chem. Ber.* **101**, 2522
52. Ashworth, F. and Burkhardt, G.N. (1928). *J. Chem. Soc.* 1791
53. Schönberg, A., with a comment by Burkhardt, G.N. (1934). *Trans. Faraday Soc.* **30**, 17
54. Schönberg, A. and Rupp, E. (1933). *Z. Naturwiss.* **21**, 561
55. Jones, S.O. and Reid, E.E. (1938). *J. Am. Chem. Soc.* **60**, 2452
56. Kharasch, M.S., Read, A.T. and Mayo, F.R. (1938). *Chem. Ind.* 752
57. Beckmann, E. and Paul, T. (1891). *Liebigs Ann.* **266**, 1
58. Schlenk, W. and Weickel, T. (1911). *Chem. Ber.* **44**, 1182

59. Doescher, R.N. and Wheland, G.W. (1934). *J. Am. Chem. Soc.* **56**, 2011
60. Sugden, S. (1934). *Trans. Faraday Soc.* **30**, 18
61. Hou, Z., Jia, X., Fujita, A., Tezuka, H., Yamazaki, H. and Wakatsuki, Y. (2000). *Chem. Eur. J.* **6**. 2994
62. Favorsky, A.E. and Nazarov, I.N. (1934). *Bull. Soc. Chim. Fr.* [5] **1**, 46
63. Hirota, N. and Weissman, S.I. (1960). *J. Am. Chem. Soc.* **82**, 4424
64. Conant, J.B. and Cutter, H.B. (1926). *J. Am. Chem. Soc.* **48**, 1016
65. Wurster, C. and Sendtner, R. (1879). *Chem. Ber.* **12**, 1803
66. Weitz, E. (1954). *Angew. Chem.* **66**, 658
67. Hünig, S. (1967). *Pure Appl. Chem.* **15**, 109
68. Ito, A., Ono, Y. and Tanaka, K. (2000). *Angew. Chem. Int.* **39**, 1072
69. Michaelis, L. (1931). *J. Biol. Chem.* **92**, 211
70. Michaelis, L. (1935). *Chem. Rev.* **16**, 243
71. Michaelis, L. and Schubert, M.P. (1938). *Chem. Rev.* **22**, 437
72. Michaelis, L. and Smythe, C.V. (1938). *Ann. Rev. Biochem.* **7**, 1
73. Michaelis, L., Schubert, M.P. and Granick, S. (1939). *J. Am. Chem. Soc.* **61**, 1981
74. Michaelis, L. (1939). *Cold Spring Harbor Sympos. Quant. Biol.* **7**, 33
75. Dimroth, O. (1933). *Angew. Chem.* **36**, 571
76. Bodenstein, M. and Lind, S.C. (1906). *Z. Physik. Chem.* **57**, 168
77. Bodenstein, M. (1926). *Trans. Faraday Soc.* **21**, 525
78. Christiansen, J.A. (1919). *Kgl. Danske Videnskabernes Selskab. Mathematisk-fysiske Meddelelser* **14**, 1
79. Herzfield, K.F. (1919). *Ann. Physik.* **59**, 635
80. Polanyi, M. (1920). *Z. Electrochem.* **26**, 49
81. Lewis, G.N. (1916). *J. Am. Chem. Soc.* **38**, 762
82. Lewis, G.N. (1916). *Proc. Natl. Acad. Sci. USA* **2**, 586
83. Hinshelwood, C.N. (1933). *The Kinetics of Chemical Change in Gaseous Systems*, 3rd edn. Oxford University Press
84. Semenov, N. (1929). *Chem. Rev.* **6**, 347
85. Semenov, N. (1935). *Chemical Kinetics and Chain Reactions.* Oxford University Press
86. Bonhoeffer, K.F. (1924). *Z. Physik. Chem.* **113**, 199
87. Paneth, F. and Hofeditz, W. (1929). *Chem. Ber.* **62**, 1335
88. Paneth, F.A. and Lautsch, W. (1931). *Chem. Ber.* **64B**, 2702
89. Paneth, F.A. and Lautsch, W. (1935). *J. Chem. Soc.* 380
90. Rice, F.O., Johnston, W.R. and Evering, B.L. (1932). *J. Am. Chem. Soc.* **54**, 3529
91. Rice, F.O. (1931). *J. Am. Chem. Soc.* **53**, 1959
92. Rice, F.O. and Rice, K.K. (1935). *Free Radicals.* Johns Hopkins Press, Baltimore
93. v. Hartel, H. and Polanyi, M. (1930). *Z. Physik. Chem.* **11B**, 97
94. Horn, E., Polanyi, M. and Style, D.W.G. (1934) *Trans. Faraday Soc.* **30**, 189
95. Gomberg, M. and Bachmann, W.E. (1927). *J. Am. Chem. Soc.* **49**, 236
96. Kharasch, M.S. and Reinmuth, O. (1954). *Grignard Reactions of Nonmetallic Substances.* Prentice-Hall, New York
97. Garst, J.F., Ungváry, F. and Baxter, J.T. (1997). *J. Am. Chem. Soc.* **119**, 253
98. Walborsky, H.M. (1990). *Acc. Chem. Res.* **23**, 286
99. Garst, J.F. (2000). In *Grignard Reagents: New Developments,* Richey, H.G., Jr. (Ed.), pp. 185–275. Wiley, New York
100. Holm, T. (2000). *J. Org. Chem.* **65**, 1188
101. Yamataka, H., Matsuyama, T. and Hanafusa, T. (1989). *J. Am. Chem. Soc.* **111**, 4912
102. Faraday, M. (1821). *Ann. Chim. Phys.* [2] **18**, 48
103. Berthoud, A. and Béraneck, J. (1927). *J. Chim. Phys.* **24**, 213

104. Wachholtz, F. (1927). *Z. Physik. Chem.* **125**, 1
105. Dickinson, R.G. and Leermakers, J.A. (1932). *J. Am. Chem. Soc.* **54**, 3852
106. Dickinson, R.G. and Carrico, J.L. (1934). *J. Am. Chem. Soc.* **56**, 1473
107. Bauer, W.H. and Daniels, F.J. (1934). *J. Am. Chem. Soc.* **56**, 2014
108. Smith, H.P., Noyes, W.A., Jr. and Hart, E.J. (1933). *J. Am. Chem. Soc.* **55**, 4444
109. Price, C.C. (1936). *J. Am. Chem. Soc.* **58**, 1834
110. Kharasch, M.S. and Mayo, F.R. (1933). *J. Am. Chem. Soc.* **55**, 2468
111. Kharasch, M.S., Engelmann, H. and Mayo, F.R. (1937). *J. Org. Chem.* **2**, 288
112. Kharasch, M.S., Mansfield, J.V. and Mayo, F.R. (1937). *J. Am. Chem. Soc.* **59**, 1155
113. Hey, D.H. and Waters, W.A. (1937). *Chem. Rev.* **21**, 169
114. Mayo, F.R. (1986). *J. Chem. Ed.* **63**, 97
115. Robinson, R. (1933). *Chem. Ind.* 219
116. Ashton, R. and Smith, J.C. (1934). *J. Chem. Soc.* 435
117. Urushibara, Y. and Takebayashi, M. (1936). *Bull. Chem. Soc. Jpn* **11**, 798
118. Urushibara, Y. and Simamura, O. (1939). *Bull. Chem. Soc. Jpn* **14**, 323
119. Wöhler, F. and Liebig, J. (1832). *Liebigs Ann.* **3**, 249
120. Baeyer, A. and Villiger, V. (1900). *Chem. Ber.* **33**, 1569
121. Bäckström, H.L.J. (1934). *Z. Physik. Chem.* **25b**, 99
122. Bates, J.R. and Spence, R. (1931). *J. Am. Chem. Soc.* **53**, 1689
123. Haber, F. and Willstätter, R. (1931). *Chem. Ber.* **64**, 2844
124. Criegee, R. (1936). *Liebigs Ann.* **522**, 75
125. Hock, H. and Lang, S. (1944). *Chem. Ber.* **77**, 257
126. Taylor, H.S. (1925). *Trans. Faraday Soc.* **21**, 560
127. Taylor, H.S. and Jones, W.H. (1930). *J. Am. Chem. Soc.* **52**, 1111
128. Cramer, P.L. (1934). *J. Am. Chem. Soc.* **56**, 1234
129. Staudinger, H. (1932). *Die Hochmolekularen Organischen Verbindungen.* Springer, Berlin, p. 151
130. Flory, P.J. (1937). *J. Am. Chem. Soc.* **59**, 241
131. Rice, O.K. and Sickman, D.V. (1935). *J. Am. Chem. Soc.* **57**, 1384
132. Grieve, W.S.M. and Hey, D.H. (1934). *J. Chem. Soc.* 1797
133. Hey, D.H. (1934). *J. Chem. Soc.* 1966
134. Gomberg, M. and Bachmann, W.E. (1924). *J. Am. Chem. Soc.* **46**, 2339
135. Schwab, G.-M. and Heyde, U. (1930). *Z. Physik. Chem.* **8b**, 147
136. Pease, R.N. and Walz, G.F. (1931). *J. Am. Chem. Soc.* **53**, 3728
137. Hass, H.B., McBee, E.T. and Weber, P. (1936). *Ind. Eng. Chem.* **28**, 333. (1935). **27**, 1190
138. Brown, H.C., Kharasch, M.S. and Chao, T.H. (1940). *J. Am. Chem. Soc.* **62**, 3435
139. Kharasch, M.S., Engelmann, F. and Urry, W.H. (1943). *J. Am. Chem. Soc.* **65**, 2428
140. Kharasch, M.S., Margolis, E., White, P.C. and Mayo, F.R. (1937). *J. Am. Chem. Soc.* **59**, 1405
141. Wohl, A. (1919). *Chem. Ber.* **52**, 51
142. Ziegler, K., Späth, A., Schaaf, E., Schumann, W. and Winkelmann, E. (1942). *Liebigs Ann.* **551**, 80
143. Pearson, R.E. and Martin, J.C. (1963). *J. Am. Chem. Soc.* **85**, 354
144. Russell, G.A., DeBoer, C. and Desmond, K.M. (1963). *J. Am. Chem. Soc.* **85**, 365
144(a). Adams, J., Gosselain, P.A. and Goldfinger, P. (1953). *Nature* **171**, 704
145. Skell, P.S., Tuleen, D.L. and Readio, P.D. (1963). *J. Am. Chem. Soc.* **85**, 2850
146. Gomberg, M. (1898). *J. Am. Chem. Soc.* **20**, 773. (1897). *Chem. Ber.* **30**, 2043
147. Wieland, H., Popper, E. and Seefried, H. (1922). *Chem. Ber.* **55**, 1816

148. Ramsperger, H.C. (1927). *J. Am. Chem. Soc.* **49**, 912; (1927). *J. Am. Chem. Soc.* **49**, 1495; (1928). *J. Am. Chem. Soc.* **50**, 714. (1929). *J. Am. Chem. Soc.* **51**, 2134
149. Leermakers, J.A. (1933). *J. Am. Chem. Soc.* **55**, 3499
150. Allen, A.O. and Sickman, D.V. (1934). *J. Am. Chem. Soc.* **56**, 2031
151. Davis, T.W., Jahn, F.P. and Burton, M. (1938). *J. Am. Chem. Soc.* **60**, 10
152. Engel, P.S. (1980). *Chem. Rev.* **80**, 99
153. Diau, E.W.-G., Abou-Zied, O.K., Scala, A.A. and Zewail, A.H. (1998). *J. Am. Chem. Soc.* **120**, 3245
154. Adam, W., Martí, V., Sahin, C. and Trofimov, A.V. (2000). *J. Am. Chem. Soc.* **122**, 5002
155. Gelissen, H. and Hermans, P.H. (1925). *Chem. Ber.* **58**, 285
156. Hermans, P.H. (1935). *Recl. Trav. Chim.* **54**, 760
157. Böeseken, Hermans, P.H. (1935). *Liebigs Ann.* **519**, 133
158. Wieland, H. and Razuvaev, G. (1930). *Liebigs Ann.* **480**, 157
159. Wieland, H., Schapiro, S. and Metzger, H. (1934). *Liebigs Ann.* **513**, 93
160. Brown, D.J. (1940). *J. Am. Chem. Soc.* **62**, 2657
161. Swain, C.G., Stockmayer, W.H. and Clarke, J.T. (1950). *J. Am. Chem. Soc.* **72**, 5426
162. Baeyer, A. and Villiger, V. (1901). *Chem. Ber.* **34**, 738
163. Blomquist, A.T. and Ferris, A.F. (1951). *J. Am. Chem. Soc.* **73**, 3408
164. Bartlett, P.D. and Hiatt, R.R. (1958). *J. Am. Chem. Soc.* **80**, 1398
165. Norrish, R.G.W., Crone, H.G. and Saltmarsh, O.D. (1934). *J. Chem. Soc.* 1456
166. Norrish, R.G.W. (1934). *Trans. Faraday Soc.* **30**, 103
167. Pearson, T.G. (1934). *J. Chem. Soc.* 1718
168. Pearson, T.G. and Purcell, R.H. (1935). *J. Chem. Soc.* 1151
169. De Feyter, S., Diau, E.W.-G. and Zewail, A.H. (2000). *Angew. Chem. Int. Ed.* **39**, 260
170. Hammond, G.S. and Moore, W.M. (1959). *J. Am. Chem. Soc.* **81**, 6334
171. Havinga, E., De Jongh, R.O. and Dorst, W. (1956). *Recl. Trav. Chim. Pays-Bas* **75**, 378
172. Zimmerman, H.E. and Sandel, V.R. (1963). *J. Am. Chem. Soc.* **85**, 915
173. Zimmerman, H.E. (1995). *J. Am. Chem. Soc.* **117**, 8988
174. Pincock, J.A. (1997). *Acc. Chem. Res.* **30**, 43
175. Nozaki, K. and Bartlett, P.D. (1946). *J. Am. Chem. Soc.* **68**, 1686
176. Bartlett, P.D. and Nozaki, K. (1947). *J. Am. Chem. Soc.* **69**, 2299
177. Cass, W.E. (1947). *J. Am. Chem. Soc.* **69**, 500
178. Horner, L. and Schwenk, E. (1949). *Angew. Chem.* **61**, 411
179. Horner, L. and Schwenk, E. (1950). *Liebigs Ann.* **566**, 69
180. Horner, L. (1955). *J. Polym. Sci.* **18**, 438
181. Greene, F.D., Adam, W. and Cantrill, J.E. (1961). *J. Am. Chem. Soc,* **83**, 3461
182. Walling, C., Heaton, L. and Tanner, D.D. (1965). *J. Am. Chem. Soc.* **87**, 1715
183. Conant, J.B. and Bigelow, N.M. (1928). *J. Am. Chem. Soc.* **50**, 2041
183(a). Zarkadis, A., Neumann, W.P., Marx, R. and Uzick, W. (1985). *Chem. Ber.* **118**, 450
184. Mendenhall, G.D. and Ingold, K.U. (1973). *J. Am. Chem. Soc.* **95**, 3422.
185. Griller, D. and Ingold, K.U. (1976). *Acc. Chem. Res.* **9**, 13
186. Rüchardt, C. and Beckhaus, H.-D. (1980). *Angew. Chem. Int. Ed. Engl.* **19**, 429; (1985). **24**, 529
187. Apeloig, Y., Bravo-Zhivotovskii, D., Bendikov, M., Danovitch, M., Botoshansky, M., Vakul'skaya, T., Voronkov, M., Samoilova, R., Zdravkova, M., Igonin, V., Shklover, V. and Struchkov, Y. (1999). *J. Am. Chem. Soc.* **121**, 8118
188. Franck, J. and Rabinowitch, E. (1934). *Trans. Faraday Soc.* **30**, 121

189. Rabinowitch, E. and Wood, W.C. (1936). *Trans. Faraday Soc.* **32**, 1381
190. Noyes, R.M. (1950). *J. Chem. Phys.* **18**, 999
191. Kiefer, H. and Traylor, T.G. (1967). *J. Am. Chem. Soc.* **89**, 6667
192. Male, J.L., Lindfors, B.E., Covert, K.J. and Tyler, D.R. (1998). *J. Am. Chem. Soc.* **120**, 13176
193. Turro, N.J., Buchachenko, A.L. and Tarasov, V.F. (1995). *Acc. Chem. Res.* **28**, 69
194. Turro, N.J. (2000). *Acc. Chem. Res.* **33**, 637
195. Hückel, E. (1934). *Trans. Faraday Soc.* **30**, 40
196. Price, C.C. (1946). *J. Polymer Sci.* **1**, 83
197. Walling, C. and Mayo, F.R. (1948). *J. Polymer. Sci.* **3**, 895
198. Mayo, F.R. and Walling, C. (1950). *Chem. Rev.* **46**, 191
199. Walling, C. and Miller, B. (1957). *J. Am. Chem. Soc.* **79**, 4181
200. Bartlett, P.D. and Rüchardt, C. (1960). *J. Am. Chem. Soc.* **82**, 1756
201. Viehe, H.G., Merényi, R., Stella, L. and Janousek, Z. (1979). *Angew. Chem. Int. Ed. Engl.* **18**, 917
202. Dust, J.M. and Arnold, D.R. (1983). *J. Am. Chem. Soc.* **105**, 1221
203. Jiang, X.-K. (1997). *Acc. Chem. Res.* **30**, 283
204. Viehe, H.G., Janousek, F. and Merényi, R. (eds) (1986). *Substituent Effects in Radical Chemistry*. NATO ASI Series C, Reidel, Dordrecht, Vol. 189
205. Melville, H.W. (1937). *Proc. Roy. Soc. (London)* **163A**, 511
206. Bartlett, P.D. and Swain, C.G. (1945). *J. Am. Chem. Soc.* **67**, 2273
207. Carlsson, D.J. and Ingold, K.U. (1968). *J. Am. Chem. Soc.* **90**, 1055
208. Zavoisky, E. (1945). *J. Physics (Moscow)* **9**, 211
209. Symons, M.C.R. (1963). *Adv. Phys. Org. Chem.* **1**, 283
210. Fessenden, R.W. and Schuler, R.H. (1963). *J. Chem. Phys.* **39**, 2147
211. Dixon, W.T. and Norman, R.O.C. (1962). *Nature* **196**, 891
212. Dixon, W.T. and Norman, R.O.C. (1963). *J. Chem. Soc.* 3119
213. Norman, R.O.C. and Gilbert, B.C. (1967). *Adv. Phys. Org. Chem.* **5**, 53
214. Krusic, P.J. and Kochi, J.K. (1968). *J. Am. Chem. Soc.* **90**, 7155
215. Hudson A. and Hussain, H.A. (1969). *J. Chem. Soc. B*, 793
216. Kochi, J.K. and Krusic, P.J. (1970). In *Essays on Free Radical Chemistry*, Special Publication No. 24, The Chemical Society, London, p. 147
217. Goldschmidt, S. and Renn, K. (1922). *Chem. Ber.* **55**, 628
218. Bartlett, P.D. and Kwart, H. (1950). *J. Am. Chem. Soc.* **72**, 1051
219. Coppinger, G.M. (1957). *J. Am. Chem. Soc.* **79**, 501
220. Bartlett, P.D. and Funahashi, T. (1962). *J. Am. Chem. Soc.* **84**, 2596
220(a). Davies, A.G. and Roberts, B.P. (1967). *J. Chem. Soc. B* 17
221. Lewis, G.N. and Lipkin, D. (1942). *J. Am. Chem. Soc.* **64**, 2801
222. Norman, I. and Porter, G. (1954). *Nature* **174**, 508
223. Pimentel, G.C. (1960). In *Formation and Trapping of Free Radicals*, Bass, A.M. and Broida, H.P. (Eds) Chap. 4, 69. Academic Press, NY
224. Porter, G. and Wright, F.J. (1955). *Trans. Faraday Soc.* **54**, 1469
225. Mackor, A., Wajer, Th.A.J.W. and de Boer, Th.J. (1966). *Tetrahedron Lett.* 2115
226. Mackor, A., Wajer, Th.A.J.W., de Boer, Th.J. and van Voorst, J.D.W. (1967). *Tetrahedron Lett.* 385
227. Iwamura, M. and Inamoto, N. (1967). *Bull. Chem. Soc. Jpn* **40**, 702
228. Janzen, E.G. and Blackburn, B.J. (1968). *J. Amer. Chem. Soc.* **90**, 5909
229. Chalfont, G.R., Perkins, M.J. and Horsfield, A. (1968). *J. Am. Chem. Soc.* **90**, 7141
230. Janzen, E.G. (1971). *Acc. Chem. Res.* **4**, 31
231. Lagercrantz, C. and Forshult, S. (1968). *Nature* **218**, 1247
232. Lagercrantz, C. (1971). *J. Phys. Chem.* **75**, 3466

233. Perkins, M.J. (1970). In *Essays on Free Radical Chemistry*, Special Publication No. 24, The Chemical Society, London, p. 5
234. Pou, S., Halpern, H.J., Tsai, P. and Rosen, G.M. (1999). *Acc. Chem. Res.* **32**, 155
235. Stone, T.J., Buckman, T., Nordio, P.L. and McConnell, H.M. (1965). *Proc. Nat. Acad. Sci. USA,* **54**, 1010
236. Bargon, J. and Fischer, H. (1967). *Z. Naturforsch. A* **22**, 1556
237. Fischer, H. and Bargon, J. (1969). *Acc. Chem. Res.* **2**, 110
238. Ward, H.R. (1967). *J. Am. Chem. Soc.* **89**, 5517
239. Ward, H.R. and Lawler, R.G. (1967). *J. Am. Chem. Soc.* **89**, 5518
240. Lawler, R.G. (1967). *J. Am. Chem. Soc.* **89**, 5519
241. Lepley, A.R. (1968). *J. Am. Chem. Soc.* **90**, 2710
242. Lepley, A.R. and Closs, G.L. (eds) (1973). *Chemically Induced Magnetic Polarization*. Wiley, New York
243. Sommer, L.H., Pietrusza, E.W. and Whitmore, F.C. (1947). *J. Am. Chem. Soc.* **69**, 188
244. Barry, A.J., DePree, L., Gilkey, J.W. and Hook, D.E. (1947). *J. Am. Chem. Soc.* **69**, 2916
245. Chatgilialoglu, C. (1995). *Chem. Rev.* **95**, 1229
246. van der Kerk, G.J.M., Luijten, J.G.A. and Noltes, J.G. (1956). *Chem. Ind.* 352
247. Menapace, L.W. and Kuivila, H.G. (1964). *J. Am. Chem. Soc.* **86**, 3047
248. Kuivila, H.G. (1968). *Acc. Chem. Res.* **1**, 299
249. Baguley, P.A. and Walton, J.C. (1998). *Angew. Chem. Int. Ed.* **37**, 3072
250. Skell, P.S., Tuleen, D.L. and Readio, P.D. (1963). *J. Am. Chem. Soc.* **85**, 2849
251. Freidlina, R.Kh. (1965). *Adv. Free Rad. Chem.* **1**, 211
252. Skell, P.S. and Traynham, J.G. (1984). *Acc. Chem. Res.* **17**, 160
253. Skell, P.S. and Allen, R.G. (1960). *J. Am. Chem. Soc.* **82**, 1511
254. Overberger, C.G. and Borchert, A.E. (1960). *J. Am. Chem. Soc.* **82**, 1007
255. Neureiter, N.P. (1959). *J. Org. Chem.* **24**, 2044
256. Vogel, E. (1960). *Angew. Chem.* **72**, 4
257. Doubleday, C., Nendel, M., Houk, K.N., Thweatt, D. and Page, M. (1999). *J. Am. Chem. Soc.* **121**, 4720
258. Davidson, E.R. and Gajewski, J.J. (1997). *J. Am. Chem. Soc.* **119**, 10543
259. Baldwin, J.E. and Shukla, R. (1999). *J. Am. Chem. Soc.* **121**, 11018
260. Staroverov, V.N. and Davidson, E.R. (2000). *J. Am. Chem. Soc.* **122**, 186
261. Dowd, P. (1966). *J. Am. Chem. Soc.* **88**, 2587
262. Borden, W. (1982). *Diradicals*. Wiley, NY
263. Dougherty, D.A. (1991). *Acc. Chem. Res.* **24**, 88
264. Ingold, K.U. (1969). *Acc. Chem. Res.* **2**, 1
265. Bartlett, P.D. and Traylor, T.G. (1963). *J. Am. Chem. Soc.* **85**, 2470
266. Howard, J.A. and Ingold, K.U. (1968). *J. Am. Chem. Soc.* **90**, 1056
267. Howard, J.A. and Ingold, K.U. (1968). *J. Am. Chem. Soc.* **90**, 1058
268. Fenton, H.J.H. (1894). *J. Chem. Soc.* **65**, 899
269. Haber, F. and Weiss, J. (1934). *Proc. Roy. Soc. London, Ser. A* **147**, 332
270. Merz, J.H. and Waters, W.A. (1947). *Disc. Faraday Soc.* **2**, 179
271. Walling, C. (1975). *Acc. Chem. Res.* **8**, 125
272. Goldstein, S. and Meyerstein, D. (1999). *Acc. Chem. Res.* **32**, 547
273. Strazisar, B.R., Lin, C. and Davis, H.F. (2000). *Science* **290**, 958
274. Zhang, D.H., Collins, M.A. and Lee, S.-Y. (2000). *Science* **290**, 961
275. Barton, D.H.R., Gastiger, M.J. and Motherwell, W.B. (1983). *J. Chem. Soc., Chem. Commun.* 41
276. Barton, D.H.R., Halley, F., Ozbalik, N., Schmitt, J., Young, E. and Balavoine, G. (1989). *J. Am. Chem. Soc.* **111**, 7144

277. MacFaul, P.A., Ingold, K.U., Wayner, D.D.M. and Que, L., Jr. (1997). *J. Am. Chem. Soc.* **119**, 10594
278. MacFaul, P.A., Arends, I.W.C.E., Ingold, K.U. and Wayner, D.D.M. (1997). *J. Chem. Soc., Perkin Trans.* 2, 135
279. Roberts, J.D. and Mazur, R.H. (1951). *J. Am. Chem. Soc.* **73**, 2509
280. Renk, E., Shafer, P.R., Graham, W.H., Mazur, R.H. and Roberts, J.D. (1961). *J. Am. Chem. Soc.* **83**, 1987
281. Kochi, J.K., Krusic, P.J. and Eaton, D.R. (1969). *J. Am. Chem. Soc.* **91**, 1877
282. Butler, G.B. and Angelo. R.J. (1957). *J. Am. Chem. Soc.* **79**, 3128
283. Marvel, C.S. and Vest, R.D. (1957). *J. Am. Chem. Soc.* **79**, 5771
284. Julia, M., Surzur, J.M. and Katz, L. (1960). *C. R. Acad. Sci.* **251**, 1030
285. Julia, M. (1967). *Pure Appl. Chem.* **15**, 167
286. Julia, M. (1971). *Acc. Chem. Res.* **4**, 386
287. Lamb, R.C., Ayers, P.W. and Toney, M.K. (1963). *J. Am. Chem. Soc.* **85**, 3483
288. Walling, C. and Pearson, M.S. (1964). *J. Am. Chem. Soc.* **86**, 2262
289. Garwood, R.G., Scott, C.J. and Weedon, B.C.L. (1965). *J. Chem. Soc., Chem. Commun.* 14
290. Beckwith, A.L.J. and Ingold, K.U. (1980). Free Radical Rearrangements. In *Rearrangements in Ground and Excited States,* Vol. 1, 161. Academic Press
290(a). Gordon, A.S. and Smith, S.R. (1962). *J. Phys. Chem.* **66**, 521
290(b). Arai, S., Sato, S. and Shida, S. (1960). *J. Chem. Phys.* **33**, 1277
291. Beckwith, A.L.J., O'Shea, D.M., Gerba, S. and Westwood, S.W. (1987). *J. Chem. Soc., Chem. Commun.* 666
292. Beckwith, A.L.J., O'Shea, D.M. and Westwood, S.W. (1988). *J. Am. Chem. Soc.* **110**, 2565
293. Dowd, P. and Choi, S.-C. (1987). *J. Am. Chem. Soc.* **107**, 3493
294. Surzur, J.-M. and Tessier, P. (1967). *C. R. Acad. Sci.* **264**, 1981
295. Tanner, D.D. and Law, F.C.P. (1969). *J. Am. Chem. Soc.* **91**, 7535
296. Beckwith, A.L.J., Crich, D., Duggan, P.J. and Yao, Q. (1997). *Chem. Rev.* **97**, 3273
297. Zipse, H. (1999). *Acc. Chem. Res.* **32**, 571
298. Newcomb, M., Horner, J.H., Whitted, F.O., Crich; D., Huang, X., Yao, Q. and Zipse, H. (1999). *J. Am. Chem. Soc.* **121**, 10685
299. Whitted, P.O., Horner, J.H., Newcomb, M., Huang, X. and Crich, D. (1999). *Organic Lett.* **1**, 153
300. Barton, D.H.R., Beaton, J.M., Geller, L.E. and Pechet, M.M. (1961). *J. Am. Chem. Soc.* **83**, 4076
301. Breslow, R. and Winnik, M.A. (1969). *J. Am. Chem. Soc.* **91**, 3083
302. Jones, R.R. and Bergman, R.G. (1972). *J. Am. Chem. Soc.* **94**, 660
303. Bergman, R.G. (1973). *Acc. Chem. Res.* **6**, 25
304. Goldberg, I.H. (1991). *Acc. Chem. Res.* **24**, 191
305. Schreiner, P.R. and Prall, M. (1999). *J. Am. Chem. Soc.* **121**, 8615
306. Danishefsky, S.J. and Shair, M.D. (1996). *J. Org. Chem. Soc.* **61**, 16
307. Barton, D.H.R., Crich, D. and Motherwell, W.B. (1983). *J. Chem. Soc., Chem. Commun.* 939. (1985). *Tetrahedron,* **41**, 3901
308. Chatgilialoglu, C., Crich, D., Komatsu, M. and Ryu, I. (1999). *Chem. Rev.* **99**, 1991
309. Russell, G.A. (1957). *J. Am. Chem. Soc.* **79**, 2977
310. Skell, P.S., Baxter, H.N., III and Taylor, C.K. (1983). *J. Am. Chem. Soc.* **105**, 120
311. Skell, P.S. and Baxter, H.N., III (1985). *J. Am. Chem. Soc.* **107**, 2823
312. Ingold, K.U., Lusztyk, J. and Raner, K.D. (1990). *Acc. Chem. Res.* **33**, 219
313. Griller, D. and Ingold, K.U. (1980). *Acc. Chem. Res.* **13**, 317

314. Newcomb, M. (1993). *Tetrahedron* **49**, 1151
315. Newcomb, M. and Toy, P.H. (2000). *Acc. Chem. Res.* **33**, 449
316. Birch, A.J. (1944). *J. Chem. Soc.* 430
317. Wooster, C.B. and Godfrey, K.L. (1937). *J. Am. Chem. Soc.* **59**, 596
318. Birch, A.J. (1995). *To See the Obvious*. American Chemical Society
319. Weiss, J. (1941). *Nature* **147**, 512
320. Kornblum, N., Michel, R.E. and Kerber, R.C. (1966). *J. Am. Chem. Soc.* **88**, 5660
321. Russell, G.A. and Danen, W.C. (1966). *J. Am. Chem. Soc.* **88**, 5663
322. Kornblum, N., Davies, T.M., Earl, G.W., Holy, N.L., Kerber, R.C., Musser, M.T. and Snow, D.H. (1967). *J. Am. Chem. Soc.* **89**, 725
323. Kim, J.K. and Bunnett, J.F. (1970). *J. Am. Chem. Soc.* **92**, 7463
324. Bunnett, J.F. (1978). *Acc. Chem. Res.* **11**, 413
325. Eberson, L. (1982). *Adv. Phys. Org. Chem.* **18**, 78
326. Eberson, L. (1999). *Acta Chem. Scand.* **53**, 751
327. Savéant, J.-M. (1990). *Adv. Phys. Org. Chem.* **26**, 1
328. Savéant, J.-M. (2000). *Adv. Phys. Org. Chem.* **35**, 117
329. Rathore, R. and Kochi, J.K. (2000). *Adv. Phys. Org. Chem.* **35**, 193
330. Stork, G. and Baine, N.H. (1982). *J. Am. Chem. Soc.* **104**, 2321
330(a). Hart, D. (1984). *Science* **223**, 883
331. Curran, D.P. and Rakiewicz, D.M. (1985). *J. Am. Chem. Soc.* **107**, 1448
332. Curran, D.P. (2000). *Aldrichimica Acta* **33**, 104
333. Giese, B. (1989). *Angew. Chem. Int. Ed. Engl.* **28**, 969
334. Porter, N.A., Giese, B. and Curran, D.P. (1991). *Acc. Chem. Res.* **24**, 296
335. Sibi, M.P. and Porter, N.A. (1999). *Acc. Chem. Res.* **32**, 163
336. Korolev, G.V. and Marchenko, A.P. (2000). *Russ. Chem. Rev.* **69**, 409
337. Veregin, R.P.N., Georges, M.K., Kazmaier, P.M. and Hamer, G.K. (1993). *Macromolecules* **26**, 5316
338. Hawker, C.J. (1994). *J. Am. Chem. Soc.* **116**, 11185
339. Hawker, C.J. (1997). *Acc. Chem. Res.* **30**, 373
340. Moad, G., Rizzardo, E. and Solomon, D.H. (1982). *Macromolecules* **15**, 909
341. Patten, T.E. and Matyjaszewski, K. (1999). *Acc. Chem. Res.* **32**, 895
342. Chiefari, J., Chong, Y.K., Ercole, F., Krstina, J., Jeffery, J., Le, T.P.T., Mayadunne, R.T.A., Meijs, G.F., Moad, C.L., Moad, G., Rizzardo, E. and Thang, S.H. (1998). *Macromolecules* **31**, 5559
343. Huisgen, R. and Horeld, G. (1949). *Liebigs Ann.* **562**, 137
344. Rüchardt, C. and Freudenberg, B. (1964). *Tetrahedron Lett.* 3623
345. Fischer, H. (1986). *J. Am. Chem. Soc.* **108**, 3925
346. Bridger, R.F. and Russell, G.A. (1963). *J. Am. Chem. Soc.* **85**, 3754
347. Binsch, G. and Rüchardt, C. (1966). *J. Am. Chem. Soc.* **88**, 173
348. Chalfont, G.R. and Perkins, M.J. (1967). *J. Am. Chem. Soc.* **89**, 3054
349. Cadogan, J.I.G., Paton, R.M. and Thomson, C. (1969). *J. Chem. Soc., Chem. Commun.* 614
350. Perkins, M.J. (1964) *J. Chem. Soc.* 5932
351. Bachmann, W.E. and Wiselogle, F.Y. (1936). *J. Org. Chem.* **1**, 354
352. DeTar, D.F. (1967). *J. Am. Chem. Soc.* **89**, 4058
352(a). Minisci, F., Fontana, F., Araneo, S., Recupero, F., Banfi, S. and Quici, S. (1995). *J. Am. Chem. Soc.* **117**, 226
353. Daikh, B.E. and Finke, R.G. (1992). *J. Am. Chem. Soc.* **114**, 2938
354. Blois, M.S., Jr, Brown, H.W., Lemmon, R.M., Lindblom, R.O. and Weissbluth, M. (eds) (1961). *Free Radicals in Biological Systems*. Academic Press, New York
355. Stubbe, J. (1988). *Biochemistry* **27**, 3893
356. Stubbe, J. (1989). *Ann. Rev. Biochem.* **58**, 257

357. Pryor, W.A. (ed.) (1976). *Free Radicals in Biology*, Vol. 1
358. Minisci, F. (ed.) (1989). *Free Radicals in Synthesis and Biology*. Kluwer, Dordrecht
359. Minisci, F. (ed.) (1997). *Free Radicals in Biology and Environment*. Kluwer, Dordrecht
360. Halliwell, B. and Gutteridge, J.M.C. (1999). *Free Radicals in Biology and Medicine*, 3rd edn. Clarendon Press, Oxford
361. Burton, G.W. and Ingold, K.U. (1986). *Acc. Chem. Res.* **19**, 194
362. Bowry, V.W. and Ingold, K.U. (1999). *Acc. Chem. Res.* **32**, 27
363. Samuelsson, B. (1972). *Fed. Am. Soc. Exper. Biol.* **31**, 1442
364. Nugteren, D.H., Vonkeman, H. and van Dorp, D.A. (1967). *Recl. Trav. Chim. Pays-Bas* **86**, 1237
365. Porter, N.A. and Funk, M.O. (1975). *J. Org. Chem.* **31**, 3614
366. Pryor, W.A. and Stanley, J.P. (1975). *J. Org. Chem.* **40**, 3615
367. Funk, M.O., Isaac, R. and Porter, N.A. (1975). *J. Am. Chem. Soc.* **97**, 1281
368. Spiteller, G. and Spiteller, G. (2000). *Angew. Chem. Int. Ed.* **39**, 583
369. Collins, P.W. and Djuric, S.W. (1993). *Chem. Rev.* **93**, 1533
370. Malkowski, M.G., Ginell, S.L., Smith, W.L. and Garavito, R.M. (2000). *Science* **289**, 1933
371. Steenken, S. (1989). *Chem. Rev.* **89**, 503
372. Steenken, S. and Goldbergerova, L. (1998). *J. Am. Chem. Soc.* **120**, 3928
373. Wu, J.C., Kozarich, J.W. and Stubbe, J. (1983). *J. Biol. Chem.* **258**, 4694
374. Flyunt, R., Bazzanini, R., Chatgilialoglu, C. and Mulazzani, Q.C. (2000). *J. Am. Chem. Soc.* **122**, 4225
375. Chatgilialoglu, C., Ferreri, C., Bazzanini, R., Guerra, M., Choi, S.-Y., Emanuel, C.J., Horner, J.H. and Newcomb, M. (2000). *J. Am. Chem. Soc.* **122**, 9525
376. Tallman, K.A., Tronche, C., Yoo, D.J. and Greenberg, M.M. (1998). *J. Am. Chem. Soc.* **120**, 4903
377. Stubbe, J. and van der Donk, W.A. (1998). *Chem. Rev.* **98**, 705
378. Licht, S.S., Lawrence, C.C. and Stubbe, J. (1999). *J. Am. Chem. Soc.* **121** , 7463
379. Gerfen, G.J., van der Donk, W.A., Yu, G., McCarthy, J.R., Jarvi, E.T., Matthews, D.P., Farrar, C., Griffin, R.G. and Stubbe, J. (1998). *J. Am Chem. Soc.* **120**, 3823
380. Lenz, R. and Giese, B. (1997). *J. Am Chem. Soc.* **119**, 2784
381. Siegbahn, P.E.M. (1998). *J. Am. Chem. Soc.* **120**, 8417
382. Aubert, C., Brettel, K., Mathis, P., Eker, A.P.M. and Boussac, A. (1999). *J. Am. Chem. Soc.* **121**, 8659
383. Logan, D.T., Andersson, J., Sjöberg, B.-M. and Norlund, P. (1999). *Science* **283**, 1499
384. Turecek, F., Carpenter, F.H., Polce, M. and Wesdemiotis, C. (1999). *J. Am. Chem. Soc.* **121**, 7955
385. Hung, R.R. and Grabowski, J.J. (1999). *J. Am. Chem. Soc.* **121**, 1359
386. He, M. and Dowd, P. (1998). *J. Am. Chem. Soc.* **120**, 1133
387. Warncke, K., Schmidt, J.C. and Ke, S.-C. (1999). *J. Am. Chem. Soc.* **121**, 10522
388. Rétey, J. (1990). *Angew. Chem. Int. Ed. Engl.* **29**, 355
389. Pfeiffer, S., Mayer, B. and Hemmens, B. (1999). *Angew. Chem. Int. Ed.* **38**, 1714
390. Fukuto, J.M. and Ignarro, L.J. (1997). *Acc. Chem. Res.* **30**, 149
391. Shustov, G.V., Spinney, R. and Rauk, A. (2000). *J. Am. Chem Soc.* **122**, 1191
392. Hodges, G.R. and Ingold, K.U. (1999). *J. Am. Chem. Soc.* **121**, 10695
393. Newcomb, M., Shen, R., Choi, S.-Y., Toy, P.H., Hollenberg, P.F., Vaz, A.D.N. and Coon, M.J. (2000). *J. Am. Chem. Soc.* **122**, 2677
394. Shilov, A.E. and Shteinman, A.A. (1999). *Acc. Chem. Res.* **32**, 763
395. Green, M.T. (1999). *J. Am. Chem. Soc.* **121**, 7939

396. Collman, J.P., Chien, A.S., Eberspacher, T.A. and Brauman, J.I. (2000). *J. Am. Chem. Soc.* **122**, 11098
397. Li, D., Zhou, H.-q., Dakoji, S., Shin, I., Oh, E. and Liu, H.-w. (1998). *J. Am. Chem. Soc.* **120**, 2008
398. Leffler, J.E. (1993). *An Introduction to Free Radicals*. Wiley, New York
399. Bauld, N. (1997). *Radicals, Ion Radicals, and Triplets: The Spin-Bearing Intermediates of Organic Chemistry*. Wiley, New York

Gomberg and the Nobel Prize

LENNART EBERSON

Department of Chemistry, Lund University, Lund, Sweden

1 Introduction

One hundred years ago, Moses Gomberg submitted a "preliminary paper" with the sensational title "An instance of trivalent carbon: triphenylmethyl" to *Journal of the American Chemical Society*. It was received on October 4, 1900 and published in the November issue the same year.[1] A German version had arrived at the office of the more widely read and prestigious *Berichte der Chemischen Gesellschaft* on October 1, was communicated at the meeting of the German Chemical Society on October 8 by R. Stelzner, and was published equally promptly in the first of two November issues of 1900.[2] Gomberg had previously presented his results in a paper at the Columbus Meeting of the American Association for the Advancement of Science in August 1899.[3] At the end of his preliminary paper, he made a statement which was not uncommon in early science: "This work will be continued and I wish to reserve the field for myself."

Only a couple of weeks later, the first two of a large number of other researchers, J.F. Norris and W.W. Sanders, made their views on Gomberg's discovery public,[4] and Gomberg soon found himself embroiled in a lively discussion of his proposal. Over a period of 15 years, he published some 30 papers in defense of the free radical concept, and in the end it prevailed. He has since been quoted as the discoverer of the first free radical in almost every textbook of organic chemistry and, in retrospect, one can see this discovery as one of the most important in 20th century chemistry, theoretically as well as practically.

ADVANCES IN PHYSICAL ORGANIC CHEMISTRY
VOLUME 36 ISBN 0-12-033536-0

For a modern observer, there are some incredible aspects in the series of events described above. Publication times were of the order of 1–2 months, so apparently neither postal offices nor referees and editors had their present-day capability to slow down the publishing process. An author was allowed to submit the same material in parallel in two languages, a practice which certainly would infuriate editors and presumably raise grave questions about ethics today. Senior authors wrote papers based on experimental work carried out by themselves. On the other hand, a more than familiar feature is the eagerness and speed with which other chemists entered the exploration of the new phenomenon. Here was an important scientific problem upon which reputations could be built or crushed, and a large number of lesser or larger luminaries entered into the discussion. This story has been covered by McBride[5] in his article "The Hexaphenylethane Riddle" and need not be repeated here. An earlier, detailed account of the development of free radical chemistry can be found in Walden's *Chemie der freien Radikale*.[6]

After the first century of free radicals, it was pertinent to ask the question: why was Gomberg not awarded the Nobel prize? The Nobel prize institution began its work in 1901 by honoring J.H. van't Hoff "in recognition of the extraordinary services he has rendered by the discovery of the laws of chemical dynamics and osmotic pressure in solution" and then in succession 1902–1906 E. Fischer, S. Arrhenius, W. Ramsay, A. von Baeyer and H. Moissan. According to A. Westgren, chairman of the Nobel committee for chemistry 1944–65, these six individuals were the truly eminent scientists who were rewarded for work entirely or almost entirely carried out during the 19th century.[7] Thus the early Nobel institution capitalized on a supply of outstanding candidates, which were used to build up credibility for the new award. From 1907 onwards, the Nobel Prizes reflect the development of chemistry in this century and more strictly adhere to the implicit stipulation in Alfred Nobel's will that the prize should be given to encourage young scientists who have made recent discoveries or improvements of the highest importance.

In the following, the imprint of Gomberg and to some extent also other pioneers of free radical chemistry on the Nobel committee for chemistry will be described. He was nominated for the first time for the Nobel prize in 1915 by L. Chugaev[8] from Petersburg, Russia in a letter dated January 12, 1915, which did not reach the committee before the deadline of January 31, 1915. The World War had intervened, and a letter from Czarist Russia on war-footing, presumably met certain obstacles on its way to Sweden. According to the statutes, this nomination was disallowed but kept resting until the next year.[9] However, in 1916 it was again disallowed[10] since Chugaev did not have the right to nominate that year! After this unlucky start, allowed nominations of Gomberg appeared fairly regularly until 1940 (Table 1). In this year, the individual professors of the whole chemistry faculty of the Department of Chemistry, University of Illinois at Urbana had apparently been asked to

Table 1 Nominations of M. Gomberg (1866–1947) for the Nobel prize in chemistry

Year	Nominator	From	Remark	Nobel prize this year
1915	L. Chugaev	Petersburg, Russia	disallowed	T.W. Richards
				R.M. Willstätter
1916	L. Chugaev	Petersburg, Russia	disallowed	reserved
1921	M.T. Bogert	New York, USA	review by O. Widman	W.H. Nernst
1922	W. Traube	Berlin, Germany		F. Soddy
				F.W. Aston
1924	J.B. Clark	New York, USA	jointly with G.N. Lewis	reserved
	A.F. Holleman	Amsterdam, Holland		
1927	W. Wahl	Helsingfors		reserved
	E. Weitz	Halle, Germany		
	D. Vorländer	Halle, Germany		
1928	M. Reimer	New York, USA		H.O. Wieland
				A.O.R. Windaus
1929	M. Kohn	Wien, Austria	jointly with W. Schlenk	A. Harden
				H.K.A. von Euler-Chelpin
1938	J. Böeseken	Delft, Holland		reserved
1940	R. Adams	Urbana, Ill., USA		reserved
	A.M. Buswell	Urbana, Ill., USA		
	R.C. Fuson	Urbana, Ill., USA		
	B.S. Hopkins	Urbana, Ill., USA		
	D.B. Keyes	Urbana, Ill., USA		
	C.S. Marvel	Urbana, Ill., USA		

nominate and they responded massively, all with different letters of nomination.

The pertinent part of the story thus lies between 1915 and 1940. In order to appreciate it, we must detail some aspects of Gomberg's discovery, know a deal about the Nobel committee for chemistry and its decision-making procedures as laid down by the statutes and by internal rules, and see how Gomberg's work was analyzed and judged in the light of this complex system of rules. In the process, we will also deal with a few other pioneers of radical chemistry and their relationship to the Nobel institution, namely W. Schlenk, F. Paneth and, briefly, M.S. Kharasch.

2   The discovery and its path to acceptance

Gomberg was first to prepare tetraphenylmethane,[11] a problem initiated during a leave of absence from the University of Michigan in 1896–1897 which was spent with A. von Baeyer, Munich and V. Meyer, Heidelberg, Germany.[12] In order to further support its structure, he wanted to prepare hexaphenylethane and test its reactivity. After some initial problems, he realized that oxygen from the air somehow must interfere with the reaction between triphenylchloromethane or triphenylbromomethane and a reducing metal like silver, mercury or, best, zinc in benzene.[1,2] He later constructed an apparatus which allowed for the reaction to be carried out in an atmosphere of dry carbon dioxide for any desired period of time and for handling the product with complete exclusion of oxygen.[13] Later, Schmidlin constructed an improved apparatus for the synthesis and handling of triarylmethyl radicals.[14]

In his preliminary paper,[1,2] Gomberg isolated a hydrocarbon, but not in pure form due to the problems with its reactivity toward oxygen. He established that "the body is extremely unsaturated" and absorbed oxygen "with great avidity to give an insoluble oxygen compound", identified as the bis(triphenylethyl) peroxide by an independent synthesis. The hydrocarbon reacted instantly with chlorine, bromine or iodine in carbon disulfide, giving the corresponding triphenylhalomethane. In the fifth section of the paper, the first paragraph states:

> The experimental evidence presented above forces me to the conclusion that we have to deal here with a free radical, triphenylmethyl, $(C_6H_5)_3\equiv C$. On this assumption alone do the results described above become intelligible and receive an adequate explanation. The reaction of zink results, as it seems to me, in the mere abstraction of the halogen, leaving the free radical,

$$(C_6H_5)_3.Cl + zn = (C_6H_5)_3C + znCl$$

> The radical so formed is apparently stable, for it can be kept both in solution and in the dry crystalline state for weeks. The radical refuses to unite with another one of its kind, and thus forms a distinct exception to all similar reactions. It might be said that, perhaps, it does polymerize to hexaphenylethane, $(C_6H_5)_3C—C(C_6H_5)_3$, but this hydrocarbon is so unstable that mere exposure to air is sufficient to break it down. Such an assumption seems to me less tenable than that of a free radical. Hexaphenylethane must, according to all our present notions of valence, be a saturated compound.

Later in the paper, Gomberg states:

> The existence of triphenylmethyl implies, of course, the existence of trivalent carbon, at least in this particular instance.

These were bold and simple statements. To put them in a modern context, the discovery of triphenylmethyl "combined the novelty of something like bucky balls with the controversial nature of something like polywater or cold fusion."[15] Thus Gomberg was soon to find that the triphenylmethyl problem was attractive and complex enough to occupy him and many others for a long time. A first period lasted until about 1911 when the phenomena observed had been clarified to the satisfaction of a majority of the research community. Theoretically, little understanding was possible before the advent of the electron pair bond[16] and, in particular, theory based on quantum mechanical concepts.[17] This meant that the theory available between 1900 and 1910 for discussion of what actually were quantum chemically based phenomena, was that of tautomerism, badly suited for the purpose. Also the nomenclature used created difficulties: the word *triphenylmethyl* was used indiscriminately to mean either the free radical proper, a dimer or a mixture of dimers, or both types of species in admixture. Therefore, many statements about triphenylmethyl in the early literature are difficult to interpret for a modern reader and were presumably so even for contemporary chemists. In the following, the expression "triphenylmethyl" will be used for the latter mixture, insofar as it is possible to understand the meaning of the author(s) in a particular context.

To simplify the listing of controversial problems appearing as a result of the free radical hypothesis, we shall follow the further development by Gomberg's own account in a review from 1914.[18] Already in 1901–1902, he had noticed that there were two forms of "triphenylmethyl", a crystalline one in the solid state and a second, orange-yellow colored one formed when the crystals are dissolved in "any solvent whatsoever" or also formed as a thin yellow coating on the initially white solid.[19] Schmidlin[20] made the important observation that the colored and colorless modifications exist side by side *in solution* in equilibrium with each other. Since Gomberg for a long time did not believe that free $(C_6H_5)_3C$ could be colored, he had great difficulties with the notion of a colored dimer, be it hexaphenylethane or the quinoid dimer **1**, postulated by Jacobson in 1905[21] and, more than sixty years later, shown to be the correct dimer structure.[22] The color problem created the only really acrimonious controversy in the history of triphenylmethyl.[5]

A seemingly minor technical problem, the ability of "triphenylmethyl" to pick up virtually any solvent as solvent of crystallization, occupied Gomberg for some time and led him into consideration of then fashionable structures involving tetravalent oxygen, which were later abandoned. Another side-track, more serious in view of the absence of a useful theory, was caused by experiments based on the known fact that triphenylchloromethane showed salt-like conductivity in solution in liquid SO_2: "It was thus definitively established that there are "carbonium" salts in the true sense of the definition applied to salts." When "triphenylmethyl" was dissolved in liquid SO_2, it was found that it too conducted the electric current quite well.[23,24] How should one explain this strange phenomenon, a hydrocarbon behaving like an electrolyte?

The most serious obstacle for the free radical nature of triphenylmethyl was the series of experiments carried out to determine the molecular weight of "triphenylmethyl". Cryoscopy was performed in a range of solvents and invariably showed that the molecular weight corresponded to that of the dimer, 486. Only in naphthalene, which in admixture with "triphenylmethyl" froze at about 80°C, was a lower value obtained, 410. This was a serious dilemma, but Gomberg in 1904[13] had a reasonable suggestion involving an equilibrium between a dimer and the free triphenylmethyl.

$$(R_3C)_n \longrightarrow (R_3C)_2 \Longleftrightarrow R_3C$$

solid   solution

This interpretation agreed with the chemical behavior of "triphenylmethyl", with the free radical as the reactive species present in a low concentration and the dimer as a reservoir for it. However, most chemists at this time preferred to leave out the free radical and instead defend the notion of an unusually reactive dimer, such as for example the quinoid structure **1** or its symmetrical analogue **2** or even hexaphenylethane.

The next five years witnessed attempts by Gomberg to get evidence for Jacobson's quinoid formula by some rather complex experimentation which actually caused him to waver for a short period in 1906. Gomberg's obituary states that he "remained unshaken in his belief in the existence of triphenylmethyl and time and time again reiterated his faith in the concept of free radicals." Only one or two sentences in a paper designed to make public preliminary results,[25] reveal a moment of doubt in a scientist dedicated to logic and truth. This is hardly surprising in view of the strong criticisms leveled at the free radical idea and the experimental results to be described below. These expressions of doubt were to play an important role later.

The background was the following ingenious experiment. If the dimer had structure **1**, the reaction between the mono-*p*-brominated triphenylchloromethane **3** and silver metal must give either **4** or **5** or a mixture of both

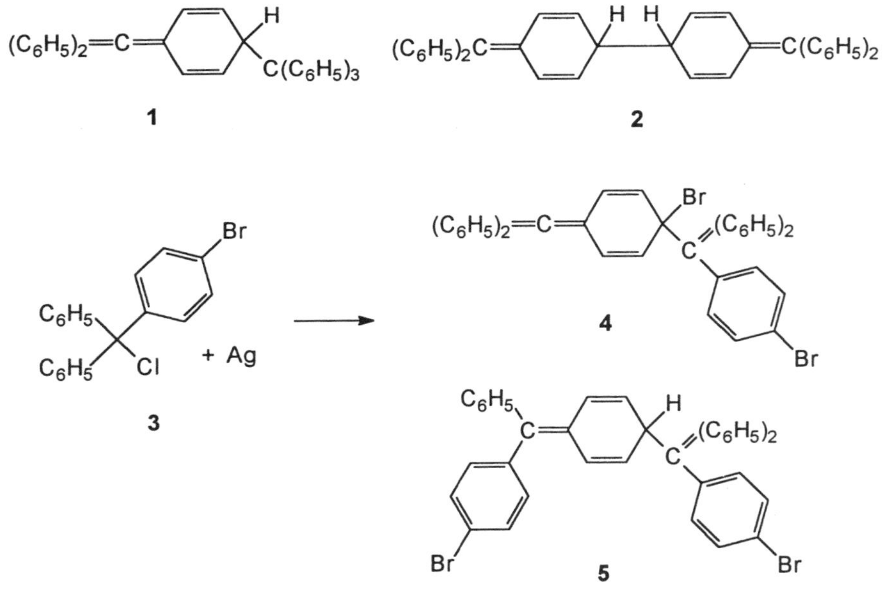

Scheme 1

(see Scheme 1). If one supposes that only **4** is formed, its quinoid bromine atom should be labile and able to be removed by reaction with silver. Thus, from two molecules of **3**, two chlorines and one bromine should be removed. The experiment showed that the reaction between **3** and silver occurred in two phases, a fast reaction giving the colored triphenylmethyl, which gave the corresponding peroxide when air was admitted into the apparatus specially designed for this type of reaction. Upon prolonged treatment with silver, the quinoid bromine atom of **4** was removed and reaction with air did not then give the same peroxide as before.

Similar experiments with other mono-, di- and trihalogenated triphenylchloromethanes gave the same type of colorations, ranging from deep-yellow to blue-red, and therefore the colored compounds should all have the same constitution as triphenylmethyl. However, in some of the di- and tri-halogenated cases, such as the tris(4-bromophenyl)chloromethane, much more than the expected amount of ring halogen, 0.5 atom per mol of starting material, was removed by silver. Also, less oxygen than expected was taken up in these experiments. Moreover, if triphenylmethyl and its analogues had the Jacobson-type structure, loss of halogen in a dimer of type **4** should lead to a tetrameric structure. Gomberg therefore ruled out Jacobson's structure **1**.

In the final section of altogether four conclusions, the second and third ones need to be quoted in full since they convey what seems to be a hesitation by Gomberg that the triphenylmethyl radical could expain the results mentioned above and were destined to play an important role later:

2. The constitution of the body formed by removal of the "carbinol-chlorine" from the halotriphenylmethyl chlorides can hardly be expressed by the formula $(C_6H_4Hlg)_3C$. Such a formula would indicate a similar function of the three phenyl groups which, in fact, does not exist. However, the same conclusion can now be drawn regarding triphenylmethyl itself: also this hydrocarbon can hardly possess the simple formula $(C_6H_5)_3C$, however satisfactorily this symbol describes all other properties of this strongly unsaturated compound;
3. The fact that the removal of the "carbinol-chlorine" causes one of the three phenyl groups (or one of the six groups of the dimolecular triphenylmethyl) to assume a function different from the two others, suggests in all probability that a conversion into chinoid compounds of some kind has taken place. None of the so far suggested formulas is, however, in full agreement with the findings reported in this paper.

However, do these conclusions really express doubt about the existence of the free radical triphenylmethyl? Or is it the nomenclature that is ambiguous? With the correct answer at hand, one cannot state today that the chemical reactivity of a solution of *ca.* 2% trityl radical and 98% dimer **1** is entirely determined by the chemistry of the radical. Maybe Gomberg was talking about "triphenylmethyl"?

The full paper on the chemistry of ring-halogenated triphenylchloro-methanes appeared in 1907,[26] six months after the previous one, and measured more than 40 pages. In the introduction, Gomberg comments upon the previous paper:

> It was concluded from these results that the halogenated analogues of triphenyl-methyl and further triphenylmethyl itself in some way must have a chinoid con-stitution.

In the light of the more complete study of ring-halogenated triphenylchloro-methanes in this paper, the free radical hypothesis was back – if it ever was excluded in the previous paper – in the final discussion of the constitution of "triphenylmethyl", now with two tautomeric triphenylmethyl radical struc-tures in equilibrium with each other and the Jacobson dimer **1** (Scheme 2). Note that the radical was symbolized by an open valence (a thick line is used here for clarity). The strong results obtained with **3** (Scheme 1) were explained by removal of the quinoid bromine atom from **4** giving a radical **6** which tautomerized to the triphenylmethyl analogue **7**. By analogy with the

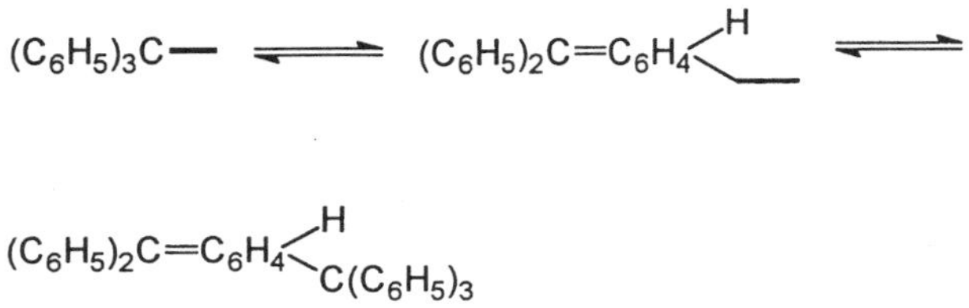

$$(C_6H_5)_3C \text{—} \rightleftharpoons (C_6H_5)_2C \text{=} C_6H_4\overset{H}{\diagdown}\text{___} \rightleftharpoons$$

$$(C_6H_5)_2C \text{=} C_6H_4\overset{H}{\underset{C(C_6H_5)_3}{\diagdown}}$$

1

Scheme 2

two tautomers of triphenylmethyl, **7** and **8** can give a tetramer **9** (Scheme 3). The formation of **7** was later verified.[27]

By 1904, Gomberg had already published studies on ring-substituted (methyl, bromo, nitro groups) triphenylmethyls and had noticed that they were more or less deeply colored and exhibited similar chemical reactions to the unsubstituted hydrocarbon, particularly the high reactivity towards oxygen.[28] Also, one phenyl could be replaced by an α-naphthyl group with a similar result. Two years later a different type of triphenylmethyl was prepared from phenylchlorofluorene and silver.[29] This compound (**10**) could not be isolated in pure form but showed the usual reactivity towards oxygen in solution, except that the reaction was unusually slow. In 1910, Schlenck[30] modified the synthetic procedure by using copper bronze as

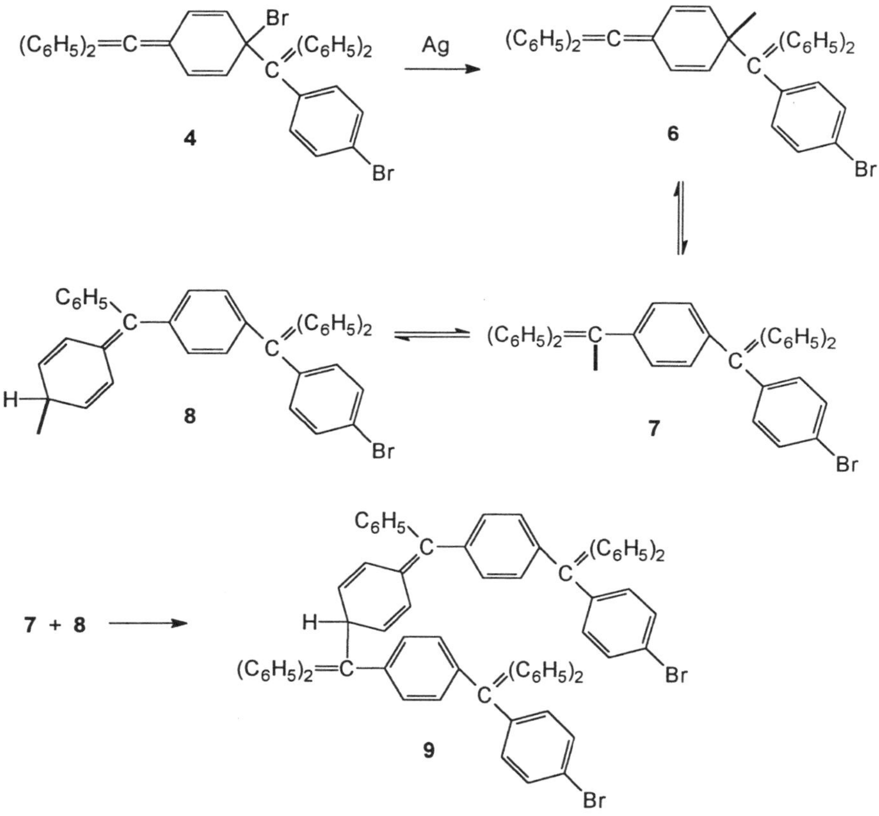

Scheme 3

reductant, and isolated **10** as white crystals with the molecular weight of a dimer. A solution of **10** in benzene was colorless and showed blue fluorescence at room temperature. It turned brown at 80°C. The color change was reversible, and Schlenk correctly stated that the phenomena depends on

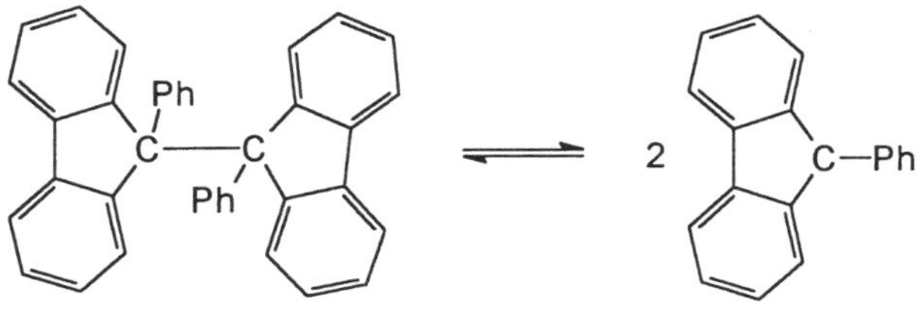

Scheme 4

the equilibrium of Scheme 4 being displaced to the right at higher temperatures, thus increasing the concentration of the colored free radical.

Schlenk was the one who first took triphenylmethyl-type radicals to the monomeric extreme and thus produced the final evidence for the existence of free radicals.[31] The first example in this direction was phenylbis(biphenylyl)-methyl (11), which was isolated as white crystals from operations carried out in the apparatus described by Schmidlin.[14] Upon dissolution of 11 in benzene, a red color developed, and cryoscopic studies revealed that the monomeric phenylbis(biphenylyl)methyl constituted 80% of the equilibrium mixture. Trisbiphenylylmethyl (12) was even more extreme; it formed black crystals and was a 100% monomeric free radical in an almost black solution. Finally, Schlenk et al. established the connection between the conducting solutions of triphenylhalomethanes and the free radical triphenylmethyl by showing that the cathodic reduction of triphenylbromomethane in liquid SO_2 gave rise to triphenylmethyl. These findings were considered the definitive evidence for the free radical hypothesis, and Schlenck was nominated for the Nobel Prize in 1918 and several times afterwards for this achievement, amongst others (Table 2).

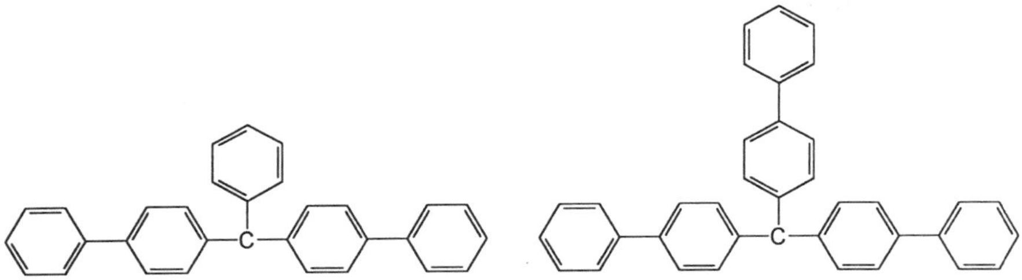

Scheme 5

Table 2 Nominations of W. Schlenk (1879–1943) for the Nobel prize in chemistry

Year	Nominator	From	Remark	Nobel prize this year
1918	W. Schneider	Jena, Germany	report by O. Widman	F. Haber 1919
1920	W. Wien	Würzburg, Germany		reserved
1924	F. Pregl	Graz, Austria		reserved
1925	A. Kötz	Göttingen, Germany		reserved
1929	M. Kohn	Wien, Austria	jointly with M. Gomberg	A. Harden H.K.A. von Euler-Chelpin

Table 3 Percentage dissociation of some historically important triarylmethyl systems (dimer ⇔ 2 Ar$_3$C$^{\bullet}$) in benzene solution[50]

Radical Ar$_3$C$^{\bullet}$	Percentage dissociation at equilibrium
triphenylmethyl	1–3
diphenyl-p-tolylmethyl	5
tris(p-tolyl)methyl	15
α-naphthyldiphenyl	60
9-fluorenylphenylmethyl	0
4-biphenylyldiphenylmethyl	15
bis(4-biphenylyl)phenylmethyl	75
tris(4-biphenylyl)methyl	100

Thus Gomberg could end his 1914 review by stating emphatically: "The supposed existence of free radicals, with carbon trivalent, becomes therefore indisputable." He still expressed uncertainty with respect to some unsettled questions, above all the color problem. However, he now had to accept that the monomeric triphenylmethyl was the colored form, and attributed this to "the capacity to undergo the same kind of tautomerization to the quinoid state as so many of its derivatives undergo." The paragraph ends: "But after all, these are minor points. The really important issue – the existence of free radicals, the trivalency of carbon – that has been established". Later studies have established the positions of the equilibria involving a large number of triarylmethyls. Table 3 shows some of these data pertaining to some historically important triarylmethyls, just to emphasize the great difficulties facing Gomberg in his uphill fight to establish his discovery.

We have described some aspects of the chemistry upon which Gomberg and Schlenk were to be judged by the Nobel committee for chemistry. Now it is time to examine the committee and its work.

3 The Nobel committee for chemistry around 1915

The setting up of the Nobel institution and its operation for the first fifteen years has been described in detail in Crawford's book *The Beginnings of the Nobel Institution*, dealing with the history of the chemistry and physics prizes.[32] Excellent chapters describe the nominating system (Chapter 4) and decision-making in the committees (Chapter 6) in relation to Nobel's will, the code of statutes of the Nobel Foundation, and the special regulations concerning the distribution of prizes (Appendix B; in English translation). The adherence to rules regarding recency, discovery and/or improvement, excellence and importance of work to be rewarded and nominations, were examined in the light of the committee decisions during these fifteen years.

As one might expect, the setting up and operation of the committees presented the problem of distribution of power between the committees and the Academy. The committees, each with its five members, were anxious to keep as much power as possible regarding prize decisions; on the other hand, the physics and chemistry classes of the Academy were required by statutory rules to examine and write a statement about the suggestions from the respective committees. Finally, it was the Academy *in plenum* who made the actual decision of which person or persons should be awarded the Nobel prize.

Much activity was spent on this problem of communication between the committees and the rest of the Academy, and by 1915, the whole Nobel institution had settled into a balanced situation which, in principle, has prevailed until this day. The chemistry committee had more initial problems than their physics counterpart: chemistry was more fragmented, which created difficulties in achieving consensus and making the committee work together as a team. This situation was not improved by the fact that the two first chairmen (1901–1910) did not exert "consistently strong leadership" and that it was "not until Hammarsten took over in 1910 that the committee acquired a reasonably strong chairman".[32] He stayed as chairman until 1926 and must have yielded considerable power during this long period. In 1915, when our story begins with the first nomination of Gomberg, the Nobel Committee for chemistry appears to have become a smoothly working instrument for achieving decisions about Nobel prize matters.

The members of the committee in 1915 and 1935 are listed in Table 4. The background of the members is given by their official positions and the areas of their scientific training. The first obvious feature one can note are the long mandate periods, between 15 and 30 years. In essence, the members of the committee of 1915 controlled the development in the first thirty years of the Nobel Prize in chemistry, while those of the 1935 committee had an almost equally long command of the Nobel Prize decisions during the next 20 years. The second point of some interest is the rather high age of committee members, averaging 65 years in 1915 and 74 years in 1924, a crucial year for Gomberg's and Schlenk's candidacies. The average age of the 1935 committee was 59 years. The high ages are easily explained: the promotion system in Swedish universities seldom allowed for attaining a professorial chair before the age of fifty, and the Academy did not elect members outside the exclusive group. This situation has improved over the years, but not much!

One can surmise that the long periods of service in the committee had a strong influence in several ways on the selection of serious candidates for the prize. One important factor that, as far as I can see, has not been emphasized before, was connected with the fact that the number of

Table 4 Members of the Nobel committee for chemistry in 1915

Name (born in)	Period	Official position	Scientific training
		In 1915	
A.G. Ekstrand (1846)	1913–1924	government service, Stockholm	organic chemistry
O. Hammarsten[a] (1841)	1905–1926	professor of medicinal and physiological chemistry (Uppsala U)	medical dr., physiology
P. Klason (1848)	1900–1925	professor of chemistry and chemical technology, Royal Inst. Technology, Stockholm	organic chemistry
H. Söderbaum (1862)	1900–1933	professor of agricultural chemistry at Academy of Agriculture, Uppsala	inorganic chemistry[b]
O. Widman (1852)	1900–1928	professor of organic chemistry, Uppsala U	organic chemistry
		In 1935	
H. von Euler-Chelpin[c] (1873)	1929–1946	professor of general and organic chemistry, Stockholms Högskola	physical chemistry
B. Holmberg (1881)	1934–1953	professor of organic chemistry, Royal Institute of Technology, Stockholm	organic chemistry
W. Palmaer[d] (1868)	1926–1942	professor of theoretical chemistry and electrochemistry, Royal Institute of Technology, Stockholm	inorganic chemistry
L. Ramberg (1874)	1927–1940	professor of chemistry, Uppsala U	organic and analytical chemistry
The Svedberg[e] (1884)	1925–1964	professor of physical chemistry, Uppsala U	physical chemistry

[a] Chairman 1910–1926,
[b] Also active in the history of chemistry.
[c] von Euler-Chelpin was mainly active as a biochemist and received the Nobel Prize in chemistry in 1929.
[d] Chairman 1934–1939.
[e] The Svedberg received the Nobel Prize in chemistry in 1926.

nominated candidates each year was rather low until about 1950, normally between 10 and 25 (see Fig. 1). This meant that in a particular year the committee had to consider a majority of candidates who had already been evaluated in previous years, once the system had reached an equilibrium. The number of new candidates was low, maybe around five, and they were subjected to an immediate evaluation the first time they were nominated. The evaluation, in the form of a special report, was in those times always commissioned from a committee member. Exceptions to this rule were the special reports requested from S. Arrhenius in his capacity as director of the Nobel Institute for physical chemistry. In addition, Arrhenius was a member of the Nobel committee for physics between 1900 and 1927. Most special reports were detailed, thorough and outspoken in a way seldom seen in

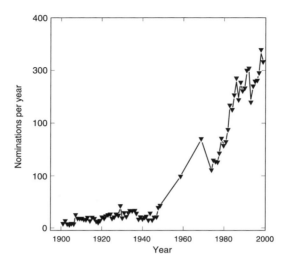

Fig. 1 Number of yearly nominated candidates for the Nobel prize in chemistry in the period 1901–1950 (see also Ref. 7, p. 320).

modern times, and it is only natural that a negative report would have only slight chances of being changed since the reporting member would be on the committee for many years. This system also meant that the work of a nominee was evaluated at an early stage, perhaps so early that the correctness of the work was still questioned by the research community, and this was bound to have consequences – a Nobel committee would avoid taking sides in a scientific controversy at almost any cost. Taken together, one can see that a person nominated early in his career might be exposed to a more negative evaluation than a late nominee who had a solidly established reputation, an effect which would have been difficult to avoid in the early Nobel committees. However, it should be stressed that the work of important candidates was often evaluated several times, usually by two members independently of each other.

The committee of 1915 had several members who had a scientific background in organic chemistry, presumably with the intention of the chemistry class and the Academy being able to properly judge the progress of organic chemistry, then a predominantly German undertaking. However, a perusal of the reports commissioned from the members at that time, shows that each member had a much broader mandate than suggested by his professional specialty or training. Thus the 1912 Academy report documented a lively but informal controversy about the prize worthiness of A. Werner (Nobel prize 1913) between a sceptical Klason on the one side and Söderbaum and Widman on the other. The committee of 1935 was more balanced, reflecting the impact of the rapidly moving areas of biochemistry and physical chemistry. In the 1940s, the proliferation of new chemical areas necessitated the election of adjunct members, in the beginning only for a special candidate and for one year, but later on a more permanent basis.

Each year the committee crowned its work by writing a report to the Academy in which all candidates were discussed and weighed against each other, with the special reports of that year and previous years as the background. The Academy report ended in most cases by giving one suggestion of Nobel prize candidate(s) in agreement with the statute that no more than three persons or two different discoveries could share the prize. However, if the committee agreed by a majority decision that no prizeworthy candidate could be found in a particular year, the recommendation was that the prize for that year should be reserved for the next year and possibly be awarded then – or reserved forever. This is not as strange as it appears to a modern observer: during the whole period 1901–1950, the number of nominees was small (Fig. 1) and thus the supply of serious candidates was easily exhausted. Reserved prizes were common in the period we are discussing (see for example Tables 1 and 2), and not only for the reason that a World War was going on.

4 Committee treatment of the nominations of Gomberg and Schlenk

As already explained, Gomberg's candidacy was disallowed in 1915–16 for formal reasons. The first time his name was mentioned in a special report was in one actually devoted to an evaluation in 1918 of Schlenk's work (for nominations of Schlenk, see Table 2). Schlenk was nominated by Schneider from Jena, Germany and Widman wrote an eleven-page special report.[33] It covered all aspects of Schlenk's research, and only two pages were devoted to the triphenylmethyl problem. The first paragraph of the latter section immediately introduced the picture of a hesitant and even retracting Gomberg, which would become part of most future judgements of his work:

> After Gomberg had discovered triphenylmethyl in 1900, this body has been the subject of great interest. Gomberg already from the beginning stated the view that this was a compound which contained a trivalent carbon atom, i.e. a "free radical". This immediately raised objections, and Gomberg himself found himself forced to give up his idea, if only for a while.

As noted above, the only documentation of this statement in Gomberg's entire scientific production consists of two sentences in an account of preliminary work from 1906.[25] After listing the problems occupying Gomberg (see above), Widman concluded that the final proof of the existence of triphenylmethyl-type radicals was provided by Schlenk's isolation of a number of nearly 100% monomeric species, for example, trisbiphenylmethyl **12**. He was also identified as the one who experimentally verified the existence of the equilibrium hexaphenylethane ⟺ triphenylmethyl by ebullioscopy in benzene at *ca.* 80°C (although here we must note that Gomberg earlier had similar indications from cryoscopy in naphthalene, but the high temperature, *ca.* 80°C, made him careful in his interpretation since one could not exclude decomposition). In his work, Schlenk developed new methods and apparatus to deal with air- and water-sensitive compounds, which earned him great praise from Widman (however, again we must note that the triarylmethyl work was done in an apparatus described by another scientist, Schmidlin[14]). Also Schlenk's discovery of metal ketyls, a new type of free radical, was quoted. However, the work on triarylmethyl radicals, even if it definitely proved the existence of free radicals, was not considered to be new and original enough. Gomberg was the one who discovered triphenylmethyl, and Schmidlin suggested the equilibrium hypothesis.

On a different note, Schlenk's work on alkylmetals, e.g. alkyllithiums, was deemed interesting, but these reagents were judged not to become of any greater use (!) in the service of organic synthetic chemistry because of the extreme difficulty in handling them.

In the 1918 report to the Academy, the committee summarized Widman's special report, citing Schlenk's rare experimental skill in handling air- and moisture-sensitive compounds, but pointed out that Gomberg made the discovery of free radicals. The committee also endorsed the statement about the bleak future of alkylmetals.[34] That year the Nobel Prize was reserved and awarded to Fritz Haber the following year.

In 1921 Gomberg was properly nominated for the first time by M.T. Bogert of New York and his work was promptly subjected to a five-page review by Widman.[35] After referring to the long discussion about the possible existence of free radicals in the period 1815–1865 and the ensuing acceptance of the dogma of tetravalent carbon, Widman described the nature and impact of Gomberg's discovery. He then pointed out the problems which Gomberg encountered in his further studies and which are detailed above: the hexaphenylethane riddle, the electrical conductivity of triphenylmethyl solutions in liquid SO_2 and the molecular weight determinations. He also referred to the Jacobson formula **1** and Gomberg's attempt to verify it by studies of ring-halogenated triphenylethyls, and cited parts of the two conclusions by Gomberg quoted fully above: "This hydrocarbon can hardly possess the simple formula $(C_6H_5)_3C$, however satisfactorily this symbol describes all other properties of this strongly unsaturated compound" and "The fact — suggests in all probability that a conversion into chinoid compounds of some kind has taken place." From this, Widman concluded again that Gomberg found himself forced to give up his original view of the trivalency of carbon in triphenylmethyl, if only for a short period.

After pointing out the contributions of Schmidlin and Wieland who suggested that an equilibrium between a dimeric species (hexaphenylethane and/

or **1**) and the monomeric free radical would explain the experimental observations, Widman stated that, as of 1910, the problem still had not been
settled. Still a majority of chemists considered triphenylmethyl to be either
a labile hexaphenylethane or a quinol (like **1**).

The next sentence introduced Schlenk's contributions. One can hardly
avoid noticing the admiration for German chemistry implicit in the following
sentence: "In this year W. Schlenk started to publish his masterly studies,
emanating from the famous Munich Laboratory." Then Widman described
Schlenk's work on monomeric triarylmethyls and also the metal ketyls,
referring to his 1918 special report. He also mentioned that Pummerer and
Frankfurter in 1914 had prepared another type of compound with trivalent
carbon, the α-ketomethyls, and drew attention to Wieland's discovery in 1911
that tetraphenylhydrazine can dissociate into free diphenylamino radicals, in
principle the same phenomenon as hexaphenylethane dissociation.[36] Thus the
discussion of the constitution of the triarylmethyls had been concluded
around 1911, and Widman went on to his final judgement of Gomberg's
discovery:

> As seen from the above, the observation made by Gomberg 21 years ago has led
> to exceedingly important theoretical results. However, the credit for these does
> not belong to Gomberg alone but, to a very significant degree, Schlenk, whose
> work in this and related areas (see my report on Schlenk's work from 1918) must
> in themselves be regarded as more prominent than Gomberg's. Even if one
> disregards the fact that Gomberg's discovery presumably is too old now to be
> awarded by the Nobel prize, it would not be fair to award him with exclusion of
> Schlenk. Anyway, the question of a possible sharing of the prize between both is
> presently not pertinent, since Schlenk has not been nominated for the Nobel
> prize this year.

Here two statutory rules were quoted and it is pertinent to comment upon
them. One strictly upheld rule is that a person has to be nominated in a given
year in order to be eligible for the Nobel prize in that year – for the obvious
reason that the committee would otherwise find itself occupied with a steadily
accumulating and unmanageable list of candidates. The second rule, about
the recency of discoveries, was (and still is) considerably more difficult to
uphold. Nobel's will stipulated that prizes should be given "to those persons
who shall have contributed most materially to benefit mankind during the
year immediately preceding." Clearly, this is an impossible rule considering
the reluctance with which the research community treats pioneering
discoveries and the time it takes to accept – or reject – them. The recency
requirement was interpreted more flexibly in Section 2 of the Code of
Statutes of the Nobel Foundation,[37] laid down by King Oscar II in 1900:

> The proviso in the Will to the effect that for the prize-competition only such
> works for inventions shall be eligible as have appeared 'during the preceding
> year', is to be understood, that a work or an invention for which a reward
> under the terms of the Will is contemplated, shall set forth the most modern

research of work being done in that of the departments, as defined in the Will, to which it belongs; works or inventions of older standing to be taken into consideration only in case their importance have not previously been demonstrated.

The most important reason for this more flexible rule is found in Section 5: "No work shall have a prize awarded to it unless it has been proved by the test of experience or by the examination of experts to possess the preeminant excellence that is manifestly signified by the terms of the will." The effect of the recency rule in the period 1901–1915 was examined by Crawford[38] who concluded that it was applied with flexibility, dependent on what kind of situations were examined, and that works carried out within the "past two decades" were considered for prizes.

Thus Widman's conclusion presumably reflected an implicit rule of the committee that the time limit for the age of a discovery was approximately 20 years. The facts that the rule of Section 4 had prohibited any award before 1910–1912 and that the World War had interrupted the awarding of Nobel prizes for two years, were not taken into account; by such counting the corroborated and generally accepted discovery of free radicals was only 7–9 years old in 1921.

The committee quoted from Widman's report almost verbatim in 1921, and in 1922 the detailed nomination by Traube was dealt with negatively by a short reference to the report of 1921. In the critical year of 1924, both Gomberg (Table 1) and Schlenk (Table 2) were nominated, the former twice and together with G.N. Lewis in one of them. The committee did not request any new special report but relied on the previous ones from 1918 and 1921, respectively, for its one-page statement.[39] In summary, it was noted that Gomberg in 1900 had discovered a compound which he denoted as triphenylmethyl, containing a trivalent carbon atom and which thus was a free radical. On the basis of his own work and criticisms from other researchers, he was forced to retract his view, if only for a short time. After ten years of scientific discussion, it was possible for Schlenk to finally prove the existence of triarylmethyls and solve this theoretically interesting valence problem. Therefore, the Nobel prize could not be awarded to Gomberg alone, especially since Schlenk's works must be considered to be more prominent. On the other hand, Gomberg made the first discovery and Schlenk's works, even if they unambiguously confirmed Gomberg's suggestion, were based on results by others, apart from Gomberg also Schmidlin. Thus none of the candidates could justly be awarded the Nobel prize with the exclusion of the other.

The possibility of a shared prize was briefly introduced, but met with a particular difficulty. This was based on Section 2 in the Code of Statutes, quoted above, and expressed as: "Gomberg made his discovery 24 years ago and its importance was clearly established in 1910, that is, 14 years ago. To award Gomberg now would, according to the views of the committee, not be in good agreement with this statute and by its consequences actually be equal to putting its rule out of force."

Thus, the candidacies of Gomberg and Schlenk were ruled out in 1924 by their recency statute, presumably after some discussion in the committee, as can be deduced from the unusually long statement in the Academy report. In that year, no Nobel prize was awarded because of the lack of suitable candidates (the nominees of 1924 are listed in Table 5), somewhat surprisingly, in view of the fact that the prize winners of the three coming years were nominated in 1924. The prize of 1924 was reserved for the next year and, in the end, forever. So, there is a question which is bound to be difficult to answer: Was the committee really so deeply concerned about the recency statute, or did it simply not want to award the discovery of free radicals? Gomberg was to be nominated in 1927, 1928, 1929 (with Schlenk), 1938 and 1940 but the committee, now with largely different members, always dealt with these nominations by reference to the Academy report of 1924 and Widman's special reports of 1921 and 1918.

Table 5 Nominees for the Nobel prize in chemistry in 1924

Name	Country	No. of nom.	Remark
A. Angeli	Italy	2	
O. Aschan	Finland	1	
C. Auer von Welsbach	Austria	1	
D. Coster	Holland	2	
T. Curtius	Germany	6	
F. Emich	Austria	1	
H. von Euler-Chelpin	Sweden	2	Nobel prize in chemistry 1929
M. Gomberg	USA	2	
O. Hahn	Germany	1	Nobel prize in chemistry 1944
A. Haller	France	1	
G. de Hevesy	Hungary	5	Nobel prize in chemistry 1943
G.N. Lewis	USA	3	
L. Meitner	Germany	1	
J. Perrin	France	1	Nobel prize in physics 1926
A. Pictet	Switzerland	1	
A. Recoura	France	1	
W. Schlenk	Germany	1	
H. Siedentopf	Germany	1	
S.P.L. Sörensen	Denmark	1	
The Svedberg	Sweden	2	Nobel prize in chemistry 1926
G. Tammann	Germany	2	
G. Urbain	France	4	
H. Wieland	Germany	2	Nobel prize in chemistry 1927
R. Zsigmondy	Germany	1	Nobel prize in chemistry 1925

5   The fate of two other pioneers of free radical chemistry, F. Paneth and M.S. Kharasch

Paneth received several nominations for the Nobel prize in chemistry (Table 6), the first one in 1927 being motivated by what turned out to be an experimental artefact, promptly retracted. In 1932, his works on the generation of free short-lived radicals and on volatile heavy metal hydrides were quoted for his nomination by O. Hönigschmid, Munich. The special report[40] was written by L. Ramberg, who had joined the committee in 1927 after Hammarsten. The introduction mentioned the role of free alkyl radicals in the time of Kolbe and Frankland but, curiously enough, said nothing about the triphenylmethyl problem. Next came a description of Paneth's experiment:[41] a stream of nitrogen containing tetramethyllead at a low partial pressure was passed at high speed through a quartz tube. By heating the tube at some point, a lead mirror was deposited in this place. After cooling the tube, another point upstream of the lead mirror was heated. A new mirror appeared, but as it grew, the first mirror diminished in size and eventually disappeared completely.

This experiment showed that some volatile component was formed in the thermal decomposition of tetramethyllead and that this compound consumed a cold lead mirror with formation of a volatile product. If, instead, a zinc mirror was first deposited and allowed to be consumed by the volatile product from decomposition of tetramethyllead, dimethylzinc could be identified as the product. Paneth concluded that free methyl radical was formed in the thermal reaction and could determine its half-life to be 0.006 seconds under the reaction conditions employed. Also, free ethyl radicals could be formed in

Table 6   Nominations of F. Paneth (1887–1958) for the Nobel prize in chemistry

Year	Nominator	From	Nominated for	Remark
1927	K. Peters		transmutation of hydrogen into helium	retracted; experimental artefact
1932	O. Hönigschmid	Munich, Germany	heavy metal hydrides; generation of the free radicals, methyl and ethyl	report by L. Ramberg
1935	M. Gomberg	Ann Arbor, USA	generation of the free radicals, methyl and ethyl	
1939	F. Soddy	Oxford, UK	use of radioactive elements as indicators	nominated jointly with G. de Hevesy
1948	W.G. Brown J. Franck T.R. Hogness W.C. Johnson H.I. Schlesinger T.F. Young	Chicago, USA	studies of free radical reactions	nominated jointly with M.S. Kharasch; report by A. Fredga

similar experiments, whereas experiments designed for study of propyl and butyl radicals indicated that these radicals decompose to methyl radicals. It was also shown that the disappearance of radicals in the apparatus used was mainly dependent on wall reactions, and accommodation coefficients (measuring the proportion of radicals reacting at a particular surface) were approximately determined.

Ramberg's conclusion about the free radical work was:

> Considering the fundamental role which according to recent work free radicals play in chemical transformations, not least in organic chemistry, Paneth's results must be granted great importance. However, his work cannot be considered more outstanding than those of many other researchers. They cause attention perhaps mostly by touching upon a classical problem which has been attacked by methods of more "chemically" oriented nature than those common in modern radical research. The most interesting results, namely the determination of the accommodation coefficients, are so far to be looked upon as provisory and require urgently supplementary and intensified studies which is expected from Paneth's ongoing investigations.
>
> Under such circumstances, the suggestion of awarding Paneth should not presently be followed.

The committee agreed with Ramberg's conclusions.

Thus Paneth's work was considered to be of equal importance to that of a number of other contemporary scientists. We can get an impression of the composition of the free radical research community at that time by looking at the list of participants and speakers at the 59th Faraday Society Discussion,[42] which took place in Cambridge, England in September 1933; discussion papers were, among others, given by J. Franck, M. Gomberg, E. Hückel, C.K. Ingold, J.E. Lennard-Jones, T.M. Lowry, R.G.W. Norrish, E. Rabinowitsch, A. Schönberg, C.P. Snow, A. Weissberger, and K. Ziegler.

In 1935, Gomberg himself nominated Paneth for the Nobel prize:

> because of the unique and original demonstration that even simple radicals, such as methyl and ethyl, are indeed a reality and that they have a measurable life-period. An examination of the various papers which have been presented at the General Discussion on Free Radicals, held by the Faraday Society, September 1933, show that Professor Paneth's contributions have served as a decided stimulus in the recent discussion of this chapter of chemistry in its various phases.

However, the committee did not change its earlier view, referring to Ramberg's special report of 1932.

It took a further 13 years, to 1948, before Paneth's free radical work was again considered by the committee after a proposal from a group of scientists at the University of Chicago. The nomination was made jointly for Paneth and M.S. Kharasch "for investigations in the field of free radical reactions". In view of the long time which had elapsed since Ramberg's first special report, A. Fredga, professor of organic chemistry at Uppsala University and a member of the committee between 1944 and 1975, was requested to evaluate the works of Paneth and Kharasch.[43] The part covering the former candidate followed the same lines as Ramberg's, and it was additionally noted that the benzyl radical, but not the phenyl radical, could be studied by the metal mirror method, and that the measurement of accommodation co-efficients had been further refined. It was pointed out that other researchers had later adopted the mirror technique in similar studies.

In the second part, Kharasch's work on organic free radical reactions was described in detail, and it was concluded that he had brought forward very extensive and valuable experimental material for the illumination of the pathways of organic reactions. His theoretical discussions of the phenomena observed were carefully conducted and alternative mechanisms often discussed. This was considered a merit but also a cause of difficulties in surveying the work. Some results were considered uncertain or not com-pletely clarified.

The conclusion regarding prizeworthiness stressed the difficulties caused by the different time perspectives. Paneth's nomination was based on invest-igations made in 1929–1935, now finished but with a great effect on later developments, whereas that of Kharasch was motivated by work begun in 1933 and still going on without any sign of slowing down. Some of Kharasch's results had to be considered as preliminary and not sufficiently well con-firmed. Neither of the two researchers should be awarded alone, but a shared Nobel prize was "a seductive thought". However, in view of the critical remarks regarding Kharasch's work, this procedure was not recommended as the committee agreed in their Academy report of 1948. Unfortunately, the first nomination of Kharasch almost coincides with the fifty-year limit imposed upon research in the Nobel Archive, so we will have to wait for the final conclusions on his candidacy.

6 Conclusions

It should be stressed that this inquiry about the fate of the pioneers of free radical chemistry in the hands of the Nobel committee is based solely on a search of the Nobel Archive of the Royal Swedish Academy of Sciences, Stockholm, Sweden. Although in principle no other written material, such as letters exchanged between committee members, should exist outside the archives (Section 8 in the Special Regulations at that time stated: "The proceedings, verdicts and proposals of the Nobel-Committees with reference to the prize-distribution shall not be published or in any other way be made known", much later to be replaced by the rule that the Nobel Archive should be made available for research of material $\geq$ fifty years old), it cannot be dismissed that such material with relation to free radical chemistry may possibly be found. The many references to correspondence between committee members in Crawford's book[32] signify that the secrecy statute was not always strictly adhered to. However, this is a research project on its own, and would require much work with a low probability of obtaining deeper insights into the problem dealt with here.

The events related above permit a tentative conclusion as to why no Nobel prize was awarded for the discovery of the first free radical. The formal reason in the critical year, 1924, was based on the recency rule. However, it is difficult to imagine that a determined champion of Gomberg in the committee would not have been able to circumvent this argument and convince the other members about the prizeworthiness of Gomberg's and Schlenk's work. No member wanted to play this role in 1924, and thus the moment was lost. The arguments used were based on Widman's special report on Gomberg 1921, which treated Gomberg's work with emphasis on predominantly negative aspects. In particular, the quotation of Gomberg's retraction of his idea, also mentioned in the special report on Schlenk in 1918, in two sentences out of a production of then more than 400 pages, appears odd and was quoted somewhat out of context. In marked contrast, the lavish praise of Schlenk for his construction of new devices to handle air- and water-sensitive compounds does not have any solid background in this context, since Schlenk used an apparatus developed by Schmidlin[14] for working with triarylmethyls. Besides, Gomberg was first to construct a special apparatus for this purpose.[13] In short, it seems that the committee did not consider the discovery of free radicals important enough to award a Nobel prize. That this was an absolute verdict is shown by the fact that the Nobel prize of 1924 was reserved forever. Later, when the ramifications of free radical chemistry had started to pervade organic chemistry, the recency rule became valid.

A similar opinion on stable free radicals was expressed later by C. Walling in his book *Free Radicals in Solution*, published in 1957, and it is difficult to find a more well-informed spokesman:[44] "However, because their structural requirements for existence are possessed by only rather complicated molecules, they have remained a rather esoteric branch of organic chemistry." The stability of Walling's opinion about stable free radicals is indicated by the following quotation from his autobiography from 1995:

> For the field I was inadvertently entering (Walling had asked Kharasch if he could join his group), 1937 was a landmark year. Free radicals of course first entered organic chemistry in 1900 with Gomberg's preparation and identification of triphenylmethyl, but the chemistry and properties of such "stable" or "persistent" species had remained largely a chemical curiosity.[45]

In 1937, three important publications concerning the role of short-lived radicals appeared: first, the review of Hey and Waters,[46] second, Kharasch's formulation of a bromine atom chain mechanism for the addition of hydrogen bromide to olefins,[47] and third, a paper by Flory (Nobel prize in 1974) analyzing vinyl polymerization as a radical chain reaction.[48]

Gomberg had the immense pleasure of seeing these important developments of free radical chemistry as they occurred after 1930.[49] He retired in 1936 and died on February 12, 1947. At the end of his obituary we get a glimpse of the man in his role as a scientist:

> He stressed the necessity of a thorough basic training in all branches of chemistry with a minimum of specialization. He believed that teaching on the university level was impossible without research, and in regard to PhD candidates he felt that the emphasis should be placed on the training of the candidate and not on the issuance of a publication. He had strong convictions on such matters and was not adverse to expressing them, but he never spoke with harshness or with intention to hurt. In his contacts with students, he was sympathetic, gave generously of his time and was always ready to offer friendly advice.
>
> Gifted with a remarkable memory, he presented his lectures with the full use of a wealth of historical material and so vividly that they left an indelible mark on his students. A great teacher and scholar, he inspired his students by his methods and ideals, and his colleagues by the vigor and clarity of his mind. To this greatness, he added an innate kindliness and unassuming modesty that endeared him to all.

Acknowledgements

I gratefully acknowledge the permission of the Royal Swedish Academy of Sciences, Stockholm, to carry out research in its Nobel Archive.

References

1. Gomberg, M. (1900). *J. Am. Chem. Soc.* **22**, 757
2. Gomberg, M. (1900). *Ber. Dtsch. Chem. Ges.* **33**, 3150
3. Gomberg, M. (1901). *J. Am. Chem. Soc.* **23**, 109
4. Norris, J.F. and Sanders, W.W. (1901). *Am. Chem. J.* **25**, 54
5. McBride, J.M. (1974). *Tetrahedron* **30**, 2009
6. Walden, P. (1924). *Chemie der freien Radikale.* S. Hirzel, Leipzig; this book was dedicated to M. Gomberg as the discoverer of the first free radical, triphenylmethyl, and the creator of the doctrine of trivalent carbon.
7. Westgren, A. (1950). In *Nobel, The Man and His Prizes.* Sohlmans Förlag, Stockholm, p. 317
8. *Nominations in chemistry.* (1915)
9. Academy Report. (1915). General report from the Nobel Committee for Chemistry to the Royal Swedish Academy of Sciences. In *Minutes concerning the Nobelprizes*, The Nobel Archive of The Royal Swedish Academy of Sciences, Stockholm.
10. Academy Report. (1916). General report from the Nobel Committee for Chemistry to the Royal Swedish Academy of Sciences. In *Minutes concerning*

the Nobelprizes, The Nobel Archive of The Royal Swedish Academy of Sciences, Stockholm.
11. Gomberg, M. (1897). Ber. Dtsch. Chem. Ges. **30**, 2043, (1898). J. Am. Chem. Soc. **20**, 773
12. Schoepfle, C.S. and Bachman, W.E. (1947). J. Am. Chem. Soc. **69**, 2921. Great Chemists (E. Farber, ed.), (1961). Interscience, New York, Ch. 85
13. Gomberg, M. and Cone, L.H. (1904). Ber. Dtsch. Chem. Ges. **37**, 2033
14. Schmidlin, J. (1908). Ber. Dtsch. Chem. Ges. **41**, 423
15. Leffler, J.E. (1993). An Introduction to Free Radicals. Wiley, New York, p. 182. The analogy is far from perfect since free radicals were eventually shown to exist.
16. Lewis, G.N. (1916). J. Am. Chem. Soc. **38**, 762
17. Hückel, E. (1934). Trans. Faraday Soc. **30**, 40. Ingold, C.K. (1934). Trans. Faraday Soc. **30**, 52
18. Gomberg, M. (1914). J. Am. Chem. Soc. **36**, 1144
19. Gomberg, M. (1901). Ber. Dtsch. Chem. Ges. **34**, 2726, (1902). **35**, 1822, 2397
20. Schmidlin, J (1908). Ber. Dtsch. Chem. Ges. **41**, 2471
21. Jacobson, P. (1905). Ber. Dtsch. Chem. Ges. **38**, 196
22. Lankamp, H., Nauta, W.Th. and MacLean, C. (1968). Tetrahedron Lett. 249
23. Walden, P. (1903). Z. Physik. Chem. **43**, 443
24. Gomberg, M. and Cone, L.H. (1904). Ber. Dtsch. Chem. Ges. **37**, 2033
25. Gomberg, M. and Cone, L.H. (1906). Ber. Dtsch. Chem. Ges. **39**, 3274
26. Gomberg, M. (1907). Ber. Dtsch. Chem. Ges. **40**, 1847
27. Bowden, S.T. and Watkins, T.F. (1940). J. Chem. Soc. 1249
28. Gomberg, M. (1903). Ber. Dtsch. Chem. Ges. **36**, 3927. (1904). **37**, 1626
29. Gomberg, M. and Cone, L.H. (1906). Ber. Dtsch. Chem. Ges. **39**, 1469, 2967
30. Schlenk, W., Herzenstein, A. and Weickel, T. (1910). Ber. Dtsch. Chem. Ges. **43**, 1753
31. Schlenk, W., Weickel, T. and Herzenstein, A. (1910). J. Liebigs Ann. Chem. **372**, 1. Schlenk, W. (1912). J. Liebig's Ann. Chem. **394**, 178
32. Crawford, E. (1984). The Beginnings of the Nobel Institution. The Science Prizes, 1901–1915. Cambridge University Press, Cambridge
33. Widman, O. (1918). Special report on W. Schlenk
34. Academy Report (1921). General report from the Nobel Committee for Chemistry to the Royal Swedish Academy of Sciences. In Minutes concerning the Nobelprizes, The Nobel Archive of The Royal Swedish Academy of Sciences, Stockholm.
35. Widman, O. (1921). Special report on M. Gomberg
36. Wieland, H. (1911). J. Liebig's Ann. Chem. **381**, 200. (1912). **392**, 156. (1911). Ber. Dtsch. Chem. Ges. **44**, 2550. (1912). **45**, 2600. Wieland made several important contributions to early free radical chemistry but was never nominated for this work; he received the Nobel prize 1927 for his investigations of the constitution of the bile acids and related substances
37. Ref. 32, p. 219ff
38. Ref. 32, p. 162
39. Academy Report (1924). General report from the Nobel Committee for Chemistry to the Royal Swedish Academy of Sciences. In Minutes concerning the Nobelprizes, The Nobel Archive of The Royal Swedish Academy of Sciences, Stockholm.
40. Ramberg, L. (1932). Special report on F. Paneth
41. Paneth, F. and Hofeditz, W. (1929). Ber. Dtsch. Chem. Ges. **62**, 1335
42. (1934). Trans. Faraday Soc. **30**, January issue
43. Fredga, A. (1948). Special report on F. Paneth and M.S. Kharasch

44. Walling. C. (1937). *Free Radicals in Solution*. Wiley, New York, p. 3
45. Walling, C. (1995). *Fifty Years of Free Radicals*. American Chemical Society, Washington, D.C., p. 11
46. Hey, D.H. and Waters, W.A. (1937). *Chem. Rev.* **21**, 169
47. Kharasch, M.S., Engelmann, H. and Mayo, F.R. (1937). *J. Org. Chem.* **2**, 288
48. Flory, P.J. (1937). *J. Am. Chem. Soc.* **59**, 241
49. Gomberg, M. (1932). *J. Chem. Educ.* **9**, 439
50. Branch, G.E.K. and Calvin, M. (1941). *The Theory of Organic Chemistry*. Prentice-Hall, New York, p. 320

Kinetics and Mechanism of the Dissociative Reduction of C—X and X—X Bonds (X = O, S)

FLAVIO MARAN,[†] DANIAL D.M. WAYNER,[‡] and MARK S. WORKENTIN[§]

[†] Dipartimento di Chimica Fisica, Università di Padova, Italy
[‡] Steacie Institute for Molecular Sciences, National Research Council of Canada, Ottawa, Ontario
[§] Department of Chemistry, The University of Western Ontario, London, Ontario

1 Introduction

STEPWISE VERSUS CONCERTED DISSOCIATIVE REDUCTION

Despite great advances in our understanding of electron transfer (ET) and subsequent reactions of radical ions over the last 20 years, work in this area continues to provide challenges and surprises. While it was recognized many years ago that the addition or removal of an electron can be used to activate molecules towards addition or fragmentation[1] it is only recently that the kinetics of a number of these reactions have been quantified systematically to allow comparison with and improvement of ET theories. Normally one

85

ADVANCES IN PHYSICAL ORGANIC CHEMISTRY
VOLUME 36   ISBN 0-12-033536-0

thinks about the one-electron reduction of a molecule, A-B, as a route to an intermediate radical anion, A-B$^-$$^\bullet$. Subsequent reaction of the radical anion leads to, among other products, the fragments A$^\bullet$ and B$^-$ (equations 1 and 2). This chemical sequence is referred to as a *stepwise dissociative reduction*. There is another mechanism that leads to the same products but does not require an intermediate radical anion (equation 3) which is referred to as a *concerted dissociative reduction* since the ET and bond breaking occur in a single step.

$$A\text{-}B + e \quad \rightarrow \quad A\text{-}B^-{}^\bullet \tag{1}$$

$$A\text{-}B^-{}^\bullet \quad \rightarrow \quad A^\bullet + B^- \tag{2}$$

$$A\text{-}B + e \quad \rightarrow \quad A^\bullet + B^- \tag{3}$$

The concept of concerted dissociative ET traces back to early studies by Hush and Eberson on the reduction of halides and the dissociative oxidation of carboxylates.[2,3] These ideas were then developed extensively by Eberson for the dissociative reduction of halides and peroxides.[4-6] Eberson employed the Marcus theory for outer-sphere ET[7-9] to describe the activation-driving force relationship of these processes. An interesting historical introduction to the matter can be found in very recent reviews by Hush[10] and Eberson.[11] In this context, one of the more interesting theories that has evolved over the last 15 years is the theory of dissociative ET, first introduced for application to solution ET by Savéant.[12] In general, the rate constant for ET, k, may be described in the usual form as in equation (4), in which Z is a pre-exponential term and $\Delta G^{\neq}$ is the activation free energy. In the case of the outer-sphere ET (equation 1), k may be predicted by Marcus theory (equation 5)[7,8] where ΔG° is the overall driving force and λ is the reorganization energy, which is four times the activation free energy at zero driving force (this latter parameter, $\Delta G_0^{\neq}$, is referred to as the *intrinsic barrier*). Although electronic coupling between reactant and product energy curves at the transition state is assumed to be enough to allow for efficient ET (unit transmission probability), it is small enough that $\Delta G^{\neq}$ is essentially unaffected. The reorganization energy has two components (equation 6): λ_s, which is the outer-sphere or solvent reorganization energy, and λ_i, which is the inner-sphere reorganization energy and accounts for changes in the bond lengths and angles upon ET. In order to provide a theoretical footing for the prediction of rates of the concerted dissociative reduction, Savéant[12] developed a theory which resulted in an equation having the same form as that of Marcus theory (equation 7) except that the intrinsic barrier includes contributions from both the above reorganization terms and the bond dissociation energy (BDE) of the breaking bond (equation 8). For simplicity, since the reactions involve only one charged species, the work terms for bringing reactants together or separating products are ignored.

$$k = Z \exp\left(\frac{-\Delta G^{\neq}}{RT}\right) \tag{4}$$

$$\Delta G^{\neq} = \frac{\lambda}{4}\left(1 + \frac{\Delta G^{\circ}}{\lambda}\right)^2 \tag{5}$$

$$\lambda = \lambda_S + \lambda_i \tag{6}$$

$$\Delta G^{\neq} = \Delta G_0^{\neq}\left(1 + \frac{\Delta G^{\circ}}{4\Delta G_0^{\neq}}\right)^2 \tag{7}$$

$$\Delta G_0^{\neq} = \frac{\lambda + \text{BDE}}{4} \tag{8}$$

A simple diagram depicting the differences between these two complementary theories is shown in Fig. 1, which represents reactions at zero driving force. Thus, the activation energy corresponds to the intrinsic barrier. Marcus theory assumes a harmonic potential for reactants and products and, in its simplest form, assumes that the reactant and product surfaces have the same curvature (Fig. 1a). In his derivation of the dissociative ET theory, Savéant assumed that the reactants should be described by a Morse potential and that the products should simply be the dissociative part of this potential (Fig. 1b).[12] Some concerns about the latter condition have been raised.[13,14] On the other hand, comparison of experimental data pertaining to alkyl halides[15,16] and peroxides (Section 3) with equations (7) and (8) seems to indicate that the simple model proposed by Savéant for the nuclear factor of the ET rate constant expression satisfactorily describes concerted dissociative reductions in the condensed phase. A similar treatment was used by Wentworth and co-workers to describe dissociative electron attachment to aromatic and alkyl halides in the gas phase.[17–19]

Much effort has been put into understanding and defining the practical differences between the concerted and the stepwise dissociative reduction mechanisms and whether or not there is a smooth transition between them (mechanistic continuum) or simply a partitioning between competing processes.[15,20–23] Savéant has described this transition in terms of three potential energy surfaces. In the dissociative reaction, the radical anion exists at a minimum energy that is above the energy of the avoided crossing between the reactant and the dissociative surfaces (Fig. 2, left). By modulating, e.g., the energy of the radical anion, the minimum of the radical anion surface eventually passes through energy of the concerted transition state (Fig. 2, center) and finally exists as an intermediate (Fig. 2, right). In most

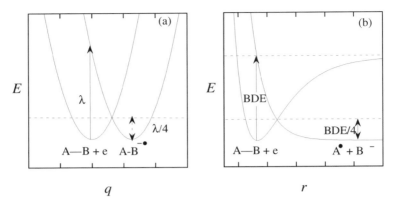

Fig. 1 Comparison of Marcus theory of outer sphere electron transfer (a) with the Savéant theory (b) of concerted dissociative electron transfer. The reaction coordinate q is a solvent parameter. The reaction coordinate, r, is the A—B bond length.

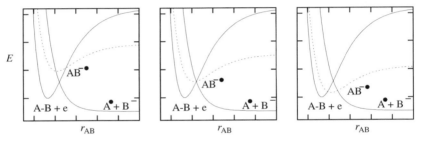

Fig. 2 Energy factors that influence the transition from the concerted (left) to the stepwise (right) dissociative reduction.

practical cases, the radical anion will be of the π^* type such as one would obtain from the one-electron reduction of an aromatic compound. The dissociative state is often associated with the one-electron reduction of a σ bond.

π^* AND σ^* INTERMEDIATES

As stated above, most radical anions encountered in the literature result from the addition of an electron to a formal π^* orbital. This is generally true because π^* orbitals are generally more accessible (energetically) than σ^* orbitals, which are more localized and more strongly perturbed by the addition of an electron. However, from an electronic viewpoint there is no reason, *a priori*, to expect that all σ bonds will be unstable to electron attachment. From simple perturbation MO theory, the interaction of a radical center with an anion leads to two new orbitals, one bonding and the other antibonding. A three-electron, two-center bond results when two electrons occupy the bonding orbital while only one electron occupies the antibonding orbital (Fig. 3). In fact, interactions of this type are particularly well characterized in the organic sulfur radical ion literature.[24] From this simple perturbation MO description, it is clear that a significant three-electron bonding interaction requires that the two interacting orbitals have similar energies and that there should be good electronic overlap. This is rarely the case for "normal" leaving groups (B⁻), which tend to have very high electron affinities (i.e. positive standard potentials) compared with the corresponding radical fragment (A•) leading to fragmentation reactions which are normally exergonic. However, in cases with less strongly driven fragmentations and in which the anionic leaving group is a softer nucleophile, the role of three-electron bonded intermediates ($2\sigma/1\sigma*$) must be considered. Such is the case for the fragmentation of disulfide radical anions that are discussed in Section 4.

RADICAL/ANION COMPLEXES

In the absence of a three-electron bond, it is possible that some interaction (Van der Waals, electrostatics, etc.) between the product radical and anion exists. This situation has been discussed in some detail for the interaction between a halide ion and an alkyl radical generated in the gas phase by dissociative electron attachment to an alkyl halide.[25] It is expected that these interactions will be more important in the gas phase, as a solvent tends to screen charge. Wentworth suggested that an appropriate potential

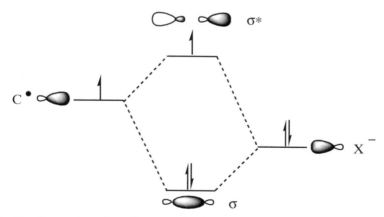

Fig. 3 Bonding and antibonding combinations of a carbon-centered radical and a nucleophile to form a two-center, three-electron bond. In this simple description, the $\sigma*$ anion radical has a bond order of one-half.

to describe the weak interaction between a radical and a nucleophile can be derived using the repulsive part of the A-B Morse potential but only a fraction, f, of the attractive part of the potential (equation 9), where $E_{AB^{-\bullet}}$ is the potential energy of the complex.[19] This is an interesting way to view the effect of one-electron reduction on the A—B bond energy. Realistically, the value of f is expected to be between 0 and 0.5. For $f = 0$ this simplifies to the Savéant model (i.e. the surface is completely dissociative). In the intermediate cases, stabilization energy of the complex becomes progressively smaller and the equilibrium "separation" increases as the contribution from the attractive part of the Morse potential decreases (Fig. 4).

$$E_{AB^{-\bullet}} = -2f\,BDE_{AB}\exp[-\beta(r - r_0)] + BDE_{AB}\exp[-2\beta(r - r_0)] - BDE_{AB} \quad (9)$$

Even a very weak interaction between $A^\bullet$ and B^- can have a dramatic effect on the kinetics of reduction. The calculated equilibrium and rate parameters for the reduction of AB as a function of f are shown in Table 1. A value of $f = 0.05$ leads to an increase in the rate constant of about one order of magnitude. It is also seen that for $f < 0.2$ the stabilization energies of the complex are similar to the barrier for diffusional separation of the fragments, which occurs with a rate constant of about $10^{10}\,s^{-1}$. At room temperature and

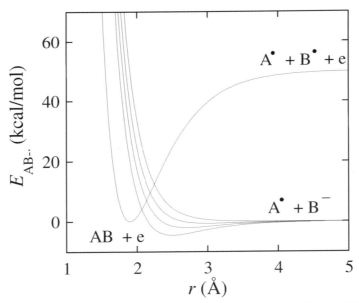

Fig. 4 Effect of the parameter, f, on the dissociative potential ($f = 0$, 0.1, 0.2, 0.3 from uppermost to lowermost curve). As the interaction between the radical and the anion increases, a transition from purely dissociative to a stepwise process is observed.

Table 1 Effect of interaction between $A^\bullet$ and B^- on the kinetics of dissociative reduction of AB.

f^a	E_S $(\mathrm{kcal\,mol^{-1}})^b$	$r\,(\text{Å})^c$	E_a $(\mathrm{kcal\,mol^{-1}})^d$	$\log\left(\dfrac{k_{ET}}{k_{ET}^{Sav}}\right)^e$
0.00	–	2.25	12.50	0
0.05	0.12	2.22	11.22	0.94
0.10	0.50	2.19	9.88	1.93
0.15	1.12	2.17	8.48	2.95
0.20	2.00	2.14	7.03	4.01

^{a}From equation (9) in which $\mathrm{BDE_{AB}}=50\,\mathrm{kcal\,mol^{-1}}$, $\beta=2$ and $r_0=1.9\,\text{Å}$.
^{b}Stabilization energy of the radical/anion complex.
^{c}A—B bond length at the transition state, $r_{TS}=\beta^{-1}\{\ln(2)+\ln(1-f)\}+r_0$.
^{d}By substitution of $r=r_{TS}$ into equation (9).
^{e}Ratio of the rate constant for ET at 298 K based on the Wentworth model compared to the Savéant model.

for $f < 0.1$, the stabilization energy is less than RT but nevertheless may still cause a significant decrease of the activation barrier. This radical/anion interaction is the basis of the substituent-dependent rate constants for reductive cleavage of substituted benzyl chlorides and bromides.[26–28] This view is also supported by very recent *ab initio* and DFT calculations of substituted benzyl chlorides.[29]

SCOPE OF THIS REVIEW

This review discusses some recent developments and methodologies that have impacted on our understanding of dissociative ET. For a detailed description of the theory and its application to carbon halogen bonds, we refer the readers to a recent complementary contribution by Savéant.[16] We will focus on the reduction of C—X and X—X bonds in which X is either oxygen or sulfur. These studies provide insights into the nature of the intrinsic barriers for the stepwise dissociative reduction reactions as well as some interesting examples that demonstrate a need to continue to develop the present dissociative ET model. In particular, the Savéant theory assumes that the electronic coupling at the avoided crossing of the A-B and $A^\bullet B^-$ surfaces is large enough ($> 200\,\mathrm{cm^{-1}}$ or $0.57\,\mathrm{kcal/mol}$) for the reaction to be adiabatic. Evidence from the reduction of peroxides points to a non-adiabatic process. The reduction of disulfides provides a clear example of a new type of stepwise process in which equation (7) cannot be employed to describe the kinetics for the formation of loose radical anions. Finally, the reduction of ethers, peroxides, sulfides and disulfides provides some insights into the three surface (Fig. 2) and two surface (Fig. 4) models of the transition from the stepwise to the concerted mechanisms.

2 Thermodynamic and kinetic methodologies

It is useful to briefly discuss some of the common and, perhaps, less common experimental approaches to determine the kinetics and thermodynamics of radical anion reactions. While electrochemical methods tend to be most often employed, other complementary techniques are increasingly valuable. In particular, laser flash photolysis and photoacoustic calorimetry provide independent measures of kinetics and thermodynamics of molecules and ion radicals. As most readers will not be familiar with all of these techniques, they will be briefly reviewed. In addition, the use of convolution voltammetry for the determination of electrode kinetics is discussed in more detail as this technique is not routinely used even by most electrochemists. Throughout this chapter we will reference all electrode potentials to the saturated calomel electrode and energies are reported in kcal mol^{-1}.

VOLTAMMETRIC METHODS

Electrochemical methods provide a measure of the rates of electron transfer and the rates of homogeneous follow-up reactions.[30,31] The most commonly employed electrochemical method is cyclic or linear sweep voltammetry, which can be used to study a wide range of electrochemical processes. For a detailed discussion of these methods we refer the readers to other sources.[35] For practical purposes we will restrict this brief summary to the two most common electrochemical mechanisms relevant to radical anion chemistry. In all cases, an initial electron transfer step is required to generate a radical anion (equation 1). The radical anion fragments (equation 2) and in most cases the product radical ($A^{\bullet}$) undergoes a second reduction either directly at the electrode (equation 10) or by diffusional encounter with another radical anion (equation 11). The first mechanism is the well-known ECE process (where E denotes an electrochemical process and C denotes a chemical process). The second is called the DISP (for electron disproportionation) mechanism. If the fragmentation is very fast ($>10^7\,s^{-1}$) then $A^{\bullet}$ is generated very close to the electrode and the ECE mechanism dominates. On the other hand, if the fragmentation is slow ($<10^4\,s^{-1}$) then the radical is produced far away from the electrode and the DISP mechanism dominates. In the intermediate range, the two mechanisms are competitive.

$$A^{\bullet} + e \quad \rightarrow \quad A^{-} \tag{10}$$

$$A^{\bullet} + AB^{-\bullet} \quad \rightarrow \quad A^{-} + AB \tag{11}$$

First and foremost, voltammetric measurements allow the determination of standard potentials. Values of $E^{\circ}_{AB/AB^{-\bullet}}$ can be directly determined when the reciprocal rate constant for fragmentation is larger than the timescale for cyclic voltammetric experiment. For most practical purposes this is limited to radical anions with rate constants $\leqslant 10^4 \, s^{-1}$ (in the majority of systems, voltammetry faster than $10^4 \, V/s$ is limited by slow ET). As a result, values of $E^\circ_{AB/AB^-\bullet}$ are often estimated using model compounds. For example, we have shown that the standard potential for the chemically irreversible reduction of a series of substituted α-phenoxyacetophenones can be estimated from the reversible potentials of the corresponding α-methoxyacetophenones.[33–36] The values of $E^\circ_{B^\bullet/B^-}$ can also be determined directly, either from electrochemical measurements in solutions of B^- or from electrochemical measurements in solutions of photogenerated $B^\bullet$. These direct electrochemical methods have been reviewed.[37,38]

When the homogeneous reactions are very fast, it is impractical to determine both the standard potential and the rate constants. In the vast majority of cases the useful scan rate (v) range is limited by the heterogeneous rate constant for formation of the radical anion (usually $v < 10\,000 \, V/s$). Below this scan rate, if the voltammetric wave is chemically irreversible, either the standard potential or the rate constant must be known in order to determine the other. At faster scan rates the electron transfer becomes the rate-limiting step so one cannot obtain any information relevant to the rate constants of the homogeneous processes. For the ECE and DISP mechanism, the relationship between the peak potential (E_p), E° and the homogeneous rate constant (k_{hom}) is given by equation (12), where the constant $m = 0.78$ for ECE and 1.107 for DISP, v is in V/s and F and R are the Faraday and gas constants, respectively.

$$E_p = E^\circ + m\frac{RT}{F} + \frac{RT}{2F}\ln\left(\frac{RT}{F}\frac{k_{hom}}{v}\right) \qquad (12)$$

In order for equation (12) to be valid, a plot of E_p vs. $\log(v)$ must have a slope of 30 mV/decade for a unimolecular process. If the slope is significantly greater, then the kinetics are not entirely limited by the rate of the homogeneous process and the electron transfer itself begins to be rate limiting. Under these conditions, other parameters such as the transfer coefficient, α, and the standard rate constant for ET, k_{het}, must also be taken into account. These concepts are discussed in more detail below. To summarize, for $\alpha = 0.5$, when the ECE/DISP process is entirely under ET control, $dE_p/d\log(v) = 60$ mV decade. When kinetic control is completely by the initial ET, an estimate of $E^\circ_{AB/AB^-\bullet}$ can be obtained using the convolution voltammetry method (see below). However, it should be noted that no information about the rate of the homogeneous reaction can be derived from these experiments (remember, one cannot learn about the kinetics of reactions that occur after the rate-limiting step). In the intermediate regime of mixed ET/homogeneous control, $30 \, mV < dE_p/d\log(v) < 60 \, mV$ deacde.[39] For mixed control, great care must be taken when extracting the rate constant.[34]

As mentioned above, the use of equation (12) presupposes that either the standard potential or the rate constant is known. In many cases it is possible to determine the rate constant using other methods such as laser flash photolysis (see later). In many other cases it is possible to obtain rough estimates of the standard potential for the reduction of AB by using model compounds that are structurally similar but less reactive. Keep in mind that an error of only 30 mV in the estimate of $E°$ leads to an error in the estimated rate constant by one order of magnitude. Under the best of conditions, the determination of standard potentials is in the order of ± 5 mV leading to errors in rate constants in the order of a factor of ± 1.5.

HOMOGENEOUS REDOX CATALYSIS

Conventional cyclic voltammetry is limited in timescale to the study of unimolecular chemical reactions with rate constants in the $5 \times 10^{-1}-10^4 \, s^{-1}$ range. With the use of ultramicroelectrodes,[37] this range can be extended by a couple of orders of magnitude only in special systems with very fast rates of heterogeneous electron transfer. A convenient method to determine the rate constants of ET or of rapid fragmentation of radical anions is homogeneous redox catalysis. This indirect method of studying the fragmentation of radical anions is well established and the reader is referred to a number of recent sources for more complete discussions of the techniques and their applications.[32,37,40–43]

Briefly, AB is reduced *homogeneously* in an ET process using an electrochemically generated radical anion donor ($D^{\bullet-}$). The donor, D, is chosen such that on a heterogeneous ET it yields a stable radical anion, $D^{\bullet-}$, both chemically and electrochemically reversible on the cyclic voltammetry timescale (equation 13) with a standard potential ($E°_{D/D^{\bullet-}}$) which is more positive than the peak potential for the direct heterogeneous reduction of AB (chemical reversibility refers to a long lifetime on the voltammetric timescale while electrochemical reversibility refers to a rapid heterogeneous ET). In the presence of AB, the voltammetric wave due to reaction (13) becomes chemically irreversible as $D^{-\bullet}$ is removed from the diffusion layer by reactions (14) and (15) or by (16) leading to an increase in the peak current, i_p. In either case, D is regenerated by the homogeneous ET reaction and subsequently re-reduced at the electrode. In the cases presented in this review, the fragmentation generates a radical, $A^\bullet$, that is generally much easier to reduce than AB itself. It follows then that $A^\bullet$ will itself be reduced by the donor radical anion (equation 17) or at the electrode (equation 18) to generate A^- at the diffusion-controlled rate. The kinetics of reactions (14), (15) or (16) (in which k_{ET}, k_{BET} and k_{frag} are the rate constants for electron transfer, back electron transfer and fragmentation, respectively) can be obtained from the quantitative determination of the increase in i_p relative to i_p° (the peak current in the presence and absence of AB, respectively) and the extent of loss of the chemical reversibility of the cyclic voltammetric wave of D/D$^{\bullet-}$. Experimentally, these current responses are measured as a function of ν and of the concentrations of AB and D. The rate constants (k_{ET}) are estimated using appropriate working curves or digital simulation of the voltammograms.

The second reduction can occur in competition with other reactions of A$^\bullet$, including coupling with D$^{\bullet-}$ (equation 19) or reaction with an H-atom donor, such as a solvent. It is necessary to account for these processes in the determination of the rate constants by including them in the treatment of the data using digital simulation. The extent of coupling and importance of competing reactions must be determined from product and coulometric analyses in preparative scale electrolyses. In some circumstances, the competition between the coupling and the reduction of the radical has been used to estimate the standard potential of the intermediate radicals.[44,45]

$$D + e \rightleftharpoons D^{\bullet-} \tag{13}$$

$$D^{\bullet-} + AB \underset{k_{BET}}{\overset{k_{ET}}{\rightleftharpoons}} D + AB^{\bullet-} \tag{14}$$

$$AB^{\bullet-} \xrightarrow{k_{frag}} A^\bullet + B^- \tag{15}$$

$$D^{\bullet-} + AB \xrightarrow{k_{ET}} A^\bullet + B^- + D \tag{16}$$

$$D^{\bullet-} + A^\bullet \longrightarrow A^- + D \tag{17}$$

$$A^\bullet + e \longrightarrow A^- \tag{18}$$

$$D^{\bullet-} + A^\bullet \longrightarrow DA^- \tag{19}$$

The application of redox catalysis also requires some knowledge or confirmation of the kinetic regime in which the chemistry occurs. For the fragmentation of AB$^{\bullet-}$ via a stepwise mechanism, the steady state approximation for [AB$^{\bullet-}$] can be applied. Therefore, the overall rate constant for reactions (15) and (16) is given by $\{k_{ET}k_{frag}/(k_{BET}[D] + k_{frag})\}$. Under these circumstances there are two limiting kinetic situations. The first occurs when $k_{BET}[D] \ll k_{frag}$. Here electron transfer is rate limiting, and the rate constant is simply k_{ET}. In the second limit, fragmentation of AB$^{\bullet-}$ is rate limiting, namely $k_{BET}[D] \gg k_{frag}$ and this leads to an observed rate constant, $k = (k_{ET}k_{frag}/[D])$, where the electron transfer step acts as a pre-equilibrium ($k_{ET} = k_{ET}/k_{BET}$). Experimentally, by varying the concentration of the donor, one can determine at which of these two limits one is operating; in the latter limit, the observed rate constant will vary with [D], while in the former, the rate is independent of [D]. The type of kinetic information that is available in these two extremes as well as in intermediate kinetic cases for a stepwise mechanism has been discussed in detail elsewhere,[46–48] and will not be discussed here, although generally the approach will allow the estimations of k_{ET} and k_{frag}. Using this method, k_{frag} values in the order of 10^5–$10^9 \, s^{-1}$ can be determined. In addition to obtaining values of the various rate constants, the method can also be used to extract standard potentials, $E°_{AB/AB^{•-}}$.

Kinetically, the dissociative homogeneous ET (equation 16) is the simplest case to treat since the rate-limiting step is the ET by definition. Bimolecular rate constants for ET determined using the technique are generally in the 10–$10^6 \, M^{-1} \, s^{-1}$. As previously mentioned, values for k_{ET} are obtained by monitoring the current response of the reversible reduction peak of the donor as it is transformed into a chemically irreversible, catalytic peak upon addition of the acceptor, AB. The current of the catalytic peak, and the extent of its reversibility, depends upon both the scan rate and the concentration of the substrate. This is illustrated in Fig. 5, which shows typical voltammograms for the mediated reduction of di-*tert*-butyl peroxide (DTBP) using anthracene radical anion as the donor. The curves were obtained (left to right) at scan rates of 0.02, 0.05, 0.1, and $0.2 \, V \, s^{-1}$, the currents being normalized with respect to $v^{1/2}$. The concentration of DTBP increases in the series from (a), (b), and (c) from 0, 1.0 and 2.0 mM, respectively. The extent of catalysis is measured by the $i_p/i_p°$ ratio and the extent of loss of the reversibility of the anodic wave. As will be described in detail in section 3, the homogeneous reduction of DTBP follows mechanism (16) and (17) in an overall two-electron process. By proper analyses of the CV data according to this mechanism, the rate constant k_{ET} can be determined. For a given AB, the rate constants are typically measured for a series of donors of varying standard reduction potential, to provide a set of $\log k_{ET}$ vs. $E°_{D/D^{•-}}$ data. By varying the potential of the donor, the rate constants can be examined as a function of the overall free energy change for ET, given by equations (20) and (21) for a stepwise and a concerted process, respectively. These data can be fitted to the quadratic activation–driving force relationship (equation 7) to provide thermochemical data, including standard dissociative reduction potentials, $E°_{AB/A^{•},B^{-}}$, and intrinsic barriers that can be further related to BDE and reorganization energies. Examples of this approach for the determination of these parameters will be presented in the following sections.

$$\Delta G° = nF(E°_{D/D^{•-}} - E°_{AB/AB^{•-}}) \tag{20}$$

$$\Delta G° = nF(E°_{D/D^{•-}} - E°_{AB/A^{•},B^{-}}) \tag{21}$$

The homogeneous catalysis method is suitable to measure rate constants over a very wide range, up to the diffusion limit. The lower limit is determined by interferences, such as convection, which occur at very slow scan rates. It is our experience that, unless special precautions are taken, scan rates below $100\,mV/s$ result in significant deviations from a purely diffusion-controlled voltammetric wave. For small values of k_{ET} rate constants (down to $10^{-4}\,s^{-1}$), other potentiostatic techniques are best suited, such as chronoamperometry at a rotating disk electrode,[49–57] UV dip probe[52] and stopped-flow UV-vis techniques.[53]

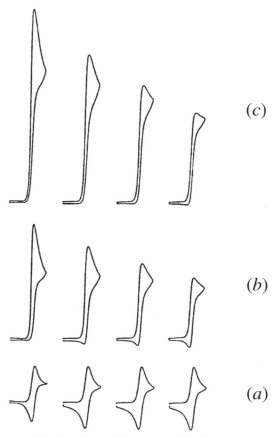

(c)

(b)

(a)

Fig. 5 Typical normalized voltammetric curves for homogeneous redox catalysis. The figure shows experimental data for the catalytic of reduction of DTBP by anthracene (1 mM in DMF/0.1 M TEAP at 25°C). The voltammetric curves were obtained, from left to right, at scan rates of 0.02, 0.05, 0.1 and $0.2\,V\,s^{-1}$, respectively. The concentrations of DTBP are, from bottom to top: (a) = 0, (b) = 1.0, and (c) = 2.0 mM. All currents are normalized to $v^{1/2}$.

CONVOLUTION ANALYSIS

One of the most powerful electrochemical methods for the study of the subtle details of heterogeneous ET processes and, particularly, dissociative ET processes is the method of convolution analysis. This method, which was developed a number of years ago,[54–57] is based on the convolutive transformation of the real voltammetric current i. However, its application to the study of electrode kinetics has been used rarely in the past.[58] In view of its relevance in the study of dissociative ET, it is worth summarizing some of the main features of this approach. In the following, some basic background will be provided, although the reader is referred to the original literature, particularly as described by Imbeaux and Savéant,[57] for the complete theoretical treatment. The main advantages of convolution over conventional voltammetric analysis will be briefly mentioned in connection with dissociative ET. Finally, some practical information on how to obtain and deal with experimental data will be discussed.

The method relies on the relationship between the surface concentration of the electroactive species O (which yields R according to: $O + ne = R$), $C_O(0,t)$, having a bulk concentration C_O^*, and the current, i. Under semi-infinite linear diffusion conditions and independently of the particular electrochemical method employed, $C_O(0,t)$ can be expressed by (22)

$$C_O(0,t) = C_O^* - (nFAD^{1/2})^{-1}\left(\pi^{-1/2}\int_0^t \frac{i(u)}{(t-u)^{1/2}}\,du\right) = C_O^* - (nFAD^{1/2})^{-1}I(t)$$

(22)

where D here is the diffusion coefficient of O. A similar expression can be obtained for the primary electrode product R. $I(t)$, defined by equation (23), is known as the convolutive current

$$I(t) = \pi^{-1/2}\int_0^t \frac{i(u)}{(t-u)^{1/2}}\,du$$

(23)

and has the dimensions of $A\,s^{1/2}$ (or $C\,s^{-1/2}$). $I(t)$ is a sigmoidal function of the applied potential E and thus it is similar in shape to the $i–E$ curve obtained by using a stationary electrochemical method.[30] It should be noted that $I(t)$ is not obtained directly but through mathematical manipulation of the experimental $i–E$ data. Under diffusion-controlled conditions ($C_O(0,t) = 0$), $I(t)$ reaches a limiting value, i.e. is independent of E (equation 24).

$$I_l = nFAD^{1/2}C_O^*$$

(24)

The I_1 value does not depend on whether or not the reduction is reversible, quasi-reversible, or irreversible. In general, the net current i is the sum of a cathodic and an anodic component. However, when the reduction of O is irreversible, because either the ET is intrinsically slow or as a consequence of a following fast reaction (e.g. bond cleavage), it can be easily shown that the link between i, $I(t)$, and the heterogeneous rate constant k_{het} is equation (25).

$$\ln k_{het}(E) = \ln D^{1/2} - \ln\{[I_1 - I(t)]/i(t)\} \tag{25}$$

Equation (25) is general in that it does not depend on the electrochemical method employed to obtain the i–E data. Moreover, unlike conventional electrochemical methods such as cyclic or linear scan voltammetry, all of the experimental i–E data are used in kinetic analysis (as opposed to using limited information such as the peak potentials and half-widths when using cyclic voltammetry). Finally, and of particular importance, the convolution analysis has the great advantage that the heterogeneous ET kinetics can be analyzed without the need of defining a priori the ET rate law. By contrast, in conventional voltammetric analyses, a specific ET rate law (as a rule, the Butler–Volmer rate law) must be used to extract the relevant kinetic information.

The convolution analysis is based on the use of convolution data and further manipulation to obtain information on the ET mechanism, standard potentials, intrinsic barriers, and also to detect mechanism transitions.[22,23,59] It is worth noting that the general outlines of the methodology were first introduced in the study of the kinetics of reduction of tert-nitrobutane in dipolar aprotic solvents, under conditions of chemical stability of the generated anion radical.[60] For the study of concerted dissociative ET processes, linear scan voltammetry is the most useful electrochemical technique.

The experimental procedure to carry out a convolution analysis experiment is usually as follows. The voltammetric behavior of the compound under investigation is studied first to verify that the electrode material employed is inert with respect to the electroactive compound and/or its reduction intermediates/products. Since strong bases and nucleophiles are often generated upon dissociative ET, care must be taken to determine whether or not the starting compound reacts with the reduction intermediates. Self-protonation and nucleophilic substitution are the most common among the so-called father–son reactions.[61] The consumption of the substrate near the electrode surface by these follow-up reactions tends to decrease the number of electrons consumed per molecule, n, from the usual two-electron stoichiometry expected for the reductive cleavage.[62,63] The convolution analysis requires that n remain constant during the experiment. In most cases it is sufficient to add a non-electroactive acid to protonate the electrogenerated bases, without otherwise affecting the electrode process.

Once an appropriate set of background subtracted voltammograms (over a range of scan rates) is obtained, the convolution analysis can be performed by using one of the possible algorithms for equation (23).[30] Best results are obtained when the sampling rate is $\geqslant 1$ point/mV. Provided n is not a function of the timescale of the experiment, I_l will be independent of the scan rate within the experimental error (i.e. typically 1–2%). The value of I_l is particularly useful to determine the diffusion coefficient of the electroactive species. Once the constancy and reliability of I_l are established, the convolution curves are analyzed according to equation (25) in order to obtain the potential dependence of k_{het}. Representative data for this approach are shown in Fig. 6. Since the convolution curve is derived from an integration procedure (more precisely, a semi-integration) it is rather insensitive to the noise affecting the original voltammetric curve. However, as the real and convoluted current data are mixed in equation (25), great care must be taken to reduce instrumental noise levels when acquiring the data.[59] Since these semi-logarithmic plots result from different experiments and scan rates, and considering that data are routinely sampled at 1 point/mV, it follows that they are normally composed of several thousand data points.

It is worthwhile commenting on the reliability of the data from the heterogeneous semi-logarithmic plots from an experimental viewpoint. It is well known that the acquisition of voltammetric i–E data requires proper compensation for the ohmic drop caused by the resistance of the solution between the working and the reference electrodes. An a posteriori indication that the ohmic drop was properly compensated (provided there are no specific heterogeneous effects) comes from the observation that at any given potential the same k_{het} is obtained, within error, from measurements performed at different scan rates. Improper ohmic-drop compensation leads to both a negative shift and a broadening of the voltammetric curves leading to poor overlap of the $\ln k_{het}$–E plots obtained in the same potential range at different scan rates.

The final step of the convolution analysis is the determination of the transfer coefficient α. This coefficient, sometimes called the symmetry factor, describes how variations in the reaction free energy affect the activation free energy (equation 26). The value of α does not depend on whether the reaction is a heterogeneous or a homogeneous ET (or even a different type of reaction such as a proton transfer, where α is better known as the Brönsted coefficient). Since the ET rate constant may be described by equation (4), the experimental determination of α is carried out by derivatization of the $\ln k_{het}$–$\Delta G°$ and thus of the experimental $\ln k_{het}$–E plots ($\Delta G° = F(E - E°)$) (equation 27).

$$\alpha = \frac{\partial \Delta G^{\neq}}{\partial \Delta G°} \qquad (26)$$

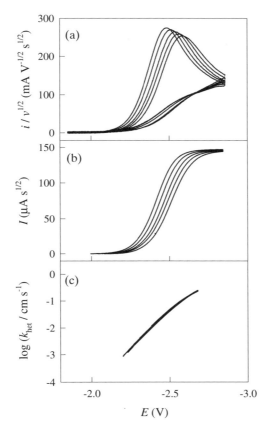

Fig. 6 Representative examples of the steps involved in the convolution analysis approach to obtaining the potential dependence of the heterogeneous rate constant. From top to bottom: (a) background-subtracted cyclic voltammograms as a function of scan rate (left to right: 0.5, 1, 2, 5, 10 V s^{-1}); (b) corresponding convolution curves; (c) corresponding potential dependence of log k_{het} obtained using equation (25). Figures shown are for the reduction of $(MeS)_2$ in DMF/0.1 M TBAP at a glassy carbon electrode.

$$\alpha = RT \frac{d \ln k_{het}}{d \Delta G^{\circ}} = -\frac{RT}{F} \frac{d \ln k_{het}}{dE} \qquad (27)$$

Derivatization is usually accomplished by linear regression of the experimental data within small E intervals (20 to 30 mV, depending on the quality of the ln $k - E$ plots). It should be noted that, upon derivatization, the contribution from the diffusion coefficient disappears. The significance and consequences of the plots of α versus E will be discussed in detail in the following sections. However, it is worth mentioning another practical aspect at this point. By using scan rates of 0.1–50 V s^{-1}, the potential range in which

α data are experimentally measurable is usually of the order of 0.5–0.7 V and 0.2–0.4 V for the concerted and the stepwise mechanisms, respectively (voltammetric waves for stepwise reactions are more narrow). Interestingly enough, we have observed that in general (because of experimental constraints) the E_p value measured at $0.2\,\mathrm{V\,s^{-1}}$ lies more or less in the middle of the investigated E range.[24(a)–25(a),60,65,66] This can be useful for planning heterogeneous ET experiments.

LASER FLASH PHOTOLYSIS

There are a number of non-electrochemical techniques that have proven invaluable in combination with electrochemical results in understanding the chemistry and the kinetics. Laser flash photolysis (LFP) is a well-established technique for the study of the transient spectroscopy and kinetics of reactive intermediates. The technique is valuable for the studying of the kinetics of the reactions of radical anions, particularly those that undergo rapid stepwise dissociative processes. The kinetics of fragmentation of radical anions can be determined using this method if (i) the radical anion of interest can be formed in a process initiated by a laser pulse, (ii) it has a characteristic absorption spectrum with a suitable extinction coefficient, and (iii) the rate of decay of the absorption of the radical anion falls within the kinetic window of the LFP technique; typically this is in the order of $1 \times 10^4\,\mathrm{s^{-1}}$ to $1 \times 10^8\,\mathrm{s^{-1}}$.

Radical anions are produced in a number of ways from suitable reducing agents. Common methods of generation of radical anions using LFP involve photoinduced electron transfer (PET) by irradiation of donor–acceptor charge transfer complexes (equation 28) or by photoexcitation of a sensitizer substrate (S) in the presence of a suitable donor/acceptor partner (equations 29 and 30). Both techniques result in the formation of a cation radical/radical anion pair. Often the difficulty of overlapping absorption spectra of the cation radical and radical anion hinders detection of the radical anion by optical methods. Another complication in these methods is the efficient back electron transfer in the geminate cation radical/radical anion pair initially formed on ET, which often results in low yields of the free ions. In addition, direct irradiation of a substrate of interest often results in efficient photochemical processes from the excited state (S*) that compete with PET.

$$[D/AB] \xrightarrow{\;h\nu\;} D^{+\bullet} + AB^{-\bullet} \qquad\qquad (28)$$

$$S \xrightarrow{\;h\nu\;} S^* \qquad\qquad (29)$$

$$S^* + AB \longrightarrow S^{-\bullet} + AB^{+\bullet} \quad \text{or} \quad S^{+\bullet} + AB^{-\bullet} \qquad (30)$$

Another approach for the formation of radical anions by LFP has been developed to overcome some of these difficulties.[67] The approach involves the formation of radical anions by trapping a solvated electron produced by photoionization of 4,4′-dimethoxystilbene (DMS) to its cation radical (equations 31 and 32). This photoionization/electron trapping method is quite general for substrates that are transparent where DMS absorbs and that are more easily reduced than dimethoxystilbene. In many ways, this method is similar to pulse radiolysis, another useful approach used to generate radical anions for optical kinetic studies.

$$\text{DMS} \xrightarrow{h\nu} \text{DMS}^{+\bullet} + e_{solv} \tag{31}$$

$$\text{AB} + e_{solv} \longrightarrow \text{AB}^{-\bullet} \tag{32}$$

In each of the above methods, if the absorption spectrum of the radical anion is properly characterized, and its decay follows first-order kinetics due to unimolecular fragmentation, an estimate of the rate constant of fragmentation can be obtained directly. As an illustrative example, the photoionization/electron trapping method was used to measure the rate constant for C–O fragmentation of the radical anion of α-phenoxyacetophenone in nitrogen-saturated acetonitrile and N,N-dimethylformamide solutions.[33,67] The radical anion of α-aryloxyacetophenone has a transient absorption spectrum with a λ_{max} at 500 nm in DMF, and decays with first-order kinetics of $7 \times 10^5 \, s^{-1}$. The failure to observe concomitant formation of a transient absorption due to the phenoxy radical (which is observed on direct excitation of the ketone) is consistent with the decay of the radical anion by β-cleavage to give the phenacyl radical and phenoxide ion (equation 33). The rate constant determined here was pivotal for a more extensive study of the substituent effect on the rates of fragmentation for a variety of substituted α-(aryloxy)arylketones discussed in detail in Section 3.

$$\tag{33}$$

PHOTOACOUSTIC CALORIMETRY

Bond dissociation energies, BDE, are required in order to understand dissociative reduction processes. While BDE values of many simple hydrocarbons have been measured using various gas phase methods, for practical purposes, reactions of interest to electrochemists occur in solution. Solution-based methods that allow the direct determination of enthalpy changes in solution preclude the need to account for solvent effects. One such technique is photoacoustic calorimetry.[68,69] The physical basis of this technique is deceptively simple; rapid heat released from a photoinitiated process in a limited, well-defined volume, results in a local change in density (thermal expansion) that generates a pressure wave that moves through the solution at the speed of sound. The detection and quantification of this pressure wave with an ultrasonic transducer (microphone) is the basis of the technique. The photoacoustic signal is linear with respect to the heat evolved, provided the chemical processes are much faster than the response time of the detector. A simple example is in the determination of the O—O bond energy of DTBP, which is relevant to discussions of its electrochemistry. Irradiation of a solution containing DTBP with a nitrogen laser (337 nm, 84.8 kcal/mol) results in the cleavage of the O—O bond with a quantum yield that depends on the viscosity of the solvent (equation 34).[70] Since 84.8 kcal/mol are absorbed, but only 37 kcal/mol are required to break the bond, the remaining 47.8 kcal/mol of energy is returned to the solution as heat. This reaction can be used to determine X—H bond energies (equations 34–38). Provided reaction (35) is fast compared with the detector response, the experiment provides a measure of the overall enthalpy change for the photointiated process (equation 36). The overall enthalpy change (equation 37) can be used to determine BDE_{XH} (equation 38) since the heats of formation of the peroxide, t-BuOH and H$^•$ are known (equation 39) where ΔH_{corr} is an empirically derived correction term that accounts for the solvation and partial molar volume changes associated with the conversion of one mole of DTBP into two moles of t-BuOH.[70] The constant 86.0 represents the collection of the heats of formation other than those for XH and X$^•$. There are a number of pitfalls and caveats that one should be aware when using this technique. These are discussed in more detail in the references cited above.

$$t\text{-BuOOBu-}t \qquad \xrightarrow{\ h\nu\ } \qquad 2\ t\text{-BuO}^• \qquad\qquad (34)$$

$$2\ t\text{-BuO}^• + \text{XH} \qquad \longrightarrow \qquad 2\ t\text{-BuOH} + 2\ \text{X}^• \qquad (35)$$

$$t\text{-BuOOBu-}t + 2\ \text{XH} \qquad \longrightarrow \qquad 2\ t\text{-BuOH} + 2\ \text{X}^• \qquad (36)$$

$$\Delta H_r = 2\Delta H_f(t\text{-BuOH}) + 2\Delta H_f(\text{X}^•) - 2\Delta H_f(\text{XH}) - \Delta H_f(t\text{-BuOOBu-}t) \quad (37)$$

$$\text{BDE}_{XH} = \Delta H_f(\text{H}^•) + \Delta H_f(\text{X}^•) - \Delta H_f(\text{XH}) \qquad\qquad (38)$$

$$
\begin{aligned}
\text{BDE}_{XH} &= \frac{\Delta H_r}{2} + \frac{\Delta H_f(\text{DTBP})}{2} - \Delta H_f(t\text{-BuOH}) + \Delta H_f(\text{H}^•)\\
&= \frac{\Delta H_r}{2} - \frac{\Delta H_{corr}}{2} + 86.0
\end{aligned}
\qquad (39)
$$

THERMOCHEMICAL ESTIMATES

The bond dissociation free energy, BDFE, for the fragmentation of a radical anion can be estimated from other available thermodynamic data: the BDFE of neutral AB and $E°$ of AB and $B^\bullet$.[38] An example of a typical thermochemical cycle is shown below (Scheme 1). In order to use these thermochemical cycles it is important to remember that by convention all electrode reactions are written in the direction of reduction and that the associated free energy change is $\Delta G_{ET} = -FE°$. In many cases BDE values can be found in standard tables or can be determined using a number of techniques including photoacoustic calorimetry (see previous section). In the absence of experimental data, reasonably reliable estimates can be obtained from group additivities[71,72] or from computational chemistry. This, however, presents a problem since the BDE values are enthalpies and must be corrected for the entropy change associated with dissociation. As with enthalpies, estimates of $\Delta S°$ can be made using group additivity methods. In the absence of entropy data it is still possible to estimate relative driving forces for a series of homologous reactions by making the reasonable assumption that the entropy changes are constant. Thus, relative driving forces can be derived from ΔBDE values.

$$
\begin{array}{lll}
AB^{-\bullet} & \rightarrow & AB + e^- & FE°_{AB/AB^{-\bullet}} \\
AB & \rightarrow & A^\bullet + B^\bullet & BDFE_{AB} \\
B^\bullet + e^- & \rightarrow & B^- & -FE°_{B^\bullet, B^-} \\
\hline
AB^{-\bullet} & \rightarrow & A^\bullet + B^- & BDFE_{AB^{\bullet-}}
\end{array}
$$

Scheme 1

$$BDFE_{AB^{\bullet-}} = BDFE_{AB} - F(E°_{B^\bullet, B^-} - E°_{AB, AB^{-\bullet}}) \qquad (40)$$

For dissociative electron transfer, an analogous thermochemical cycle can be derived (Scheme 2). In this case the standard potential includes a contribution from the bond fragmentation. Using equations (40) and (41) one can derive another useful expression for $BDFE_{AB^{\bullet-}}$, equation (42). While direct electrochemical measurements on solutions may provide $E°_{B^\bullet, B^-}$, for example, of phenoxides[73] and thiophenoxides (Section 4), the corresponding values for alkoxyl radicals are not as easily determined.[59] Consequently, these values must be determined from a more circuitous thermochemical cycle (Scheme 3), using equation (43). The values of $E°_{H^+/H^\bullet}$ in a number of common solvents are tabulated elsewhere.[38] Values of pKa in organic solvents are available from different sources.[74–76] A comparison of some estimated $E°$ values with those determined by convolution voltammetry can be found in Section 3.

AB	$\rightarrow$	$A^{\bullet} + B^{\bullet}$	$BDFE_{AB}$
$B^{\bullet} + e$	$\rightarrow$	B^-	$-FE^{\circ}_{B^{\bullet}, B^-}$
$AB + e$	$\rightarrow$	$A^{\bullet} + B^-$	$E^{\circ}_{AB/A^{\bullet}, B^-}$

Scheme 2

$$E^{\circ}_{AB/A^{\bullet}, B^-} = E^{\circ}_{B^{\bullet}/B^-} - BDFE/F \tag{41}$$

$$BDFE_{AB^{\bullet-}} = F(E^{\circ}_{AB, AB^{\bullet-}} - E^{\circ}_{AB/A^{\bullet}, B^-}) \tag{42}$$

$RO^{\bullet} + H^{\bullet}$	$\rightarrow$	ROH	$-CBFE$
ROH	$\rightarrow$	$RO^- + H^+$	$2.303RTpKa$
$H^+ + e^-$	$\rightarrow$	$H^{\bullet}$	$-FE^{\circ}_{H+/H^{\bullet}}$
$RO^{\bullet} + e^-$	$\rightarrow$	RO^-	$E^{\circ}_{RO^{\bullet}/RO^-}$

Scheme 3

$$E^{\circ}_{RO^{\bullet}/RO^-} = BDFE/F - (2.303\,RT/F)pK_a + E^{\circ}_{H^+/H^{\bullet}} \tag{43}$$

3 Reduction of C—O and O—O bonds

In the introduction, the concept of having two limiting dissociative ET processes, namely the stepwise and concerted processes, was introduced. In this section we discuss the ET reduction of C—O bonds of arylethers and phenoxyacetophenones and the O—O bonds of peroxides and endoperoxides. Reduction of the C—O and the O—O bonds represent classic examples of the stepwise and concerted dissociative mechanisms, respectively. This is partly the function of the significant difference between C—O and O—O bond energies, with C—O bond energies typically more than $70\,kcal\,mol^{-1}$ and the latter seldom being greater than $40\,kcal\,mol^{-1}$. This feature is exemplified by O—O generally being easily reduced (good oxidant) compared with C—O bonds. Because of the differences in bond energies, it is expected that for the same RO^- as a leaving group, the concerted mechanism is much more likely for peroxides, while a stepwise is more likely for C—O systems; this is indeed the case.

The role of ET and cleavage intrinsic barriers on the classic stepwise reduction of aryl ethers and α-phenoxyacetophenones, is discussed first (see below). In most of the examples the initial ET is governed primarily by solvent reorganization. For some α-phenoxyacetophenones ET, is sufficiently endergonic that cage escape of the $A^{\bullet}/B^-$ pair and not the fragmentation itself becomes rate limiting. The ET reduction of peroxides and endoperoxides demonstrates the clearest examples to date of a parabolic driving force relationship. In addition, while an adiabatic ET model has described other concerted dissociative systems such as benzyl and alkyl halides, we demonstrate that the reduction of O–O bonds is a non-adiabatic concerted ET. When this latter aspect is properly considered, this class of compounds provides excellent support of Savéant's theory of concerted dissociative ET. Finally, there is a discussion of the reduction of substituted perbenzoates, which provides the best evidence for the experimental observation of a transition between the two mechanistic extremes.

REDUCTION OF ETHERS

In general, alkyl ethers are thought to be chemically inert to reductive fragmentation. In part, this is because of strength of the C–OR bond in simple alkyl ethers, the inaccessibility of the σ^* orbital, and the instability of the alkoxide leaving groups. Aryl ethers, on the other hand, are more labile and undergo stepwise dissociative processes. This increase in reactivity is the result of the weaker C–OAr bond, the availability of a π^* orbital and the much higher stability of phenoxide ions. This section deals entirely with the stepwise reduction of aryloxy ethers.

Cleavage of the C–O bond of aryloxy ethers takes place with regioselectivity and with rates that are a function of environmental (solvent, counter-ions) and intrinsic parameters.[77–79] The presence of electron-withdrawing substituents significantly increases the lifetime of the radical anion, as shown with diaryl ethers and benzyl aryl ethers.[80–83] The latter class of compounds was also the subject of an investigation of the effect of the intramolecular reorganization on the cleavage rate.[82,84] A similar topic was investigated by using families of phenoxyacetophenones, substituted at either side of the C–O bond.[33–36] These data lead to some interesting generalizations about the intrinsic barriers in relation to the mechanism of cleavage.

One of the key issues in understanding these stepwise dissociative reductions is to define the thermodynamics (or at least relative thermodynamics) of the fragmentation itself. It is equally important to understand on which side of the scissile bond the charge actually resides, as this has important mechanistic implications. This is most easily inferred by comparison of the measured standard (or peak) potential with standard potentials of similarly substituted aromatic molecules that make stable radical anions.

Benzyl aryl ethers

The reduction of benzyl aryl ethers has been thoroughly investigated by voltammetric reduction, homogeneous redox catalysis,[83,85] and currently, by convolution analysis.[86] A family of ethers activated by proper substitution on the phenoxy side were chosen to provide a wide variation in the ET and bond cleavage properties of the molecule.[83,85]

$$X = H, Ph, CN, COMe, NO_2$$

The reduction, carried out in DMF/0.2 M TBAP, takes place with cleavage of the C—O bond to form the benzyl radical and the appropriate phenoxide anion (equations 44–46). The radical is then reduced at the same potential (applied electrode potential or donor $E°$) to yield the carbanion.

$$ArO\text{-}CH_2Ph + e \rightleftharpoons ArO\text{-}CH_2Ph^{\bullet-} \tag{44}$$

$$ArO\text{-}CH_2Ph^{\bullet-} \rightleftharpoons ArO^- + PhCH_2^{\bullet} \tag{45}$$

$$PhCH_2^{\bullet} + e \longrightarrow PhCH_2^- \tag{46}$$

Some protonation of the benzyl carbanion by the starting ether (self-protonation reaction)[61,87] and other side reactions, such as hydrolysis caused by *in situ* generation of OH^- (through protonation of the benzyl anion by traces of water),[88] can be avoided by addition of a suitable acid. Under these conditions, electrolysis leads to an effective conversion of the ether into toluene and phenoxide ion with an electron consumption of 2 F/mol.

The voltammetric data and other relevant kinetic and thermodynamic information are summarized in Table 2. While for X = H the initial ET controls the electrode rate, as indicated by the rather large E_p shift and peak width, the electrode process is, at low scan rates, under mixed ET-bond cleavage kinetic control (see Section 2) for X = Ph, and CN. Although the voltammetric reduction of these ethers is irreversible, in the case of the COMe derivative, some reversibility starts to show up at 500 V s^{-1}; in fact, this reduction features a classical case of Nernstian ET followed by a first-order reaction. The reduction of the nitro derivative is reversible even at very low scan rate although, on a much longer timescale, this radical anion also decays.

There is a linear relationship between $E°$ values of the benzyl aryl ethers and the corresponding PhX compounds; the relationship being $E°$(ether) $= -0.042 + 1.04\ E°$(PhX) ($r^2 = 0.996$) suggesting that the SOMO of the radical anions is largely delocalized on the substituted aryl phenoxyl ring. The 0.08–0.18 $E°$ difference is due to the electron-donating property of the OBz substituent. The inner contribution to the intrinsic barrier is, on the average, 1.8–2.0 kcal mol higher than expected compared with the values found for stable aromatic radical anions.[90] Nevertheless, these heterogeneous and homogeneous intrinsic barriers are remarkably low for such reactive intermediates, suggesting that very little intramolecular reorganization takes place in the formation of the radical anion and, particularly, that little C—O bond

Table 2 Electrochemical, kinetic, and thermodynamic parameters for ET to benzyl aryl ethers in DMF/0.2M TBAP at 25C.[a]

X	E_p^b (V)	E° (V)	E°(PhX) (V)	$\Delta G_{0\,het}^{\neq}$ [c] (kcal/mol)	$\Delta G_{0\,het}^{\neq}$ [d] (kcal/mol)	$\Delta G_{0\,hom}^{\neq}$ [e] (kcal/mol)	$\Delta G_{0\,hom}^{\neq}$ [f] (kcal/mol)	$\log k_{frag}$ (s^{-1})
H	-2.83^g	-2.87^e	na^h	6.0	3.9	5.8	3.2	$> 8.1^e$
Ph	-2.51	-2.70^i -2.64^e	-2.54	5.3	3.5	4.7	3.1	6.97^e
CN	-2.33	-2.44^i -2.43^e	-2.26	5.8	3.8	4.4	3.2	7.67^e
COMe	-2.11	-2.15^i -2.13^j	-2.01	6.0	3.7	n.d.^{k}	3.1	3.18^j
NO$_2$	-1.23	-1.20^j	-1.12	5.3	3.7	n.d.^{k}	3.2	-3.82^l

[a]Redox catalysis and voltammetric data from ref. 83; convolution data from ref. 86.
[b]Hg electrode, $v = 1\,\mathrm{V\,s}^{-1}$.
[c]Double-layer uncorrected data; from eq. 4.
[d]Calculated from $4\Delta G_{0\,het}^{\neq}$ [kcal/mol] $= 55.7/r$[Å], where r is the radius of the ether.[59]
[e]From redox catalysis.
[f]Calculated from $4\Delta G_{0\,hom}^{\neq}$ [kcal/mol] $= 95[(2r_D)^{-1} + (2r_A)^{-1} - (r_D + r_A)^{-1}]$, where the radii of the donor and the acceptor are in Å.[89]
[g]Extrapolated from scan rates $\geqslant 4$ V/s because of background discharge.
[h]Beyond background discharge.
[i]From convolution, double-layer uncorrected data, at both Hg and glassy carbon.
[j]From reversible voltammetry. [k]Not determined. [l]From amperometric measurements.

elongation occurs. This is reinforced by the fact that, when the double layer effect is taken into account (heterogeneous data), a slight decrease of the *apparent* value of the intrinsic barrier occurs. Depending on the potential and the electrolyte concentration, this correction corresponds to a typical decrease of 1–1.6 kcal mol with the system Hg/DMF/0.2 M TBAP. It is also of particular significance that the heterogeneous inner barrier of the nitro derivative is similar to the other values. In fact, nitro derivatives are known to localize the π^* orbital onto the nitro group, leading to very small intramolecular reorganization in other parts of the molecule. It appears that some slight increase of the inner reorganization is brought about by a decrease of the electron-acceptor property of the substituent. Unfortunately, the reduction potential of more deactivated ethers would shift the experimental peak into the solvent/electrolyte discharge, preventing any possible measurement.

The rate constant for the fragmentation (k_{frag}) (equation 45) increases along the series as the electron-donating character of the aryl substituent increases. This can be explained on the basis of equation (40). By comparison with the BDE of the corresponding phenols,[91] the BDE and thus BDFE of benzyl ethers is expected to increase when going along the series from X $=$ H to X $=$ NO$_2$. The corresponding variation of the redox potential of the PhO$^\bullet$/PhO$^-$ couples is *ca.* 0.7 V [92] and that of the ethers is *ca.* 1.7 V. The latter factor (with some contribution from the BDE) is thus the principal driving force for the cleavage when going from the nitro-substituted to the unsubstituted ether. Finally, the cleavage rate in the ethers seems to be about one order of magnitude slower than that of the equivalent thioethers (Section 4). For example, the cleavage of $PhCH_2OPhNO_2$ and $PhCH_2SPhNO_2$ is 1.5×10^{-4} and 1.8×10^{-3} s^{-1}, respectively.[83,85] The same trend is observed when PhOPh[93] is compared with PhSPh,[94] the two rate constants (DMF/TBAP) being 4×10^5 and 6×10^6 s^{-1}, respectively. In both cases, this was attributed to the C—O bond being stronger than the C—S bond.

Phenoxyacetophenones

The unimolecular cleavage of $ArC(O)CH_2X^{-\bullet}$ species has been suggested as a suitable clock-reaction to distinguish hydride transfer from electron transfer/radical pathways in the reduction of carbonyls with different hydride donors.[95,96] The idea follows from the well-established free radical clocks that led to the development of a number of useful chemical probes to report the existence of short-lived free radical intermediates. When used as chemical probes, the main consideration is to ensure that the "clock reaction" is much faster than the other competing processes. This is in contrast to the use of clock reactions as a kinetic tool in which the rate constant of the competing processes must be of the same order of magnitude. Thermodynamic parameters for some relevant acetophenone derivatives are given in Table 3.

In order to make use of electron transfer probes, the rate constants for the reactions of the intermediate radical ions must either be known or simple to estimate. Tanner and his co-workers attempted to determine the rate constant for cleavage of the α-phenoxyacetophenone radical anion from competition by assuming the rates of cleavage were independent of α- and

Table 3 Bond energies of C—O-containing $X\text{-}C_6H_4C(O)CH_2B$ radical anions ($\Delta G^{\circ}_{BDE^{-\bullet}}$).

X	B	$E_{B^{\bullet}/B^-}$ (V)	$E^{\circ}_{AB/AB^{-\bullet}}$ (V)	BDE_{AB} (kcal/mol)	$BDE(AB^{-\bullet})$ (kcal/mol)	$BDFE(AB^{-\bullet})$ (kcal/mol)
4-MeO	PhO	0.24	−2.02	56	4.0	−0.4[a]
4-Me			−1.95		5.6	1.2[a]
H			−1.88		7.4	3.0[a]
3-MeO			−1.86		8.7	3.3[a]
3-C(O)Me			−1.73		10.6	6.3[a]
3-CF$_3$			−1.67		12.0	7.6[a]
3-CN			−1.62		13.2	8.8[a]
4-CF$_3$			−1.59		13.9	9.5[a]
4-MeOC(O)			−1.47		16.6	12.2[a]
4-CN			−1.47		16.6	12.2[a]
4-C(O)Me			−1.41		18.0	13.6[a]
4-MeO	PhCO$_2$	1.24	−1.97	74	0.2	−4.2[b]
H			−1.81		3.8	−0.6[b]
4-NO$_2$			−0.79		27.3	22.9[b]
H	MeO	0.06	−1.80	75	32.2	27.8[b]

[a]Ref. 33.
[b]Ref. 97.

ring-substituents.[95] α-Aryloxyacetophenones are ideal substrates for a systematic study of the cleavage of radical anions and have provided insights into the intrinsic barriers.[33–36,98] While these studies provided information regarding the rate constants for cleavage of the radical anions, they also pointed to a situation in which the cleavage is not rate limiting; i.e. if the cleavage is sufficiently endergonic, the dynamics are dominated by escape of the fragments from the initial solvent cage. When fragmentation occurs in a solvent, the separation of the fragments into independently solvated pieces competes with the back reaction (i.e. reforming the anion radical, equation (47)). The observed rate constant (k_{obs}) is given by equation (48) where k_f and k_{-f} are unimolecular rate constants for breaking and remaking the A—B bond and k_{-d} is the rate constant for diffusional separation of A$^{\bullet}$ and B^{-}. This latter term is sometimes referred to as counterdiffusion.

$$A\text{-}B^{-\bullet} \underset{k_{-f}}{\overset{k_f}{\rightleftharpoons}} \left[A^{\bullet}\ B^{-}\right] \underset{k_d}{\overset{k_{-d}}{\rightleftarrows}} A^{\bullet} + B^{-} \tag{47}$$

$$k_{obs} = \frac{k_f k_{-d}}{k_{-f} + k_{-d}} \tag{48}$$

This simple model predicts that the observed kinetics is determined by the rate of fragmentation only when the reverse process is much slower than counterdiffusion (i.e. when $k_{-f} \ll k_{-d}$). Under these conditions $k_{obs} = k_f$ and the slope of a plot of $\log(k_{obs})$ vs. BDFE$_{(AB^{-\bullet})}$ is simply the derivative of equation (4) (equation (49)). For moderately driven processes, this slope is about $-0.5/(2.303RT)$ and the reactions are under activation control. On the other hand, for an endergonic fragmentation it is expected that $k_{-f} \gg k_{-d}$ and $k_{obs} = (k_f/k_{-f})k_{-d}$. The reaction now is described as a pre-equilibrium followed by rate limiting counterdiffusional separation of the fragments.[35,98] Since $\Delta G^{\circ}_{AB^{-\bullet}} = -2.303 \log(k_f/k_{-f})$, the plot of $\log(k_{obs})$ vs. $\Delta G^{\circ}_{AB^{-\bullet}}$ now has a slope of $1/2.303RT$. Kinetic studies in this regime can give no information about the intrinsic barrier for fragmentation.

$$\frac{\partial \log(k_{obs})}{\partial \Delta G^{\circ}_{AB^{-\bullet}}} = \frac{-1}{2.3RT}\left(\frac{1}{2} + \frac{\Delta G^{\circ}_{AB^{-\bullet}}}{8\Delta G_0^{\neq}}\right) \tag{49}$$

Savéant and co-workers have shown that the kinetics for C—C cleavage of radical cations of NADH model compounds fall into this pre-equilibrium regime.[98] Similarly, the slope of $\log(k_{obs})$ vs. $\Delta G^{\circ}_{AB^{-\bullet}}$ for a number of C—C containing ion radicals also is about $-1/(2.303RT)$.[99] The first clear demonstration of the transition from activation to counterdiffusion control was found in a study of the fragmentation of anion radicals of α-aryloxyacetophenones (ArC(O)CH$_2$OAr$^{-\bullet}$). This study used a combination of electrochemistry and laser flash photolysis to determine rate constants over a range of almost ten orders of magnitude.[35] The relative driving forces were determined using thermochemical cycles. The absolute driving forces were obtained by making two key assumptions: that the pre-expontial term for the cleavage step is $10^{13}\,s^{-1}$ and that the rate constant for counterdiffusion (k_{-d}) is $10^{10}\,s^{-1}$. The second assumption allows the point at which $\Delta G^{\circ}_{AB^{-\bullet}} = 0$ to be determined. The experimental data, along with some theoretical curves, are shown in Fig. 7. The theoretical curves represent different values for the intrinsic barrier. It is clear from the figure that if the intrinsic barrier is too small, then all of the kinetics are under counterdiffusion control. On the other hand, if the intrinsic barrier is too large then all of the kinetics are under activation control. The ability to clearly observe the transition in this case is a result of the intrinsic barrier being intermediate in magnitude; in this case $\Delta G_0^{\neq} \approx 8\,kcal/mol$. The fact that all of these data fit to a single theoretical curve supports the suggestion by Savéant that the intrinsic barriers are determined largely by solvent reorganization.[97] Within this series the C—O bond energy is expected to change by $ca.$ 10 kcal/mol.

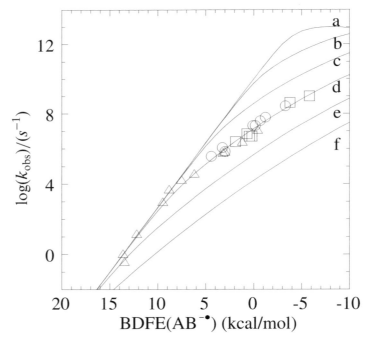

Fig. 7 Plot of $\log(k_{obs})$ versus BDFE(AB$^{-\bullet}$) for the fragmentation of ArC(O)CH$_2$OPh$^{-\bullet}$ (circles),[33] PhC(O)CH$_2$OAr$^{-\bullet}$ (triangles)[39] and 3,4-(MeO)$_2$C$_6$H$_4$C(O)CH$_2$OPh (squares).[36] The lines represent theoretical curves based on equations (47) and (48) using $\Delta G_0^{\neq}$ = (a) 2 kcal/mol, (b) 4 kcal/mol, (c) 6 kcal/mol, (d) 8 kcal/mol, (e) 10 kcal/mol and (f) 12 kcal/mol.

Homolysis versus heterolysis of radical anion fragmentation

One of the first kinetic studies of the fragmentation of a C—O bond in an ether radical anion was reported by Maslak and Guthrie.[82,84] In this study substituted benzyl phenyl ethers (as well as some other benzyl-type phenyl ethers) were treated with 2,4,6-tri-*tert*-butylnitrobenzene radical anion to produce $^{-\bullet}ArCH_2OPh$ or $PhCH_2OAr^{-\bullet}$ and the unimolecular decay of the anion radical was monitored using EPR. Despite some discrepancies between the values of the reported rate constants,[82,83,85] the kinetic trends are clear. While there is a thermodynamic advantage for the fragmentation of $PhCH_2OAr^{-\bullet}$, the fragmentation of $^{-\bullet}ArCH_2OPh$ is faster: $k_{heterolysis}/k_{homolysis} = 10^2 - 10^4$, depending on the compound. The origin of these differences is not yet fully understood and may be related either to differences in the intrinsic barriers or in the electronic coupling between the reactant and product surfaces, or both. Originally, the difference was assigned entirely to differences in the intrinsic barriers. The fragmentation of $A\text{-}B^{-\bullet}$ can occur in one of two ways (Scheme 4). If the extra electron is largely localized on the A fragment as in $^{-\bullet}ArCH_2OPh$, as shown for the 4-nitrobenzylphenyl ether radical anion below (equations 50 and 51), then the loss of B^- is a formal

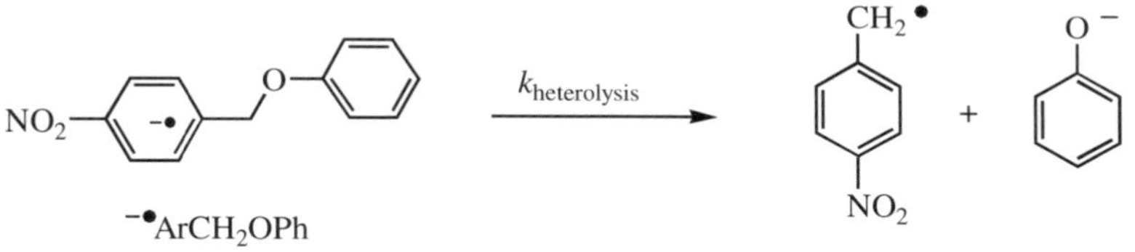

$$(50)$$

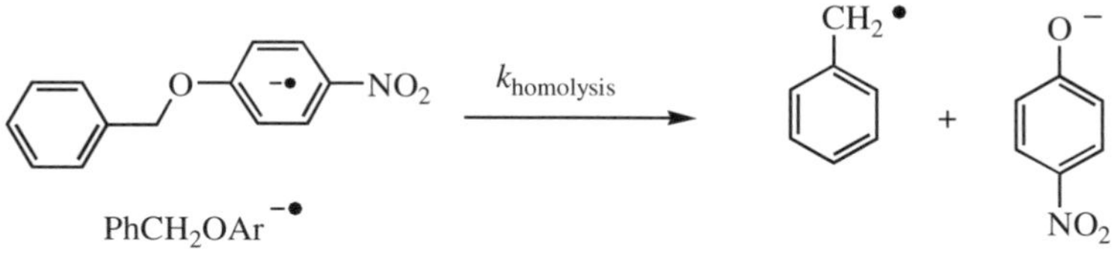

$$(51)$$

heterolysis of the A—B bond (Scheme 4(a)). The heterolysis is conceptually similar to the first step of an S_N1 reaction. On the other hand, if the extra electron is localized on the B fragment as in $PhCH_2OAr^{-\bullet}$ (Scheme 4(b))

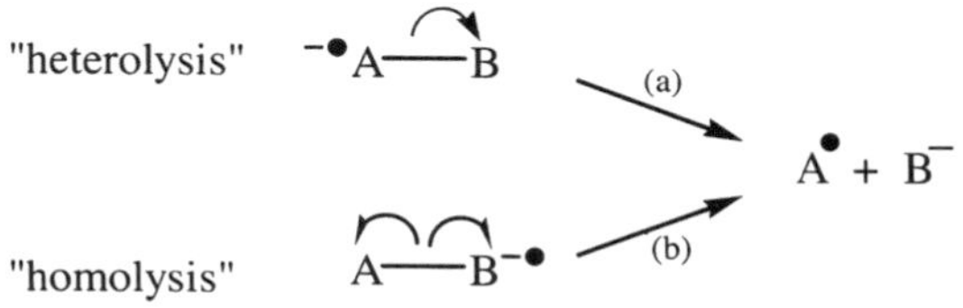

Scheme 4

then the loss of B^- is a formal homolysis of the A—B bond. The homolysis and heterolysis pathways were discussed (Maslak and Guthrie)[82] in terms of Shaik's valence bond configuration mixing model (Scheme 5).[100] In this

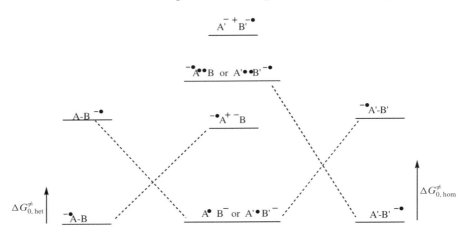

Scheme 5

scheme, the reactants correlate with the lowest excited states of products and *vice versa*. The intersection is an approximation of the position of the transition state. Scheme 5 is drawn for the thermal neutral reaction in order to illustrate the relative intrinsic barriers. The excited state of the reactants ($^-{}^\bullet$A-B and A'-B'$^{-\bullet}$ for $^-{}^\bullet$ArCH$_2$OPh and PhCH$_2$OAr$^{-\bullet}$, respectively) represent single electron transfer from A (or B') to B (or A'). There are two excited-state configurations to consider for the products. Homolysis of the A—B bond in the anion radical results in the formation of a radical and what is formally an excited state of the anion. Since it is assumed that the extra electron does not interact with the radical center, the radical pairs from $^-{}^\bullet$A-B and A'-B'$^{-\bullet}$ will have about the same relative energy. The heterolysis of the A—B bond correlates with an excited state of the products, which is formally the product of electron transfer within the radical pair. For the situation in which the anionic fragment is a good nucleophilic leaving group, the ion pair will always be lower in energy than the radical pair. It was argued that for this reason, the heterolysis pathway should, in general, have a lower intrinsic barrier compared with homolysis. This argument is, of course, limited to systems in which the B^- fragment is a competent nucleophilic leaving group. For the disulfides discussed in Section 4 this is not the case and the radical pair is lower in energy than the ion pair.

An alternative or complementary explanation is based on consideration of the fragmentation as an intramolecular dissociative ET.[101–104] In particular, Savéant extended the theory of concerted dissociative ET to include this situation. Briefly, one may consider the fragmentation as being coupled to the stretch of the A—B bond. If one considers the simple state correlation diagram in Scheme 6 for the fragmentation of the allyl bromide radical anion, it is clear that as the A—B bond stretches, the σ^* energy decreases more quickly than the π^* energy. This system has been nicely described in terms of potential energy curves in a study of dissociative electron attachment to some alkyl chlorides.[101,102] When these energies cross, the intramolecular ET can occur in a manner similar to that described above for the intermolecular concerted ET. Consideration of this view of the mechanism of fragmentation led to an alternate explanation[105] for the apparently lower intrinsic barrier for the heterolytic cleavage of $^{-\bullet}$A-B. These differences may be attributed to differences in the electronic coupling at this avoided crossing. Maslak and Theroff suggested that there is greater delocalization of charge across the scissile bond in the heterolytic cleavage compared with the homolytic cleavage. A kinetic advantage of four orders of magnitude for thermal neutral processes would require an increase in the avoided crossing energy of about 10 kcal/mol (i.e. a lowering of the barrier by about 5 kcal/mol).

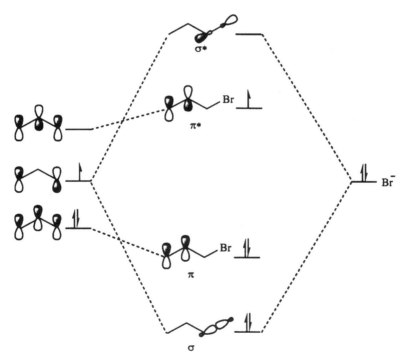

Scheme 6 Simple orbital correlation diagram depicting the interaction of a bromide ion with an allyl radical. The reverse process represents the intramolecular concerted ET.

It is difficult to assess the magnitude of the electronic coupling at the avoided crossing without additional spectroscopic information or a number of assumptions. First, the bond energy of the radical anion ($^-{}^\bullet A - B \rightarrow {}^-{}^\bullet A^\bullet + B^\bullet$) must be known or estimated from changes in the C—O stretching frequency. Second, it must be assumed that the curvature of the dissociative potential for the reactant and the product ($A^- + B^\bullet$) is the same. This may allow the energy of the avoided crossing to be estimated using theoretical calculations, and then compared with the measured activation parameters.

Similar relative reactivities for homolysis versus heterolysis have been observed in the fragmentation of 1-NMOPh$^{-\bullet}$ versus 1-NpOBz$^{-\bullet}$ and 2-NMOPh$^{-\bullet}$ versus 1-NpOBz$^{-\bullet}$.[84,106] In these cases, both the heterolytic and the homolytic pathways were observed. However, the heterolytic reactions were reported to be about 10^3 times faster than the homolytic reactions.

1-NMOPh$^{-\bullet}$ **2-NMOPh$^{-\bullet}$**   **1-NpOBz$^{-\bullet}$**   **2-NpOBz$^{-\bullet}$**

Interestingly, it was observed that the heterolytic fragmentation of 1-NMOPh$^{-\bullet}$ was 10^4 times faster than the heterolytic fragmentation of 2-NMOPh$^{-\bullet}$. In this case, the difference was attributed to the electronic configuration of the anion radical itself. In the 1-naphthyl system there is high negative charge density at the 1-position, while in the 2-naphthyl position the breaking bond is located at a node in the electronic structure of the anion radical. In addition to the intrinsic barrier, electronic factors also are important in determining the rate of fragmentation; there must be orbital overlap between the half-filled π^* of the anion radical and the σ^* of the breaking bond. This is exemplified by the determination of rate constants for intramolecular dissociative ET in *cis* and *trans* isomers of aryl-substituted 4-benzoyloxy-1-methylcyclohexyl bromides which differ by one order of magnitude.[64,107] Any electronic reorganization (which requires configuration mixing with higher states) to achieve this overlap will contribute to weaker electronic coupling between the reactant and product surfaces. While this point seems obvious, it has not been discussed in detail in the context of stepwise dissociative reduction. Other reports in the literature support the idea that electronic configuration can be, at times, a dominant factor. The rate constants for the fragmentation of 3-nitrobenzyl chloride anion radicals are 10^4 times slower than the rate constants for the corresponding 4-nitrobenzyl halide chloride anion radicals.[108,109] The overall driving force for the fragmentation of the benzyl halide anion radicals is independent of whether the substituent is in the *meta* or *para* position. Again, the difference in the kinetics is associated with differences in electronic coupling between reactants and products..

REDUCTION OF PEROXIDES AND ENDOPEROXIDES

Although there are numerous investigations of concerted dissociative ET reported, particularly those involving alkyl and benzyl halides,[15] examples of other molecular systems that undergo putative concerted dissociative ET are not as well documented. Peroxides and endoperoxides are another class of compounds where ET to the oxygen—oxygen bond has recently been shown conclusively to follow a concerted dissociative mechanism. The concerted nature of the dissociative ET is, in part, a result of the very weak O—O bond, which is a necessary condition, as illustrated by equation (41).

Eberson introduced the concept of a dissociative ET to peroxides some time ago.[4,5] There have been attempts to apply Marcus Theory to the ET reduction of diaroyl peroxides in connection with the mechanism of the chemically initiated electron exchange luminescence (CIEEL).[4,5,10] The CIEEL mechanism was originally proposed by Schuster[111–114] to account for intense luminescence (or bioluminescence) in the decomposition of endoperoxides and dioxetanes. The relevance and importance of ET in the latter has recently been discussed.[115,116] While the mechanism of reduction of peroxides in these early studies was described essentially as a concerted dissociative process, little insight into the fine detail of the mechanism could be provided.

In addition to the CIEEL mechanism, peroxides and endoperoxides are key intermediates in a number of chemical and biological processes.[117–120] There are a growing number of examples where ET to the O—O bond in these systems is accepted as an important step in their activity. For example, it is now generally agreed that the first step in the bioactivity of the recently discovered potent antimalarial, artemisinin,[121–123] involves an ET from Fe-heme to the O—O bond, leading to fragmentation and a number of psytotoxic radical intermediates.[124–128] In contrast to the enormous amount of literature on the thermal and photochemical reactivity of peroxides, there is relatively little known about their ET chemistry. It is this lack of kinetic data on ET to peroxides and endoperoxides and the possible relationship of this data to Savéant's model for dissociative ET that initiated our own interest in this chemistry.[22,23,59,89,129–133]

In this section, we will present examples of the concerted ET reduction of the O—O bond in a number of simple alkyl peroxides (RO-OR) and endo-peroxides. These systems provide the first clear examples of the parabolic activation/driving force relationships. The necessary background is provided in the section below. The data provided by the peroxide systems also allow us to introduce important new insights into concerted dissociative processes, particularly the importance of steric and nonadiabatic effects. Finally, data for perbenzoates, another peroxide system related to the early studies, provide evidence for the transition between the concerted and stepwise dissociative mechanisms.

Rate/free energy relationships and the potential dependence of α

We have already seen that modeling of the dissociative ET theory, in its more simple form, leads to a quadratic equation relating $\Delta G^{\neq}$ to ΔG° through equation (7). The kinetic sensitivity of a simple process on ΔG° is described by the transfer coefficient α, which is a linear function of ΔG° (equation 52). An important feature of equation (52) is that α is expected to be 0.5 for $\Delta G^{\circ} = 0$, less than 0.5 for favored ETs and larger than 0.5 for unfavored ETs. The second derivative (equation 53) describes the curvature of the parabola (or the slope of the α–ΔG° plot).

$$\alpha = \frac{\partial \Delta G^{\neq}}{\partial \Delta G^{\circ}} = 0.5 + \frac{\Delta G^{\circ}}{8\Delta G_0^{\neq}} \tag{52}$$

$$\frac{\partial \alpha}{\partial \Delta G^{\circ}} = \frac{\partial^2 \Delta G^{\neq}}{\partial (\Delta G^{\circ})^2} = \frac{1}{8\Delta G_0^{\neq}} \tag{53}$$

Since the curvature is inversely proportional to $\Delta G_0^{\neq}$, it follows that it might be difficult to detect the expected quadratic activation/driving force relationship for reactions characterized by large $\Delta G_0^{\neq}$ values. Conversely, when the latter values are not too large, the expected parabolic pattern should be detectable beyond experimental error.

In general, data can be collected by studying either the homogeneous or the heterogeneous ET at different donor strengths or applied potentials, respectively. To better understand the problems associated with these studies, a few examples in the field of dissociative ETs are worth mentioning at this point. A relevant example of the role of $\Delta G_0^{\neq}$ is the homogeneous ET to *tert*-butyl bromide from a radical anion donor $D^{\bullet-}$ (equation 54). This is by far the most studied dissociative ET with data from homogeneous redox catalysis and pulse radiolysis experiments covering 13 orders of magnitude in the bimolecular rate constants.[41,43,134,135]

$$D^{\bullet-} + RBr \longrightarrow D + R^{\bullet} + Br^{-} \tag{54}$$

In this reaction the experimental data appears to fit almost equally to a parabola, as predicted by the Savéant theory, or to a straight line.[136,137] Although the possible role of an inner-sphere component and thus of a rate increase (relative to pure ET) when the ET becomes more endergonic[137] should not be neglected, the "almost linear" or "slightly curved" activation/driving force relationship is primarily caused by a large intrinsic barrier. A recent attempt to shed light on this specific problem has been described by using well-defined intramolecular donor-spacer-acceptor systems[64] where any inner-sphere contributions to the ET are precluded because of the controlled distance between the electron-exchanging centers. The reduction of a series of ring-substituted 4-benzoyloxy-1-methylcyclohexyl bromides, having a cis-equatorial-axial configuration, was studied by cyclic voltammetry to obtain the rate constant for the intramolecular dissociative ET from the electrogenerated benzoate radical anions to the tertiary C-Br function (equation 55).

$$ \text{(structure with } e,\ Br,\ Y,\ O \text{)} \xrightarrow{k_{ET}} \text{(products)} + Br^- \quad (55) $$

However, even the intramolecular approach could not provide a real answer to the problem of the shape of the activation/driving force relationship of alkyl halides reduction. In fact, the rate constants were found to be more sensitive to the variation of ΔG° than the corresponding intermolecular reductions. For the intermolecular ETs, the α is distinctly smaller than 0.5 (ca. 0.38–0.41), as expected for such exergonic processes, but the value of α for the intramolecular ET is 0.51, a value that would be expected only at $\Delta G^\circ \approx 0$. This effect was attributed to a substituent-induced shift of the π^* orbital of the donor away from the acceptor moiety, resulting in a more rapid rate drop (larger α) compared with the intermolecular reaction when smaller driving forces are considered. As stated above, the failure to clearly observe the parabolic dependence of the rate constant with the driving force for bromide reductions is related to the large intrinsic barrier that is dominated by the bond energy. In principle, the curvature should be clearly evident in dissociative ETs to weaker bonds. In the following, we will describe examples of concerted dissociative ET to peroxides having small $\Delta G_0^{\neq}$ values, thus allowing a better observation of parabolic patterns.

There are a number of problems associated with measuring bimolecular rate constants for ET. Only a small set of data can be obtained. In addition, since a wide range of donor anion radicals is used, there are variations in the reorganization energies that influence local curvature (and thus intrinsic barrier: equation 53) for each point. In principle, electrochemical measurements such as those described in Section 2 can provide similar information.

The advantage is that the electrode potential, E, can be varied continuously and that the intrinsic barrier is defined only by the acceptor. A drawback, however, is related to the effect of the electric double layer. If this effect is neglected, the electrochemical equivalents of equations (7) and (53) are equations (56) and (57). Now, $E = E°$ when $\alpha = 0.5$

$$\Delta G^{\neq} = \Delta G_0^{\neq}\left(1 + F\frac{E - E°}{4\Delta G_0^{\neq}}\right)^2 \tag{56}$$

$$\alpha = 0.5 + \frac{F}{8\Delta G_0^{\neq}}(E - E°) \tag{57}$$

The reduction of di-cumyl peroxide in DMF is a representative example showing how the above concepts apply.[59] The voltammetric data were elaborated by convolution to obtain the potential dependence of k_{het}.[59] The data reported in Fig. 8 compare the analogous semi-logarithmic plot obtained by studying the same system by homogeneous ET.[89] It is interesting to compare these approaches. As already observed, since in the electrochemical approach the free energy of the reaction and thus E can be varied continuously, the number of collectable heterogeneous data points is huge compared with the restricted number of electron donors that can be reasonably used in a study of homogeneous ET. The fact that both plots are curved shows the agreement between the two sets of data. Some scatter in the homogeneous data is expected. Whereas in the heterogeneous case the overall intrinsic barrier depends only on the acceptor molecule, in the homogeneous case it depends also upon the structure of the donor. Nevertheless, the two approaches are complementary and provide information that covers a very wide range of driving force (in this case, $ca.$ 28 kcal/mol or 1.2 eV). For practical reasons, the most negative donor employable has about the same potentials as the most positive E values accessible by convolution.

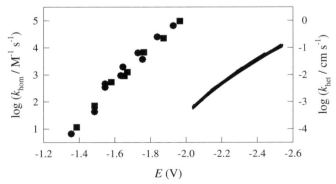

Fig. 8 Plot of $\log(k_{hom})$ (left: MeCN, ■) and $\log(k_{het})$ (right: DMF, ●) versus potential for the mediated and direct reduction of $(PhMe_2CO)_2$.

Electroreduction of peroxides and endoperoxides

The O—O bond of peroxides and endoperoxides is electrochemically reducible.[138–140] The peroxides that will be discussed in this section are illustrated below. In general, electroreduction of simple peroxides and endoperoxides at mercury or glassy carbon electrodes exhibits a single, irreversible, and broad two-electron peak.[22,23,59,89,124,130,141] In addition, the voltammetric peaks of these peroxides exhibit a number of features that indicate that the heterogeneous ET cannot be described by Butler–Volmer kinetics. Namely, the peak potential E_p shifts to more negative potentials values with increasing potential scan rate v with a slope in the order of 110–170 mV/log v, the peak widths $\Delta E_{p/2}$ are scan-rate dependent and the normalized peak current, $i_p/C^* v^{1/2}$, where C^* is the concentration, decreases on increasing v. All of these features should be independent of v by Butler–Volmer kinetics.[30] The deviations are related to a potential dependence of α and allow analysis of the voltammetric data using heterogeneous activation/driving force relationships, as already discussed.

$(CH_3)_3CO\text{-}OC(CH_3)_3$

di-*tert*-butyl peroxide

$CH_3(CH_2)_3O\text{-}O(CH_2)_3CH_3$

di-*n*-butyl peroxide

$Ph(CH_3)_2CO\text{-}OC(CH_3)_2Ph$

di-cumyl peroxide

$Ph(CH_3)_2CO\text{-}OC(Ph)_3$

cumyl triphenylmethyl peroxide

$(Ph)_3CO\text{-}OC(Ph)_3$

bis-triphenylmethyl peroxide

$(CH_3)_3CO\text{-}OC(Ph)_3$

tert-butyl triphenylmethyl peroxide

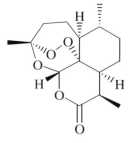

artemisinin   ascaridole   dihydroascaridole

Preparative scale electrolyses of RO–OR results generally in the formation of the corresponding alkoxide ions with the consumption of two electrons per molecule. The two-electron stoichiometry and the dissociative nature of the initial ET are consistent with reduction occurring according to the reaction sequence shown in equations (58)–(60), where the first ET results in concerted dissociative reduction of the O—O bond and the resulting alkoxy radical is then reduced in a second step, since it is easier to reduce than the peroxide itself. Similar results are obtained for simple endoperoxides although the initial ET results in a distonic radical anion ($^\bullet$O-R-R-O$^-$), which is then reduced formally to the corresponding dianion (equations 61–63). Ultimately, the products obtained from reduction of peroxides and endoperoxides are the corresponding alcohols or diols, respectively.[89,130,131] We now have a number of examples where there is evidence for rapid competing alkoxy radical rearrangement in the distonic radical anion, formed by reduction of endoperoxides that competes with the second ET. These processes are being investigated as possible clock reactions.[133,142]

$$RO\text{-}OR + e \longrightarrow RO^\bullet + RO^- \tag{58}$$

$$RO^\bullet + e \longrightarrow RO^- \tag{59}$$

$$RO\text{-}OR + 2e \longrightarrow 2\,RO^- \tag{60}$$

$$R\text{-}O\text{-}O\text{-}R + e \longrightarrow \,^\bullet O\text{-}R\text{-}R\text{-}O^- \tag{61}$$

$$^\bullet O\text{-}R\text{-}R\text{-}O^- + e \longrightarrow \,^- O\text{-}R\text{-}R\text{-}O^- \tag{62}$$

$$R\text{-}O\text{-}O\text{-}R + 2e \longrightarrow \,^- O\text{-}R\text{-}R\text{-}O^- \tag{63}$$

One of the most challenging problems in the study of dissociative ETs concerns the calculation of the standard potential. As described in Section 2, it is possible to derive standard potentials from thermochemical cycles. These calculations require estimates of both the BDFE and the E° of the leaving group. While the relevant BDE values may be available in the literature, correction of these values for entropy changes associated with fragmentation in solution introduces further uncertainty in the calculations. Since the concerted dissociative ET reaction is completely irreversible, the standard potential cannot be determined directly by cyclic voltammetry as with other redox systems (see Section 2). With concerted dissociative ETs, as well as with stepwise dissociative ETs in which the heterogeneous ET is the rate-determining step, the peak potential does not provide any thermodynamic information. As a matter of fact, the overpotential, i.e. the difference between the actual reduction potential and the standard potential, can be so large for the concerted mechanism that the position of the reduction peak may be more negative than the standard potential by as much as 1–1.5 V. Fortunately, it is sometimes possible to obtain the required thermodynamic information by analyzing kinetically-controlled voltammetric peaks in the framework of non-linear activation/driving force relationships obtained from convolution analysis. The analysis of the potential dependence of α is based on the idea that the electrode potential and the free energy are linearly related and that there may be experimental systems providing non-linear rate/free energy (activation/driving force) relationships, as predicted by contemporary ET theories. In this regard, it has to be observed that equations (56) and (57) are not strictly correct since they do not account for the effect of the electric double layer. Modified equations must be used, as previously described.[143] This procedure was applied to study the reduction of a variety of dialkyl peroxides.

The possibility of studying the heterogeneous ET to dialkyl peroxides at the mercury electrode has provided the opportunity to test the dissociative ET theory using experimental activation/driving force relationships. It was thus possible to observe parabolic patterns in agreement with the theory and to use the potential dependence of α to determine the double-layer corrected $E°$ values. Thus, using the convolution analysis approach, values for $E°_{ROOR/RO^•,RO^-}$ were determined for a number of peroxides in both acetonitrile and DMF solutions. Representative results are summarized in Table 4.

Table 4 Summary of the voltammetric reduction peak potentials (E_p), standard dissociative reduction potentials ($E°_{ROOR/RO^•,RO^-}$) for a variety peroxides and endoperoxides in DMF/0.1 M TBAP at $T = 25°C$. Also summarized are the BDFEs and the standard potentials of the corresponding leaving group.[a]

Substrate	E_p (V)	$E°_{ROOR/RO^•,RO^-}$ (V)	$E°_{RO^•/RO^-}$ (V)	BDFE (kcal mol^{-1})
(PhMe$_2$CO)$_2$	−2.23	−1.32	−0.12	27.7
(t-BuO)$_2$	−2.50	−1.48	−0.23[b]	28[b]
		−1.62		32
(n-BuO)$_2$	−2.08	−1.38	−0.15	28.3
(Ph$_3$CO)$_2$	−1.91	−1.13	−0.03	25.4
t-BuOOCPh$_3$	−2.18	−1.22	−0.03	27.4
PhMe$_2$COOCPh$_3$	−2.04	−1.15	−0.03	22
ascaridole	−1.88	−1.20	−0.23[c]	22
dihydroascaridole	−1.93	−1.10	−0.23[c]	24.4
artemisinin	−1.68	−0.82	na	na

[a]Data are are from refs 59, 89, 131, 132.
[b]Thermochemical calculation, from refs 89 or 129.
[c]Assumed to be the same as t-butoxide oxidation.

These values were compared with independent estimates of the $E^°_{ROOR/RO^•,RO^-}$ values from thermochemical cycles, where data were available to evaluate them. In the case of di-cumyl peroxide, for example, the $E^°$ obtained experimentally differs from the result of a thermodynamic calculation by only 30 mV. It is of interest to note that the uncorrected α data would have led to $E^°_{ROOR/RO^•,RO^-}$ values only slightly negative to the corrected ones (0.06–0.07 V). The good agreement in these cases was used as the basis to support the use of the convolution approach to estimate $E^°_{ROOR/RO^•,RO^-}$ for systems where the necessary values for thermochemical estimates are not available. This has been particularly useful in the study of endoperoxides and was used to estimate the standard reduction potential of the antimalarial agent, artemisinin.[131]

The analysis of the curvature of the experimental parabola led to very reasonable determinations of the intrinsic barrier. The measured values are relatively large, ca. 10–13 kcal mol^{-1}, i.e. larger than usually found in stepwise dissociative processes but still not as large as found with other dissociative-type acceptors, such as halides.[15,136] On the other hand, if the intrinsic barriers are calculated by the Eyring equation (equation 4) the values are larger by a few kcal mol^{-1} (using the collision frequency factor Z). This is because the heterogeneous ET is actually non-adiabatic (which means that the actual pre-exponential factor is smaller). This is a very important aspect, which will be covered below.

Using equation (41), and the values of $E^°_{ROOR/RO^•,RO^-}$ determined as described above, values for BDFE can be determined if $E^°_{RO^•/RO^-}$ is known. In fact, in favorable conditions, the standard potential for the $RO^•/RO^-$ couple can be determined through analysis of the voltammetric oxidation of the RO^- anion. In this way, reasonable estimates of solution $O-O$ BDFEs were obtained for some peroxides. The data are also reported in Table 4 and are the same within experimental error. Since the entropy term for this series of compounds is not expected to be very different, this implies that the BDE of these compounds is also the same; consistent with what is known about the substituent effects on BDE for simple peroxides.[117,144–146] Using a common entropy correction for the acyclic peroxides, the BDE of the peroxides is in the range 34–37 kcal mol^{-1}.

The same method was also used to derive the standard potential for the concerted reduction of some endoperoxides, these values are also listed in Table 4. The BDE of endoperoxides is smaller than that for acyclic peroxides, which is reasonable due to the added strain and the eclipsing interactions of the lone pairs on the oxygen.[132]

Homogeneous reduction of peroxides and endoperoxides

ET rate constants can also be determined using solution donors. Indirect reduction of peroxides and endoperoxides was accomplished by homogeneous redox catalysis using electrogenerated radical anions as the donors (Section 2); for the peroxides the relevant reactions are summarized by equations (64)–(66). By using a series of electrogenerated bases of varying standard potentials, values of k_{hom} were measured for the acyclic peroxides di-*tert*-butyl peroxide and di-cumyl peroxide[89,124] and the endoperoxides ascaridole and dihydroascaridole[130,132] (where k_{hom} values pertains to the dissociative ET of equation (65)). One possible complication in the analysis of homogeneous reduction of peroxides is the occurrence of base-induced peroxide decomposition.[89] Another is some consumption of the catalyst because of radical-induced reactions involving the solvent. This complication for the homogeneous ET reduction of di-*tert*-butyl peroxide in DMF for slow reactions was utilized to estimate the standard potential of the DMF-derived N,N-dimethylaminocarbonyl radical, $Me_2NC^\bullet O$, to be $-1.62\,V$.[141]

$$D + e \; \underset{\longleftarrow}{\overline{}} \; D^{\bullet-} \qquad\qquad (64)$$

$$D^{\bullet-} + RO\text{-}OR \longrightarrow RO^\bullet + RO^- + D \qquad\qquad (65)$$

$$D^{\bullet-} + RO^\bullet \longrightarrow RO^- + D \qquad\qquad (66)$$

Using the values of $E^\circ_{ROOR/RO^\bullet,RO^-}$ determined from thermochemical cycles or convolution analysis, the log k_{hom} can be plotted as a function of the reaction free energy shown in Figs 8 and 9. The data convincingly illustrate the parabolic nature of the expected quadratic-activation driving force relationship and thus equation (7). Because of the low BDE(O-O), and thus low intrinsic barrier, the parabolic nature is much more apparent in these systems than in others that undergo dissociative ET.

Fitting of the homogeneous kinetic data for di-*tert*-butyl peroxide according to Savéant's original theory and the Eyring equation using equations (4), (7) and (8) with log $Z = 11.5$, it was shown that the predicted rate constants overestimated the actual rate constants by 2–2.5 orders of magnitude,[89] once account was made for the fact that in the original report BDFE was used instead of BDE in equation (8). In the preliminary account of this work it was suggested that steric inhibition was partly responsible for this discrepancy owing to the exponential decrease of the electronic coupling between reactant and product states caused by the bulky *tert*-butyl groups blocking access of the reductants to the O—O bond.[129]

This aspect was investigated later by comparing the heterogeneous ET kinetics of di-*tert*-butyl peroxide with that of the less hindered di-*n*-butyl peroxide by convolution analysis. A plot comparing the results of a logarithmic

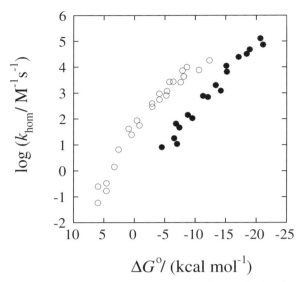

$$\Delta G^{\circ}/ \ (kcal \ mol^{-1})$$

Fig. 9 Plots showing the variation in the logarithm of the homogeneous rate constant for ET, $\log(k_{\mathrm{hom}})$, with the driving force, $-\Delta G^{\circ}$, for the ET reactions of a number of aromatic radical anions with (a) ascaridole (○) and (b) $(t\text{-}BuO)_2$ (●) at 25°C.

analysis of k_{het} as a function of driving force for these two peroxides is shown in Fig. 10. Examination of this figure makes it clear that the heterogeneous rate contant for ET to the sterically unhindered di-n-butyl peroxide is greater than to di-$tert$-butyl peroxide at the same driving force by a factor of 6. This represents the decrease in k due to the steric effect. Accounting for the steric effect, the discrepancy between measured and predicted rate constants falls to 1.2–1.7 orders of magnitude.

Since the kinetic discrepancy of the homogeneous data for di-$tert$-butyl peroxide was originally reported,[129] Savéant and co-workers developed an extension of their original model that takes cage effects and entropy into account.[147] Their work suggests that the available thermodynamic driving force relates energies of solvent separated reactants to solvent separated products (equation 3), where e is the homogeneous reductant, whereas the relevant activation energy is the one for a reaction in which the reactants are solvent separated species, while the products are formed in a solvent cage (equation 67). The products diffuse apart and become independently solvated in a separate step with an activation barrier that is much less than the barrier for the ET. In order to solve this complex problem it was assumed that the entropy change associated with the formation of the fragments in a cage is a fraction of the overall entropy change, $\Delta S^{\circ}_{\mathrm{C}}$. Accordingly, the activation free energy (equation 68) differs from equation (7), because of $\Delta G^{\circ}_{\mathrm{C}}$ (the actual

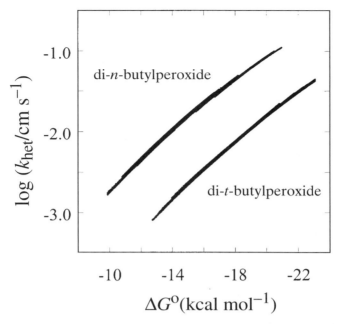

Fig. 10 Logarithm of the heterogeneous rate constant, $\log(k_{\text{het}})$ versus free energy, for the reduction of $(t\text{-BuO})_2$ and $(n\text{-BuO})_2$ in MeCN/0.1 M TEAP at the glassy carbon electrode. $T = 25°C$.

free energy, equation 69) and an additional term. The transfer coefficient, α, can also be calculated at a given driving force (equation 70).

$$A\text{-}B + D^{-\bullet} \longrightarrow (A^{\bullet} B^{-} D)_{\text{sol}} \tag{67}$$

$$\Delta G^{\neq} = \frac{\Delta G^{\neq}}{4}\left(1 + \frac{\Delta G°_{\text{C}}}{\Delta G_0^{\neq}}\right)^2 - \frac{(T\Delta S°_{\text{C}})^2}{4\text{BDE}} \tag{68}$$

$$\Delta G°_{\text{C}} = \Delta G° + T(\Delta S° - \Delta S°_{\text{C}}) \tag{69}$$

$$\alpha = 0.5 + \frac{\Delta G°_{\text{C}}}{8\Delta G_0^{\neq}} \tag{70}$$

To examine the extent that cage and entropy had on the original data, activation parameters for the reduction of di-*tert*-butyl peroxide were measured from a temperature study using a series of donors. These values are compared with those predicted by the model that accounts for cage and entropy effects and are summarized in Table 5. Examination of the two series of $\Delta G^{\neq}$ appears to account for the original discrepancy in the ET rate constants. However, the measured pre-exponential factors are two orders of magnitude lower than those predicted by the theory. In addition, the experimental α values, being significantly smaller than those calculated from equation (70), are in agreement with reactions that are occurring with larger driving forces. Again, the adiabatic dissociative ET model does not account for the experimental kinetic data for the peroxides and endoperoxides. Similar activation parameters were found for ascaridole and dihydroascaridole endoperoxides supporting the generality of non-adiabaticity in these reactions.

The unusually low measured pre-exponential factors are, however, predicted by the theory for non-adiabatic dissociative ET.[13] Unlike Savéant's original treatment, this theory examines the effect of a non-adiabatic ET, which occurs when the electronic coupling energy between the reactant and product states, H_{RP}, is low. This occurs when the reactant and product potential energy surfaces do not interact strongly. Generally, an ET is viewed as non-adiabatic when H_{RP} is distinctly below RT, namely $0.6\,\text{kcal mol}^{-1}$ (or $200\,\text{cm}^{-1}$). Table 6 summarizes the H_{RP} and α values obtained using the German and Kuznetsov approach at varying driving forces for two cases: (i) the dissociative reduction of $tert$-butyl bromide, which is generally accepted as an adiabatic ET; and (ii) the dissociative reductions of di-$tert$-butyl peroxide and di-cumyl peroxide. Details of these calculations are provided elsewhere and will not be given here.[89] The data reported in this table show that for di-$tert$-butyl peroxide, H_{RP} lies significantly below the non-adiabatic upper limit and suggests a non-adiabatic ET, while that for $tert$-butyl bromide is close to the limit. Therefore, the small rate constant values are not the result of a particularly large $\Delta G^{\neq}$, but a result of weak electronic coupling between the reactant and product energy surfaces. Since one implication of the concerted ET model is that there should be some correlation of nuclear and electronic motion near the transition state, it can be argued that all dissociative processes should be inherently non-adiabatic.

Table 5 Experimental and predicted activation parameters for the reduction of di-$tert$-butylperoxide by a number of radical anion homogeneous donors.[a]

Donor	$\Delta G^{\neq}_{exp}$[a] (kcal/mol)	$\Delta G^{\neq}_{calc}$[b] (kcal/mol)	α_{exp}	α_{calc}	$\log(A)$ (exp)	$\log(A)^c$ (calc)
chrysene	8.81	7.59	0.23	0.38	7.06	10.68
isoquinoline	9.72	8.99	0.27	0.41	7.47	10.60
pyrene	10.15	9.87	0.30	0.43	8.08	10.56
anthracene	10.91	10.63	0.32	0.45	8.15	10.52
9,10-diphenylanthracene	11.47	11.60	0.35	0.47	8.76	10.48

[a]$\Delta G^{\neq} = \Delta H^{\neq} - T\Delta S^{\neq}$, from Arrhenius and equation (4) plot. [b]Based on equation (68). [c]Using $\log(Z) = 11.5$.

Table 6 Non-adiabaticity calculations for the homogeneous electron transfer to di-*tert*-butylperoxide, di-cumylperoxide and *t*-butyl bromide (*t*-BuBr).

Acceptor	Donor	$\Delta G^{\circ\ a,b}$ (kcal mol^{-1})	$\log k_{hom}$ (DMF)	α	H_{RP}^{c} (cm^{-1})
(*t*-BuO)$_2$	Pyrene	−12.1	4.05	0.386	6.0–15.4
(*t*-BuO)$_2$	Fluoranthene	−5.7	2.15	0.445	5.8–15.1
(PhMe$_2$CO)$_2$	9,10-diphenylanthracene	−11.9	4.40	0.383	6.2–16.1
(PhMe$_2$CO)$_2$	naphthacene	−5.2	2.54	0.449	7.3–18.9
t-BuBr	Quinoxaline	−13.3	1.66	0.418	82–212
t-BuBr	Azobenzene	−6.0	−0.92	0.463	63–163

$^a E^{\circ}_{DTBP} = -1.48$ V, $E^{\circ}_{DCP} = -1.32$ V.
$^b \lambda_{s\,DTBP} = 15.5$ kcal mol^{-1}, $\lambda_{s\,DCP} = 14.7$ kcal mol^{-1}.
^{c}See reference 89.

Indeed, this idea is being further developed for other chemical systems and also being tackled theoretically.[148,149]

A question that arises is, why would the reduction of ROOR be non-adiabatic while the reduction of R—Br is apparently adiabatic? Consider that the stretching of the R—Br bond must result in a change in the dipole moment of the bond as a result of electron redistribution that occurs along the molecular trajectory in the reaction coordinate for the dissociative reduction. This simple picture is suited for the concerted dissociative reduction since the bromine atom becomes more electron deficient as the bond lengthens and thus more able to accept an electron. On the other hand, the peroxides are symmetrical so while the stretching of the O—O bond may lead to a change in polarizability of the bond, there is no change in dipole moment. At the transition state there is no clear differentiation of which fragment will be the radical site. Under these conditions there may be poor electronic coupling between the reactant and the product surfaces. A similar mechanism accounts for the smaller rate constants measured for endoperoxides where the steric effects are less important than di-*tert*-butyl peroxide.[132] A very recent investigation on the heterogeneous, homogeneous, and intramolecular reduction of alkyl peresters led to determine rate constants that are many orders of magnitude smaller than the adiabatic limit.[150] The results suggested that the intrinsic nonadiabaticity of peroxide reduction might be related also to the breakdown of the Born–Oppenheimer approximation near the transition state.

Transition between concerted and stepwise dissociative electron transfers

We have seen in previous sections that the determination of the potential dependence of α is a very powerful tool in the study of dissociative ETs. α is obtained from the experimental activation/driving force plots and, being a derivative, is also particularly sensitive to changes in the slope of these plots.

This feature is thus very important in detecting the transition between concerted and stepwise dissociative electron transfers, provided a large amount of α data is collectable in a sufficiently large free energy interval. This has been verified during an electrochemical investigation of the reduction of a family of perbenzoates,[22,23] as will be described in the next section. Since this is a general problem in the field of dissociative reductions (and oxidations), it is now useful to review the necessary background. The two competitive mechanisms are the two ETs given in equations (1) and (3). This representation is of course an oversimplification of the actual system because the reaction coordinates describing the two ET reactions may be very similar (being related in both cases to the elongation of the breaking bond and to solvent reorganization). In the next section, however, we shall see that the mechanistic transition may indeed be described as a simple competition. The concerted mechanism is better viewed as a possible reaction pathway independent of the fact that the $AB^{\bullet-}$ radical anion might exist as a discrete intermediate species. Therefore, the actual formation (or non-formation) of $AB^{\bullet-}$ from AB must be considered a function of the competition between the stepwise and the concerted pathways.

The fact that one mechanism may prevail over the other depends on several factors. The thermodynamics of the two ETs is of course the first parameter to be considered. Once we define the reducing properties of the medium (either the applied electrode potential or the standard potential of the solution electron donor), the chances for a concerted dissociative ET to provide the preferred reaction path are enhanced when its standard potential $(E^{\circ}_{AB/A^{\bullet},B^-})$ is (significantly) more positive than the standard potential of the ET of the stepwise process $(E^{\circ}_{AB/AB^{\bullet-}})$. Because of the relationship defined by equation (41), this is more likely when the BDFE is small and/or $E^{\circ}_{B^{\bullet}/B^-}$ is sufficiently positive. It is also worth noting that the free energy for the cleavage of the putative radical anion is also given by the difference $E^{\circ}_{AB/AB^{\bullet-}} - E^{\circ}_{AB/A^{\bullet},B^-}$ as can be obtained from equation (42). This implies that a large E° difference is also most likely associated with a fast cleavage of the radical anion.

The E° difference is a necessary but not a sufficient condition. The rate constant for either ET (in general, k_{ET}) may be described in a simple way by equation (4). The activation free energy $\Delta G^{\neq}$ is usually expressed as a quadratic function of ΔG°, no matter whether we deal with an outer-sphere ET[9] or a dissociative ET.[12] However, even if the condition $(\Delta G^{\circ})_C < (\Delta G^{\circ})_{ST}$ holds (hereafter, subscripts C and ST will be used to denote the parameters for the concerted and stepwise ETs, respectively), the kinetic requirements (intrinsic barriers and pre-exponential factors) of the two ETs have to be taken into account. While $\Delta G^{\neq}_{0,s}$ depends only slightly on the ET mechanism, $\Delta G^{\neq}_{0,i}$ is dependent on it to a large extent. For a concerted dissociative ET, the Savéant model leads to $\Delta G^{\neq}_{0,i} \approx BDE/4$.[12] Thus, $(\Delta G^{\neq}_0)_C$ is significantly larger than $(\Delta G^{\neq}_0)_{ST}$ no matter how significant $\Delta G^{\neq}_{0,i}$ is in $(\Delta G^{\neq}_0)_{ST}$ (see, in particular, Section 4). In fact, within typical dissociative-type systems such as halides and peroxides, the contribution of the BDE term to $\Delta G_0^{\neq}$ is typically 70–80%. Because of the intrinsic barrier difference, the two ETs respond to changes in the driving force in a different way and this may result in having $(\Delta G^{\neq})_{ST}$ smaller than $(\Delta G^{\neq})_C$, in spite of a less favorable driving force. Besides the nuclear term of equation (4), Z_{ST} and Z_C also might differ. Although the formation of $AB^{\bullet-}$ is most likely an adiabatic ET process, we have seen that there is enough evidence indicating that non-adiabaticity affects the concerted ET to dialkyl peroxides. This would result in Z_C being smaller than Z_{ST} and thus, at any given experimental condition, to a less relevant contribution (to the observed rate) of the rate of the concerted ET relative to the stepwise ET.

Let us now focus specifically on electrochemical reductions. Provided only one ET mechanism obeying equation (7) takes place, the apparent value of α depends upon the applied potential E according to equation (57). The value of α may allow an approximate discrimination to be performed between the two mechanisms. Because of the large activation overpotential suffered by the concerted dissociative ET, the potentials at which the voltammetric peak for the reduction of AB occurs, are much more negative than $E^{\circ}_{AB/A^{\bullet},B^-}$. Equation (57) shows that values of α significantly lower than 0.5 are thus expected. On the other hand, if the initial ET leads to the formation of $AB^{\bullet-}$ that fragments only successively (equations 1 and 2), then the usual effect of the chemical reaction is to cause the peak to appear close to or even before $E^{\circ}_{AB/AB^{\bullet-}}$; thus apparent α values close to or larger than 0.5 are expected. However, there may be situations where the heterogeneous ET rate can be slow compared to the cleavage rate. In this circumstance, the voltammetric peak is electrochemically irreversible and is pushed to more negative potentials than $E^{\circ}_{AB/AB^{\bullet-}}$. Thus, α can be significantly lower than 0.5, even though the mechanism is stepwise.

When the standard potential for the formation of the electron donor (homogeneous ET) or the electrode potential E is changed to more positive values, it may be possible to observe a transition from a stepwise to a concerted mechanism. Therefore, there will be a borderline situation when the system is in an energy range such that reduction may occur through both mechanisms, although with different rates. This competition has been described by expressing the heterogeneous rate constant as the sum of the rate constants of the two competitive ETs; $k_{ET} = k_C + k_{ST}$.[23] An analogous description can be applied to the homogeneous counterpart. In line with the above discussion, it was demonstrated that the potential dependence of α responds to variations of three main parameters: (a) the difference between the two standard potentials, $\varepsilon = (E^{\circ}_{AB/A^{\bullet},B^-} - E^{\circ}_{AB/AB^{\bullet-}})$; (b) the ratio between the two pre-exponential factors, $\zeta = Z_{ST}/Z_C$; and (c) the ratio between the two intrinsic barriers $\beta = (\Delta G_0^{\neq})_C/(\Delta G_0^{\neq})_{ST}$. Under certain conditions (particularly, small but positive ε values and large values of ζ and β), a wave-like potential dependence of α, connecting the two linear variations describing the pure mechanisms, is evident. An example is provided in Fig. 11. The wave-like potential dependence of α magnifies as ε decreases because we are now exploring E values where the contribution of k_{ST} to k_{ET} becomes increasingly significant. Accordingly, the apparent α detects that when E is positive of $E°_{AB/AB•-}$ the stepwise-type α contribution is larger than 0.5 (equation 57).

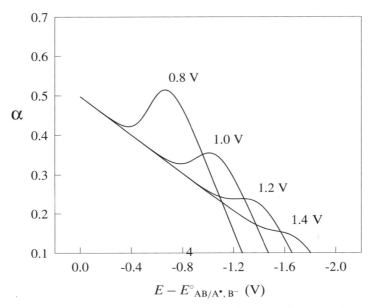

Fig. 11 Typical effect of the parameter ε on the potential dependence of the α value for a mixed dissociative ET mechanism: $\zeta = 1$, $\beta = 3.5$, BDE $= 34$ kcal mol^{-1}.

Electroreduction of perbenzoates

The sensitivity of α to the ET mechanism is particularly useful in revealing deviation from the parabolic behavior expected on the basis of equation (7). This is exemplified by the application of the α convolution analysis to the reduction of a series of perbenzoates in DMF at the glassy carbon electrode.[22,23]

X = H, 4-OCOMe, 4-COMe, 4-CN, 3-NO$_2$, 4-NO$_2$

The electrochemical measurements were carried out in the presence of one equivalent of a weak acid (acetanilide) to ensure protonation of the electro-generated *tert*-butoxy anion. This was necessary to avoid the interference of the father–son reaction between t-BuO$^-$ and the perbenzoate, leading to the corresponding ester. The initial one-electron reduction proceeds with O—O bond cleavage leading to the formation of t-BuO$^\bullet$ and ArCOO$^-$ according to a stepwise (equations 71, 72) or concerted (equation 73) mechanism. At the working potentials, t-BuO$^\bullet$ is reduced (equation 74) to the anion t-BuO$^-$ ($E^\circ = -0.23$ V)[129] and thus the overall process is a two-electron reduction.

$$t\text{-BuOOCOAr} + e \rightleftharpoons t\text{-BuOOCOAr}^{\bullet-} \tag{71}$$

$$t\text{-BuOOCOAr}^{\bullet-} \longrightarrow t\text{-BuO}^\bullet + \text{ArCOO}^- \tag{72}$$

$$t\text{-BuOOCOAr} + e \longrightarrow t\text{-BuO}^\bullet + \text{ArCOO}^- \tag{73}$$

$$t\text{-BuO}^\bullet + e \longrightarrow t\text{-BuO}^- \tag{74}$$

The oxidation of ArCOO$^-$ is detectable through an irreversible oxidation peak that occurs at very positive potential values. The voltammetric data are reported in Table 7, together with the E° of the t-butyl esters corresponding to the above perbenzoates. Quantitative information on the ET mechanism was obtained by convolution analysis. The logarithmic analysis was carried out by using equation (25). Whereas, for some compounds, parabolic $\log k_{het}$–E plots were obtained, for other compounds the $\log k_{het}$–E plots were neither parabolic nor linear (see Fig. 12). The analysis was carried out on the basis of the simple competition approach described in the previous section, using reasonable estimates for the inner barriers and standard poten-tials. Best fitting of the data led to relatively small variations of these initial

Table 7 Electrochemical and thermochemical data for the dissociative ET to ring-substituted perbenzoates.

Substituent	$E_p{}^a$ (V)	E° (ester)^b (V)	$E_{p,\text{ox B}^\bullet/B^-}{}^a$ (V)	BDE^c (kcal/mol)	$E^\circ{}_{\text{AB/A}^\bullet,\text{B}^-}{}^d$ (V)	$E^\circ{}_{\text{AB/A}^\bullet,\text{B}^-}{}^e$ (V)
H	−1.38	−2.29	1.43	32.6	0.07	−0.20
4-(-OCOMe)	−1.35	−2.20	1.48	33.7	0.07	−0.12
4-COMe	−1.25	−1.58	1.50	33.3	0.11	0.02
4-CN	−1.26	−1.63	1.56	36.1	0.04	0.02
3-NO$_2$	−0.88	−1.01	1.57	35.3	0.22	0.12
4-NO$_2$	−0.76	−0.89	1.58	35.4	0.23	0.09

$^a v = 0.2$ V s^{-1}. ^{b}Obtained from the reversible reduction peaks of the corresponding esters. ^{c}See ref. 23. ^{d}Estimated on the basis of thermochemical and peak potential data. ^{e}From convolution analysis.

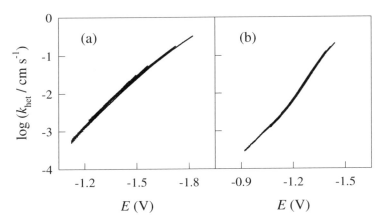

Fig. 12 Potential dependence of the logarithm of the heterogeneous rate constant for the reduction of PhCO$_3$Bu-t (graph (a)) and 4-MeCO-PhCO$_3$Bu-t (graph (b)) in DMF/0.1 M TBAP.

parameters. Figure 13 shows the result of this analysis for a typical concerted ET (X = H), transitional behavior (X = 4-acetyl, 4-CN), and stepwise dissociative (X = 4-NO$_2$). The slopes of the linear sections are inversely proportional to the intrinsic barrier (equation (57)). A similar potential dependence of α has been found very recently with peresters.[150]

Full transition from one linear behavior to the other requires no less than 0.7 V. In the framework of detecting a mechanistic change, the temperature effect on the potential dependence of α is very important. By studying the reduction of the 4-acetyl perbenzoate,[23] it has been shown that the transition is shifted toward a stepwise pattern by lowering the temperature and thus by shifting the voltammetric peak closer to $E°_{AB/AB^{\bullet-}}$ and away from $E°_{AB/A^{\bullet},B^-}$. A similar observation has been reported for the reduction of a sulfonium salt by using conventional voltammetry.[151] The opposite shift is caused by an increase of temperature, as observed with 3-nitro perbenzoate[23] and two aryl iodides.[152] The agreement between the simulation and the experimental data as well as the reasonable values obtained for the relevant parameters of perbenzoate reduction ($E°$s and ET barriers), suggest that the simple competition model describes satisfactorily the transition between the two mechanisms. The observed transition is between the two limiting dissociative mechanisms, i.e. concerted and stepwise mechanisms (where solvent reorganization is the most important contribution to the intrinsic barrier). According to the $E°$ values resulting from the best fitting procedure, the free energy for the radical anion cleavage (equation 42) is largely exergonic (-23, -26, -30 and -31 kcal mol^{-1} for X = 4-NO$_2$, 3-NO$_2$, 4-CN, and 4-COMe). Less driving force for X = NO$_2$ is associated with more O—O bond elongation, more solvent reorganization (the negative charge moves

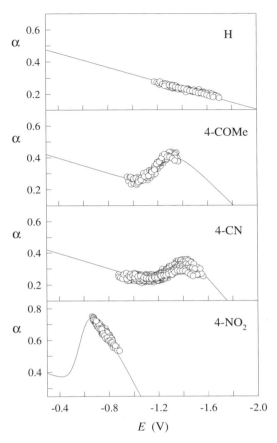

Fig. 13 Experimental (○) and calculated (solid line) potential dependencies of the apparent transfer coefficient α for the electroreduction of 4-X-PhCO$_3$Bu-t in DMF/ 0.1 M TBAP at 25°C.

from the nitro group to the incipient carboxylate leaving group), and more electronic reorganization (the COOBu-t group is less affected by the initial electron uptake) at the transition state of the homolytic fragmentation. Although these effects, which can be described as an actual intramolecular dissociative ET, diminish when going to less electron-withdrawing substituents, they do not disappear. In fact, despite the large driving forces involved, the indirect evidence for the formation of the radical anion (under appropriate conditions) also means that the cleavage is not barrierless. The fact that the cleavage is of the homolytic type (the charge is not transferred across the scissile bond) is also favoring a finite lifetime for the radical anion. The reduction of perbenzoates provides the first example of strongly exergonic cleavages still requiring appreciable activation energy.

Besides the reduction of peresters,[22,23,50] other reports have dealt with the problem of detecting a mechanistic transition by varying the driving force provided to the same acceptor. The first concepts were introduced for the homogeneous redox catalysis approach.[40] The first experimental report came from the C—S bond cleavage caused by homogeneous ET to triphenylmethyl phenyl sulfide from a series of aromatic electron donors,[153] although in a more recent study the transition was not as evident.[154] The homogeneous reduction of some nitro benzyl chlorides has provided a similar transition.[155] We have already pointed out that the homogeneous approach is intrinsically less sensitive than the corresponding heterogeneous one. Indeed, voltammetric effects (peak width variation with the scan rate) consistent with a transition behavior were reported for the reduction of two sulfonium cations,[151,156] and two aryl iodides.[152] However, since the conventional voltammetric analysis was applied, only an approximate, though indicative, picture of the ET mechanism could be obtained. In terms of sensitivity to ET rate changes, the convolution approach is thus recommended, as exemplified by the reduction of peresters.[22,23,150] An important result stemming from the study of the reduction of perbenzoates is that, at least within a family of related compounds, a transition behavior can be predicted on the basis of relatively simple considerations. Understanding the subtle factors causing the progressive shift of one mechanism to the other, in terms of the driving force, intrinsic barrier, and environmental aspects (temperature, solvent, counterions), is believed to be of particular relevance in future practical applications of these reactions.

4 Reduction of S—S and C—S bonds

The reduction of disulfides and sulfides provides new insights into the mechanism of stepwise dissociative electron transfers. Normally, the stepwise mechanism is one in which the radical anion $AB^{\bullet-}$ forms without significant structural reorganization with respect to its precursor. While the intrinsic barrier for solvent reorganization of common molecules is usually $\Delta G_{0,s}^{\neq} = 2.3–3\,\text{kcal mol}^{-1}$ (remember, the intrinsic barrier is one-quarter of the reorganization energy), the inner component is normally considered to be much smaller ($\Delta G_{0,i}^{\neq} = 0.7–1\,\text{kcal mol}^{-1}$) and in many cases is ignored altogether. While this assumption is often reasonable, there are examples in literature that suggest it is not always justifiable. For example, the electroreductive C—S cleavage in thiocarbonates $(X\text{-PhS})_2C{=}S^{157}$ has been reported to have heterogeneous rates that, depending on the substituent, are lower than expected. Although this was attributed to specific solvation effects at the C=S bond, on the basis of the present state of knowledge (*vide infra*) a contribution from C—S bond elongation may be envisaged as the main reason for such a slow ET rate.

Although the possibility of significant internal reorganization in stepwise processes should not be ignored with other classes of compounds, the majority of the data supporting the idea comes from studies where the cleaving bond is C–S or S–S. The first detailed studies in this field dealt with the heterogeneous and homogeneous reduction of a series of benzyl aryl sulfides.[62,153,158,159] These studies, particularly that on the reduction of 4-CNC$_6$H$_4$S-CPh$_3$, provided evidence[159] that the inner reorganization energies can be substantially larger than $\Delta G^{\neq}_{0,s}$ (*vide infra*). Analogous information was obtained by studying the homogeneous ET to other *para*-substituted triphenylmethyl aryl sulfides.[154,160] The unusually large intrinsic barriers were attributed to a lengthening of the C–S bond upon the formation of the radical anion. Some support for this was gained by semi-empirical theoretical calculations.[159] However, a specific study of the relevance of the inner reorganization energy was not available until very recently, thanks to a series of comparative studies carried out on the homogeneous and heterogeneous dissociative reduction of series of dialkyl, alkyl-aryl, and diaryl disulfides[65,161–163] and sulfides.[154,164] These studies, together with theoretical calculations,[162,163,165] and ET modeling[166] on the formation of loose radical anions, provide the basis for conceptual modifications to the dissociative ET theory that are currently being developed. The reduction of disulfides will be considered first, including data on the redox properties of the related RS•/RS⁻ couples and theoretical calculations on the formation and cleavage of the disulfide radical anions. Heterogeneous and homogeneous ET data will be provided and a later section will focus on the inner intrinsic barriers. The reduction of sulfides will be described in the final part of this section.

REDUCTION OF DISULFIDES

ET to disulfides leads, as a rule, to the cleavage of the S–S bond by a stepwise mechanism.[167–175] For the purposes of this review, we will focus only on the data obtained at inert electrodes, particularly glassy carbon electrodes. The reduction of the disulfide bond, in both simple organic compounds and proteins,[176,177] is complicated at the mercury electrode by adsorption phenomena, leading to complex reaction pathways which are beyond the scope of this review. However, it is worth noting that the reduction of some epidithiodioxopiperazines at mercury was reported to generate stable radical anions, most likely because of the inherent constraint in the disulfide bridge.[178]

In general, the reduction of disulfides is an irreversible two-electron process leading to the formation of two thiolate anions (equations 75–78) where the two R groups may be different. The standard potential of the RS•/RS⁻ couple is generally at least 1 V more positive than the potential at which the disulfide is reduced.

$$RS\text{-}SR + e \rightleftharpoons RS\text{-}SR^{\bullet-} \tag{75}$$

$$RS\text{-}SR^{\bullet-} \rightleftharpoons RS^{\bullet} + RS^{-} \tag{76}$$

$$RS^{\bullet} + e \longrightarrow RS^{-} \tag{77}$$

$$RS\text{-}SR + 2e \longrightarrow 2\,RS^{-} \tag{78}$$

The lifetime of the RSSR$^{\bullet-}$ radical anions is usually very short; on the microsecond timescale in water.[169] However, they have been detected and characterized by time-resolved optical methods. In one early study, γ irradiation of matrices containing alkyl and aryl disulfides provided spectroscopic evidence for the formation of the corresponding radical anions.[179] Subsequently, the formation of RSSR$^{\bullet-}$ radical anions has been well documented, particularly by EPR, flash photolysis, and pulse radiolysis. In fact, $2\sigma/1\sigma^*$ three-electron bonded radical anion species, particularly from sulfur compounds, constitute significant and interesting intermediates.[24] The RSSR$^{\bullet-}$ radical anions may be obtained from different approaches. One is by one-electron reduction of disulfides (equation 75), such as by pulse radiolysis.[169] However, the most common approach is by association of RS$^{\bullet}$ and RS^{-} (equation 79).[180–183]

The formation of RSSR$^{\bullet-}$ from RS$^{\bullet}$ and RS^{-} species is particularly relevant in the present context because it is the reverse of the electro-induced radical anion cleavage (equation 76). Actually, the formation of RSSR$^{\bullet-}$ from reaction (79) is as well studied as the reaction between aryl carbon radicals and anionic nucleophiles, the fundamental step of the $S_{RN}1$.[103,184] Equilibrium constants in the range 10^2–10^4 M for reaction (79) were determined for a number of alkyl-type systems in water,[183,185] although the corresponding values for aryl-type systems are smaller.[186] The rate constants for the formation of RSSR$^{\bullet-}$ are nearly diffusion controlled $(3–5 \times 10^9 \, \mathrm{M^{-1}\,s^{-1}})$.[185]

$$RS^{\bullet} + RS^{-} \rightleftharpoons RS\text{-}SR^{\bullet-} \tag{79}$$

Before proceeding to describe the mechanistic features of disulfide reduction, it is useful to first describe the effect of substituents on the stability of thiyl radicals and disulfide radical anions as well as the consequences, from a theoretical viewpoint, of the unpaired electron on both the bond energy and the S—S bond length of disulfides.

The RS$^{\bullet}$/RS^{-} standard potentials

The redox properties of the RS$^{\bullet}$/RS^{-} couples have been described by a number of authors. Thermodynamic calculations also have been carried out to estimate the standard potentials of these and related redox couples in water.[183,185,186] Electrochemical studies provide irreversible potential data[91,187] and thus will not be considered here. However, accurate determinations of several $E°$ values in non-aqueous solvents, pertaining to *para*-substituted phenylthiyl radicals, have been reported. The oxidation of RS⁻ anions, generated in MeCN by deprotonation of the corresponding thiophenols, has been studied by using gold micro or ultramicroelectrodes.[188] It is noteworthy that reversibility could be observed in the kV s⁻¹ range for the OMe and Me derivatives, consistent with the observed slow self-reaction of electron-rich arylthiyl radicals.[189–191] Very recently, voltammetric measurements have been carried out in DMF by using platinum and glassy carbon electrodes; in this study, the anions were generated by reduction of the corresponding disulfides.[162] This study, which is not affected by hydrogen-bonding interactions of the electroactive RS⁻ anion, provided a particularly reproducible and self-consistent set of data. Again, in agreement with the above discussion the rate constants were found to be smaller for anions bearing electron-donating substituents. For example, some reversibility is evident with the NH₂ derivative at 100 V s⁻¹. The $E°$ values were obtained by studying the scan rate dependence of the peak[192] and by digital simulation. Peak potentials and $E°$ data are reported in Table 8. A very good Hammett correlation, with $E°_{RS•/RS^-} = 0.076 + 0.604\sigma$ ($r^2 = 0.997$), was found.

Theoretical calculations on disulfides and their radical anions

Typical BDE values for the S–S bond of disulfides are in the range 50–80 kcal mol⁻¹.[193] On the other hand, bond energies in the RSSR•⁻ radical anions should range from about half to one-third of the BDE of neutral disulfides.[24] For radical anions of dialkyl disulfides, the strength of the S–S bond decreases as the electron donating ability of R increases. This is presumably a consequence of increased electron density in the σ^* antibonding orbital and is characterized by a red shift in the optical absorption and the very good correlation with the Taft's σ^*.[187] EPR characterization of some

Table 8 Peak potentials at the platinum electrode and standard potential for the oxidation of X-Ph-S⁻ in DMF/0.1 M TBAP at 25°C.[a]

X =	NH₂	OMe	H	F	Cl	CO₂Me	CN	NO₂
$(E_p)_{ox}$[b] (V)	−0.41	−0.14	−0.02	0.03	0.12	0.28	0.37	0.42
$E°_{RS•/RS^-}$ (V)	−0.34	−0.07 (−0.04)[c]	0.07 (0.10)[c]	0.12	0.21 (0.18)[c]	0.37	0.47	0.53 (0.46)[c]

[a]Reference 162. [b]$v = 0.2$ V s⁻¹, Pt electrode.
[c]Reference 188, MeCN, Au electrode; the $E°$ of the Me derivative is 0.04 V.

dialkyl disulfide radical anions indicates that the lifetime of t-BuSSBu-t is particularly short.[182]

Unlike radical anions of most aryl-containing molecules, the radical anion of PhSSPh, like dialkyl disulfide radical anions, is characterized by localization of the odd electron mostly on the S—S bond.[179] These data suggest that dialkyl, PhSSPh, and probably PhSSR disulfide radical anions are short-lived but well-defined σ^*-type radical anions.

Theoretical data support the fact that the disulfide radical anion, because of the weakness of the three-electron bond vs. the two-electron bond, has a bond length that is significantly larger than that of the precursor. For example, by using *ab initio* calculations, it was reported that upon formation of the radical anion, HS–SH increases the S—S bond length from 2.08 to 2.78 Å[165] and MeS-SMe from 2.06 to 2.62 Å[195] or 2.05 to 2.84 Å.[196] Very recent results have provided a much deeper insight into this problem, confirming that a decrease in the BDE value is matched by an increase of the bond length.[162,163]

Theoretical calculations were carried out on the disulfides shown below as well as the corresponding radical anions.[163]

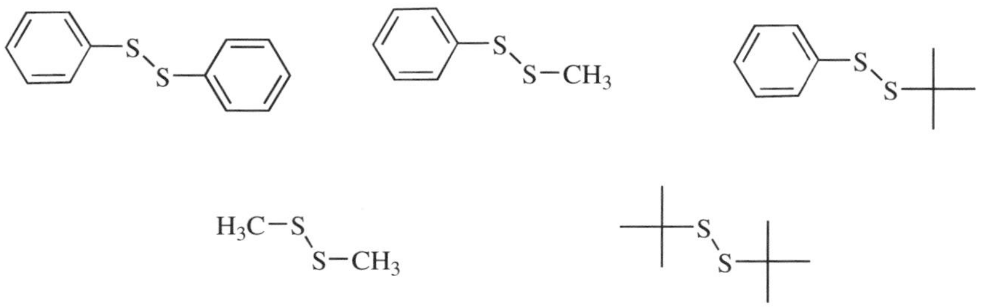

The total molecular energies for all these compounds were determined by MO *ab initio* calculations at MP2/3-21G*//MP2/3-21G* level. The BDE values were obtained as the difference between the total molecular energy of the neutral molecules or of the radical anions and that of the S—S cleavage products. They are reported in Table 9 with the relative results obtained by simulating the presence of a solvent having the dielectric constant of DMF (36.7). While it has been suggested that the absolute BDE values calculated for the neutral molecules may be smaller than those determined experimentally or by using the heats of formation,[193] relative values and trends are considered to be meaningful. The energy data were fitted by Morse-like potential functions (equation (9) $f = 1$) of the S—S coordinate and the corresponding exponential β factors are also reported. As expected, the solvent has a much larger effect on radical anions than in the neutral molecules and the calculated BDEs are smaller in solution.

From the data of Table 9, it is seen that the S—S bond length increases upon reduction of the disulfide from the neutral molecules to the radical anions by 0.76–0.81 Å. This represents a very significant structural change. The calculations indicate that the other bonds also are affected, but not as much as the S—S bond. For example, the C—S bond in $PhSSMe^{\bullet-}$ and $PhSSBu^{\bullet-}$ contracts by 0.03–0.04 Å. Therefore, it appears that taking the length of the bond undergoing the dissociation as the main reaction coordinate describing the energy profile of the inner contribution for both ET and bond breaking is a very good approximation to describe the dynamics of disulfide reduction.

Besides the above data on PhSSPh, theoretical calculations were carried out also on a series of *para*-substituted diaryl disulfides and corresponding radical anions.[162]

$$X = NH_2, H, F, CN, NO_2$$

BDEs, calculated as described above, are reported for these disulfides and their radical anions in Table 10, together with the β Morse factors. Again, although the BDE values may be underestimated,[193] relative comparisons are expected to be reliable.

The BDE values of the neutral disulfides do not change significantly along the series, although there is a slight increase when going toward more electron-withdrawing substituents. This is consistent with the data pertaining to *para*-substituted thiophenols.[91,186] Already it was suggested that electron-withdrawing groups stabilize the S—S bond by decreasing the electric

Table 9 Calculated parameters for neutral disulfides and relative radical anions.

Compound	$BDE_{(g)}{}^{a,b}$ (kcal mol^{-1})	$BDE_{(s)}{}^{a,c}$ (kcal mol^{-1})	$BDE(^{\bullet-})_{(g)}{}^{d,a}$ (kcal mol^{-1})	$BDE(^{\bullet-})_{(s)}{}^{d,c}$ (kcal mol^{-1})	$\beta^{a,b}$ (Å^{-1})	$\beta(^{\bullet-})^{b,d}$ (Å^{-1})	Δr^{e} (Å)
PhSSPh	46.8	46.2	15.0	1.8	1.930	1.558	0.765
PhSSMe	51.6	50.3	19.4	7.6	1.929	1.478	0.768
PhSSBu	55.0	53.7	22.3	7.9	1.906	1.297	0.757
MeSSMe	56.7	55.0	26.9	9.9	1.896	1.164	0.759
t-BuSSBu-*t*	61.2	59.5	29.8	12.5	1.873	1.025	0.807

[a]Values refer to the neutral molecules. [b]Gas phase. [c]Solution. [d]Values refer to the radical anions. [e]S—S length increment from neutral to radical anion.

Table 10 Calculated parameters for the neutral diaryl disulfides and their radical anions.

X	$BDE^{a,b}$ (kcal mol^{-1})	$BDE(\bullet^-)^{b,c}$ (kcal mol^{-1})	$r_0{}^{a,b}$ (Å)	$r_0(\bullet^-)^{b,c}$ (Å)	$\Delta r^{\neq\,d}$ (Å)	$\Delta E_0^{\neq\,e}$ (kcal mol^{-1})
NH$_2$	44.6	10.5	2.078	2.866	0.39	12.25
H	46.8	15.0	2.069	2.831	0.36	11.67
F	47.6	16.1	2.070	2.835	0.36	11.93
CN	55.1	11.7	2.070	2.858	0.39	14.02
NO$_2$	49.6	−5.9	2.070	2.175		

^{a}Values refer to neutral molecule. ^{b}Gas phase. ^{c}Values refer to the radical anion.
^{d} Increase in bond length at the ET transition. ^{e}Activation energy for ET.

repulsion between the electrons on the sulfur atoms; this affects both the HOMO and the LUMO.[172] Calculations show that in solution (DMF, $\varepsilon = 36.7$) the BDE of the neutral compounds are not significantly different from those in the gas phase, except for X = NH$_2$ which shows a marked decrease of the BDE in solution. This would suggest that the p-NH$_2$C$_6$H$_4$S$^\bullet$ radical is particularly stabilized in solution, in agreement with above kinetic results on the particularly low coupling rate of this radical (which may be considered to have a structure such as $^{+\bullet}$H$_2$NC$_6$H$_4$S$^-$).

For the radical anions, the BDE values in gas phase are considerably lower than those of the neutral molecules. For the nitro-substituted radical anion the enthalpy change is even negative suggesting the cleavage of a π^* radical anion. Unlike the other substituted radical anions, the calculated equilibrium S—S bond distance of this particular radical anion is only slightly larger than that of the corresponding neutral molecule (0.1 Å). For the other diaryl disulfides, the structures of the corresponding radical anions are characterized by force constants that are markedly smaller than those of the corresponding neutral molecules. This is an important observation, in line with other observations,[197] and will be discussed later on. The Morse β values also decrease upon radical anion formation, although generally less than observed for the other disulfides (see Table 9).

From the crossing point of the Morse curves of the neutral molecule and of the radical anion, obtained by using the calculated parameters (uncorrected for the avoided crossing and by using the same energy minimum for the two Morse curves), the bond elongation at the ET transition state ($\Delta r^{\neq}$) and the activation energy at zero driving force ($\Delta E_0^{\neq}$) were calculated (Table 10). These values show that the calculated S—S bond elongation in the transition state for the reduction of X = NH$_2$, H, F, and CN is similar and quite large. A different situation is found for the nitro substituted disulfide. As pointed out above, the apparent "negative" BDE can be explained by considering the initial intermediate as a π^* radical anion. The cleavage of the radical anion is then an intramolecular ET to an antibonding orbital mostly localized on the

S–S bond. This intramolecular ET requires inner activation through S–S bond elongation that is not evident in the initial ET.

Electrochemical reduction of disulfides

The voltammetric reduction of a series of dialkyl and arylalkyl disulfides has recently been studied in detail, in DMF/0.1 M TBAP at the glassy carbon electrode[163] The ET kinetics was analyzed after addition of 1 equivalent of acetic acid to avoid father–son reactions,[61] such as self-protonation or nucleophilic attack on the starting disulfide by the most reactive RS⁻ anion. Father–son reactions have the consequence of lowering the electron consumption from the expected two-electron stoichiometry. Addition of a suitable acid results in the protonation of active nucleophiles or bases. The peak potentials for the irreversible voltammetric reduction of disulfides are strongly dependent on the nature of the groups bonded to the sulfur atoms. Table 11 summarizes some relevant electrochemical data. These results indicate that the initial ET controls the electrode kinetics. In addition, the decrease of the normalized peak current and the corresponding increase of the peak width when v increases, point to a potential dependence of α, as discussed thoroughly in Section 2.

Logarithmic analysis of the convolution curves, using the equation holding for irreversible processes, led to very good ($r^2 = 0.995$–0.999) second-order plots of the potential dependence of $\log k_{het}$.

From the derivative of these plots, the potential dependence of α was obtained and the $E°$ for each disulfide was estimated, using the approach described in Section 2. The double-layer uncorrected $E°$ values and corresponding standard rate constants were optimized by reproducing the experimental curves by digital simulation. The data are reported in Table 11. By using the Eyring equation (4) with the pertinent pre-exponential

Table 11 Electrochemical and kinetic parameters for the reduction of disulfides in DMF/0.1 M TBAP at 25°C.

Disulfide	$E_p{}^a$ (V)	α^a	$\alpha^{c,d}$	$E°{}^c$ (V)	$\log k°_{het}{}^c$ (cm s^{-1})	$\Delta G_0^{\neq}$ (kcal mol^{-1})
PhSSPh	−1.65	0.432	0.430	−1.37	−4.22	10.7
PhSSMe	−1.97	0.398	0.373	−1.62	−4.45	11.1
PhSSBu	−2.19	0.366	0.356	−1.71	−5.20	12.1
MeSSMe	−2.43	0.350	0.337	−1.88	−5.45	12.6
BzSSBz	−2.36	0.393	0.380	−1.89	−5.39	12.3
t-BuSSBu-*t*	−2.72	0.376	0.374	−2.34	−4.53	11.2

$^a v = 0.2\,\mathrm{V\,s^{-1}}$. ^{b}Calculated from $\Delta E_{p/2}$. ^{c}Convolution, double-layer uncorrected data.
^{d}Calculated for $E_p - 0.5\Delta E_{p/2}$, where $E = E_p\,(0.2\,\mathrm{V\,s^{-1}})$.

Z factor (adiabatic ET, $Z_{het} = (k_B T/2\pi m)^{1/2}$), the intrinsic barriers $\Delta G_0^{\neq}$ were calculated from $k°_{het}$. It is worth noting that the $k°_{het}$ values are unusually low and $\Delta G_0^{\neq}$ values unusually large for the formation of radical anions.

Some literature reports, particularly on the reduction of PhSSPh on platinum or glassy carbon electrodes, have stressed the irreversible nature of the electrode process leading to the corresponding thiol anions.[168,170,173–175] A recent report, making use of a carbon-fiber ultramicroelectrode, describes the reduction of PhSSPh in MeCN to be reversible for $\nu > 1000\,V\,s^{-1}$.[198] Using double-potential step chronoamperometry, the lifetime of the radical anion was estimated to be 0.4 ms. An extensive study on the voltammetric reduction of diaryl disulfides, X-PhS-SPh-X where X = NH_2, OMe, H, F, Cl, CO_2Et, CN, and NO_2, was reported very recently.[65,162] As for dialkyl and alkyl-aryl disulfides, the voltammetric reduction is irreversible and the peak potential strongly depends on the substituent. As can be observed in Table 12, E_p spans more than 1 V. In the timescale domain employed ($\nu \leqslant 100\,V\,s^{-1}$), the electrode reduction is a two-electron process. For disulfides bearing electron-donating or moderately electron-withdrawing substituents, the peak width values at $0.2\,V\,s^{-1}$ correspond to α values in the range 0.37–0.43. For the disulfides with more electron-withdrawing substituents, the peaks become sharper and α increases accordingly. A similar trend can be observed analyzing the E_p shifts caused by the variation of the scan rate.

The value of α and the normalized peak currents $i_p/\nu^{-1/2}$ are scan rate dependent, pointing to a non-linear dependence of the heterogeneous ET kinetics on the applied potential. As in the case of aryl-alkyl and dialkyl disulfides described above, the kinetics of the heterogeneous ET was studied by convolution voltammetry. The results are also reported in Table 12, in

Table 12 Electrochemical, kinetic and thermodynamic parameters for the reduction of *para*-substituted diaryl disulfides $(XPhS)_2$.

X	$E_p^{\,a}$ (V)	$\alpha^{a,b}$	$\alpha^{c,d}$	$E°^{\,c}$ (V)	$\log k°_{het}^{\,c}$ (cm s^{-1})	$\Delta G_0^{\neq}$ (kcal mol^{-1})
NH_2	−1.86	0.422	0.410	−1.60	−3.95	10.3
OMe	−1.71	0.404	0.388	−1.38	−4.36	10.8
H	−1.65	0.434	0.430	−1.37	−4.22	10.7
F	−1.55	0.404	0.408	−1.27	−3.84	10.1
Cl	−1.43	0.367	0.410	−1.18	−3.73	10.0
CO_2Et	−1.23	0.508	0.482	−1.15	−2.69	8.5
CN	−1.15	0.438	0.471	−1.06	−2.60	8.4
NO_2	−0.79	0.737	0.727	−0.90	−0.80	5.9

$^a\nu = 0.2\,V\,s^{-1}$. ^{b}Calculated from $\Delta E_{p/2}$.
^{c}Convolution, double-layer uncorrected data.
^{d}Calculated for $E_p - 0.5\Delta E_{p/2}$ where $E = E_p$ $(0.2\,V\,s^{-1})$.

terms of $E°$, α and $k°_{het}$. Figure 14 shows that the logarithmic plots can be fitted by second-order regression ($r^2 = 0.995$–0.999), allowing extrapolation of reliable standard rate constants, $k°_{het}$, using the $E°$s determined through the α analysis. Again, the results were checked and optimized by reproducing the experimental curves using digital simulation in the entire scan-rate range investigated.

The values of the standard rate constants vary considerably along the series of disulfides, the $\log k°_{het}$ going from -0.80 for the nitro to -4.36 for the methoxy derivatives. Again, as observed for the other class of disulfides, most of them are unusually low for substrates undergoing a stepwise mechanism. By using the Eyring equation (4), the values of the intrinsic barriers $\Delta G_0^{\neq}$ reported in Table 12 were obtained.

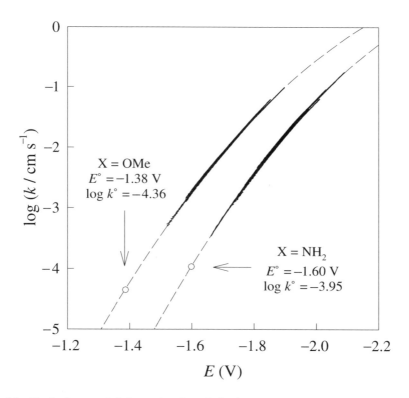

Fig. 14 Typical potential dependencies of the heterogeneous rate constant for the electroreduction of *para*-substituted diaryl disulfides in DMF/0.1 M TBAP. The dashed lines represent the parabolic fitting to the experimental data. The extrapolated standard potential and rate constant values (see text) are indicated.

Homogeneous reduction of disulfides

There have been some reports on the reduction of diaryl disulfides by solution electron donors in organic solvents. The reduction of a series of *para*-substituted diaryl disulfides was studied in tetrahydrofuran by generating the radical anion electron donors through metal reduction or flash photolysis.[172] For any given disulfide, the ET rate was found to increase, as expected, with a decrease of the donor $E°$. The results, however, were discussed on the basis of what we now know to be incorrect assumptions, such as $E°(PhSSPh) \sim -1.8\,V$, as measured from irreversible voltammetric curves, and intrinsic barriers of $\sim 2.3\,kcal/mol$, i.e. solvent-driven ET reactions. The ET data showed that the rate increases when the electron-withdrawing character of the substituent on the disulfide increases. A similar report was published on the homogeneous ET of a series of *para*-substituted diaryl disulfides.[171] Measurements were carried out in DMF by the homogeneous redox catalysis approach. The results allowed for some rough estimates of $E°$ values, providing some evidence that the direct electroreduction occurs at more negative potentials than $E°$. This work also showed, in particular, how direct electroreduction may be affected by the presence of even small amounts of electroactive impurities that can act as homogeneous donors.

A more recent and detailed investigation of the mediated ET to PhSSPh, MeSSMe and *t*-BuSSBu-*t* in DMF, led to results in agreement with the transient formation of the RSSR$^{•-}$ radical anion.[161] This was supported by thermochemical calculations, using BDE and standard potential estimates, showing that the stepwise mechanism was thermodynamically favored over the concerted pathway. The experimental data were analyzed, by using a linear dependence of the activated process on $\Delta G°$, to estimate the $E°$ for the formation of the PhSSPh radical anion $(-1.40\,V)$. The same analysis estimated the cleavage rate constant to be around $10^8\,s^{-1}$, which would correspond to a lifetime that is shorter by at least a factor 10^4 than is observed by other electrochemical means.[198] The experimental reorganization energy of PhSSPh was found to be significantly larger than that attributable to solvent reorganization. Although the absence of a counter-diffusion region did not allow for the determination of the intrinsic barrier for the other two dialkyl disulfides, the data were in agreement with an even larger value than that of PhSSPh.

A more recent investigation has been carried out on the homogeneous ET to an extended series of diaryl disulfides $(X = NH_2, OMe, H, F, CO_2Et, CN, NO_2)$ in DMF.[65,162] The redox catalysis approach was applied extensively. The mechanism of the homogeneous reaction between electrogenerated radical anion donors $D^{•-}$ and $(ArS)_2$ takes place according to the sequence (equations 80–83):

$$D + e \rightleftharpoons D^{•-} \qquad (80)$$

$$D^{\bullet-} + (ArS)_2 \underset{}{\overset{k_{\text{hom}}}{\rightleftharpoons}} D + (ArS)_2^{\bullet-} \tag{81}$$

$$(ArS)_2^{\bullet-} \rightleftharpoons ArS^{\bullet} + ArS^- \tag{82}$$

$$D^{\bullet-} + ArS^{\bullet} \longrightarrow D + ArS^- \tag{83}$$

According to the above scheme outlined by equations (80)–(83), the rate constant k_{hom} may be expressed as shown in equation (84).

$$\frac{1}{k_{\text{hom}}} = \frac{1}{k_{\text{d}}} + \frac{1}{k^{\circ}{}_{\text{hom}} \exp[(\alpha_{\text{hom}} F/RT)(E^{\circ} - E^{\circ}{}_{\text{D}})]}$$

$$+ \left(\frac{1}{k_{\text{d}}} + \frac{1}{Z_{\text{hom}}} \right) \frac{1}{\exp[(F/RT)(E^{\circ} - E^{\circ}{}_{\text{D}})]} \tag{84}$$

The parameter k_{d} is the diffusion-controlled rate constant in DMF ($\approx 10^{10}\,\text{M}^{-1}\,\text{s}^{-1}$), Z_{hom} is the collision frequency ($= 3 \times 10^{11}\,\text{M}^{-1}\,\text{s}^{-1}$), α_{hom} is the homogeneous transfer coefficient and E° is the standard potential of the disulfide. The best fit values of E°, $k^{\circ}{}_{\text{hom}}$, and α_{hom} from equation (84) are reported in Table 13.

Table 13 Electrochemical, kinetic and thermodynamic parameters for the homogeneous reduction of *para*-substituted diaryl disulfides (XPhS)$_2$.

X	$E^{\circ}{}_{\text{hom}}$ (V)	α_{hom}	$\log k^{\circ}{}_{\text{hom}}$ (M^{-1} s^{-1})
NH$_2$	−1.52	0.52	4.59
OMe	−1.42	0.52	3.79
H	−1.40	0.47	4.28
F	−1.31	0.52	4.55
CO$_2$Et	−1.23	0.58	5.74
CN	−1.14		5.77
NO$_2$	−0.90		

The intrinsic barrier for disulfide reduction

Intrinsic barriers define the intrinsic velocity by which an ET (or any other reaction) proceeds. Although they are tailored to the particular acceptor considered, chemical intuition suggests that if the main reaction site is kept constant, e.g. the S–S bond, the intrinsic ET rate should be some function of the substituents at the atoms of concern. Let us consider first the data pertaining to the heterogeneous and homogeneous reduction of diaryl disulfides.[65,162] Although some of the reduction features change with X (see below) for all compounds, the apparent α values, measured by voltammetry or convolution, are consistent with a stepwise dissociative ET, where for most compounds the initial ET is rate controlling. In fact, there is enough information (coming from the reduction of different classes of compounds) to believe that when α is larger than 0.35–0.4 the mechanism is stepwise. As discussed above, theoretical calculations and other information agree with this conclusion. As further mechanistic support, the heterogeneous experimental $E°$s can be compared to those estimated for a concerted mechanism, using equation (41). The corresponding values of $E°_{AB/A•,B^-}$[162] are shown in Table 14, together with other relevant data. The experimental $E°$ values are more positive than the corresponding $E°_{AB/A•,B^-}$ by 0.22–0.36 V (remember, the peak potential for a concerted process is much more negative than the corresponding $E°$ value). Moreover, as discussed in particular in Section 3, a stepwise process is always associated with a lower activation barrier than the concerted ET and thus it is favored on a kinetic basis.

The theoretical prediction and the experimental observation of the weakening of the S—S bond upon radical anion formation are in satisfactory agreement (Table 14). These data give strong support to the suggestion that the mechanism is stepwise, the cleavage being endergonic. Significant differences between theory and experiment arise when the fragmentation of the radical anion cannot be simply described by a Morse curve, as for the nitro compound. On the other hand, calculations refer to the gas phase. In solution, the BDE value should decrease, as shown with PhSSPh•– (Table 9).

Table 14 Thermodynamic results for the reduction of X-PhS-S-Ph-X.

X	$E°_{het}$ (V)	$E°_{AB/A•,B^-}$[a] (V)	ΔBDE_{theo}[b] (kcal mol^{-1})	ΔBDE[c] (kcal mol^{-1})	$\Delta G°_{AB•-}$[c] (kcal mol^{-1})
NH$_2$	−1.60	−1.91	34.1	29.1	7.1
OMe	−1.38	−1.70		30.2	7.4
H	−1.37	−1.60	31.8	33.2	5.3
F	−1.27	−1.56	31.5	32.1	6.7
Cl	−1.18	−1.49		32.1	7.2
CO$_2$Et	−1.15	−1.37		35.1	5.0
CN	−1.06	−1.30	43.4	35.3	5.5
NO$_2$	−0.90	−1.26	55.5	33.0	8.2

[a]Concerted ET standard potential (equation 41).
[b]From the calculated gas phase values of neutral and disulfide.
[c]From equation (42).

By using the electrochemical $E°$ estimates and the experimental activation-potential relationship, the values of $k°_{het}$, were derived (Table 12). Figure 15 illustrates $\log k°_{het}$ values as a function of the Hammett σ and shows that the heterogeneous kinetics for reduction of disulfides is, as a rule, very sluggish. However, when the electron-withdrawing properties of the aryl substituent are enhanced and thus when the reduction becomes more facile on a thermodynamic ground, the $k°_{het}$ value increases significantly. In fact, the $k°_{het}$ value of the nitro derivative is of the same order as that for ET to common non-dissociative organic compounds. The $E°$ values compare well, within 0–80 mV, to those estimated by homogeneous redox catalysis. Similar agreement is found between $\log k°_{het}$ and $\log k°_{hom}$, the linear relationship being $\log k_{het} = -8.14 + 0.95 \log k_{hom}$ ($r^2 = 0.971$); the unit slope is particularly significant.

The reduction data indicate that the intrinsic barrier (heterogeneous or homogeneous) is very large when the orbital hosting the unpaired electron

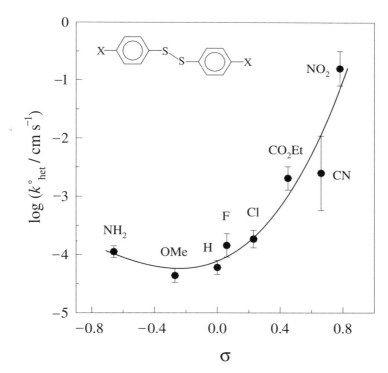

Fig. 15 Hammett plot of the logarithm of the heterogeneous ET rate constant for the electroreduction of diaryl disulfides in DMF. The solid line illustrates the experimental trend.

is localized close to the S—S bond and that substituents may significantly influence the stepwise dissociative ET mechanism by changing the nature of the LUMO. This conclusion is also supported by theoretical calculations. The reduction of alkyl disulfides is analogous, although here the reorganization energies are even larger. The data indicate that the reduction of disulfides proceeds by a mechanism involving the formation of σ^* radical anions, having apparent BDFEs of *ca.* 5–8 kcal mol^{-1} range. In contrast to the stepwise reduction of ethers described in Section 3, the significant bond lengthening upon ET to disulfides leads to a significant inner reorganization and, consequently, slow kinetics. In fact, unlike "normal" stepwise reactions, in which the inner intrinsic barrier is in the order of 20–30% of the overall intrinsic barrier, the inner intrinsic barrier associated with the reduction of disulfides is in the order of 70–75% of the total. A similar result is found with the dialkyl and alkyl aryl disulfides. The results for the diaryl disulfides are consistent with a gradual change in the ET mechanism along the disulfide series. This is illustrated in Fig. 16, which shows how the inner reorganization energy associated with the reduction increases when the electron-donating properties of R increase. This points to a transition between the "classical" stepwise pathway and a borderline stepwise mechanism, which is, however, still distinct from the purely concerted process.

Finally, the follow-up cleavage can be described as changing from a simple decay, where the unpaired electron is mostly located at the fragmentation site, to an intramolecular ET that now occurs from the aryl-substituent system to the S—S σ^* orbital, particularly with the nitro-substituted compound. The observed change in the ET rate would thus monitor a change in the overall ET-bond fragmentation mechanism.

REDUCTION OF SULFIDES

The dissociative reduction of sulfides proceeds through a two-electron mechanism in which C—S bond cleavage takes place. Most of the work on these processes has been carried out on benzyl aryl sulfides having the general formula RSAr (R = PhCH$_2$, Ph$_2$CH, Ph$_3$C; Ar = *para*-substituted phenyl). These compounds have provided a significant amount of information on stepwise dissociative reductions, particularly on the bond cleavage in radical anions and the effect of substitution on the dynamics of radical anion formation and fragmentation. As a rule, the reduction (heterogeneous or homogeneous) can be described by the two-electron stepwise process described by equations (85)–(87) and the overall stoichiometry given in equation (88).

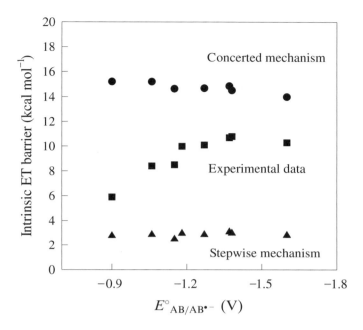

Fig. 16 Comparison between experimental (■) and calculated (●: concerted dissociative ET; ▲: stepwise dissociative ET) intrinsic ET barriers for the reduction of *para*-substituted diaryl disulfides in DMF/0.1 M TBAP. The data are reported as a function of the corresponding standard potentials.

$$R\text{-}SAr + e \rightleftharpoons R\text{-}SAr^{\bullet-} \tag{85}$$

$$R\text{-}SAr^{\bullet-} \rightleftharpoons R^{\bullet} + ArS^{-} \tag{86}$$

$$R^{\bullet} + e \longrightarrow R^{-} \tag{87}$$

$$R\text{-}SAr + 2e \longrightarrow ArS^{-} + R^{-} \tag{88}$$

The reduction scheme (equations 85–88) may be complicated by other reactions induced by the initial ET. The most important of these is the self-protonation, a reaction between an electrogenerated species and the starting material. Self-protonation is the most common case of the so-called father–son reactions.[62,86] This type of reaction has been characterized both theoretically and experimentally for the case of an initial slow ET by Vianello and co-workers in a study concerning the reduction of $Ph_2CH\text{-}SPh$, as shown in equation (89).[63]

$$Ph_2CH\text{-}SPh + Ph_2CH^{-} \longrightarrow {}^{-}Ph_2C\text{-}SPh + Ph_2CH_2 \tag{89}$$

This reaction, which has a rate constant of $5 \times 10^4 \, M^{-1} \, s^{-1}$ and thus affects the voltammetric pattern for $v < 50 \, V \, s^{-1}$, can be inhibited by addition of an acid. The acid must be strong enough to trap the electrogenerated carbanion without affecting the lifetime of the radical anion. Acid addition leads to an increase of the peak current, which is now governed by the "uncomplicated" two-electron stoichiometry (equation 88). Other reactions may be triggered by the electrogenerated carbanion. One such example, found by studying the reduction of $Ph_3CSPhCN$ in formally aprotic DMF, is due to the formation of OH^- through protonation of the benzyl-type carbanion by residual water.[88] The OH^- then causes a base-catalyzed decomposition of the aryl cyano group in the starting material, with formation of the corresponding amide. As in the self-protonation case, a suitable acid was added which was able to protonate the carbanion but not the radical anion. In general, these chemical complications cause an increase of the rate of the electro-induced decomposition of the starting material. This may affect both the characterization of the heterogeneous ET kinetics and the determination of the radical anion lifetime. For example, as will be seen below, some interesting data were published on the fragmentation of nitro-substituted diphenylmethyl aryl sulfides.[105] Based on the above discussion, however, these data should be treated cautiously because they may be affected by self-protonation complications, as already shown.[62,199]

The data on the dissociative ET to sulfides provide complementary information to those described in the previous section on disulfides. Specifically, they provide: (i) further evidence of the large intrinsic barrier affecting the reductive cleavage of sulfur-containing σ bonds; (ii) evidence of a smooth transition between the stepwise and concerted dissociative ET mechanisms; (iii) data illustrating the effect of the substitution on the cleavage rate in the radical anion; and (iv) the effect of the cleavage mechanism on the cleavage rate.

The electrochemical reduction of sulfides in dipolar aprotic solvents (most of the data obtained is in DMF) is scarcely affected by the electrode material and essentially the same features are observed at mercury, platinum, or glassy carbon electrodes. The process is irreversible and the initial ET (equation 85) is usually rate determining, except for those sulfides containing a 4-nitrophenyl group, in which the ET step is electrochemically fast (i.e. $k^{\circ}_{het} > 0.1 \, cm/s$). In general, the values of the transfer coefficient α are in the 0.4–0.55 range at low scan rate, which suggests that the experimental peak potential is within 100–200 mV from the standard potential value. Both the heterogeneous and the homogeneous reductions have been studied in detail with a series of related phenyl sulfides, $PhCH_2$-SPh,[158] Ph_2CH-SPh,[62] and Ph_3C-SPh.[153] The most detailed investigation was carried out on the reduction of Ph_3C-$SPhCN$ in DMF.[159] Further homogeneous redox catalysis data were reported for Ph_3C-$SPhX$, with $X = OMe$, H, COMe,[154] and Cl.[160] EPR, voltammetric, and/or homogeneous redox catalysis data on the reduction of nitro-substituted sulfides were also reported.[105,199–201]

The reduction data of substituted triphenylmethyl arylsulfides will be considered first. The reduction of the unsubstituted sulfide was investigated in detail both heterogeneously and homogeneously.[153,200] The voltammetric reduction at Hg exemplifies the typical behavior of triphenylmethyl arylsulfides: a two-electron irreversible peak at quite negative potentials (-2.25 V at $1\,\mathrm{V\,s^{-1}}$) having a rather large width ($\Delta E_{p/2} = 110\,\mathrm{mV}$, $\alpha = 0.43$). On the positive scan the reversible oxidation of Ph_3C^- ($E^\circ = -1.10$ V) could be observed in carefully dried DMF.[201] The homogeneous reduction was studied by the redox catalysis approach. As in the heterogeneous reduction, whose standard rate constant is $4.5 \times 10^{-3}\,\mathrm{cm\,s^{-1}}$, the initial ET is rate determining. The data are consistent with a very fast bond cleavage, the rate constant being $8 \times 10^{11}\,\mathrm{s^{-1}}$. No real counter-diffusion region was evident. Instead, the data were in agreement with the pattern expected[40] for a transition from stepwise to concerted dissociative ETs when the driving force decreases by using less powerful reductants (i.e. donors with a more positive E°). The intrinsic barrier for the solution ET was calculated, from the experimental data, to be 6.2 kcal/mol, although more recent data indicate that the value could be as large as 10.1 kcal/mol.[154] By correcting for the donor contribution (3.3 kcal/mol: see below) and for the self-exchange solvent intrinsic barrier of the sulfide (3.5 kcal/mol[159]), a rather large inner intrinsic barrier of 2.8–6.7 kcal/mol is derived. Analogously, the heterogeneous rate constant may be used, together with the Eyring equation (adiabatic ET, $Z_{\mathrm{het}} = (k_B T/2\pi m)^{1/2}$), to estimate an intrinsic barrier of 8.0 kcal/mol. By extracting the solvent contribution (using the method described in reference 59), the inner intrinsic barrier is found to be 3.9 kcal/mol, in agreement with the homogeneous estimates. These inner intrinsic barriers are well outside experimental error and can be attributed to a significant elongation of the C—S bond in the formation of the radical anion, analogous to the disulfides.

More recent data were collected on the reduction of triphenylmethyl sulfides having the formula Ph_3C-SPhX. The data pertains to X = CN,[159] Cl,[160] OMe, H, and COMe.[154] The voltammetric pattern is similar to that of the unsubstituted compound.[164] The homogeneous reduction of each compound provided curved $\log k_{\mathrm{hom}}$ vs. $E^\circ_{\mathrm{D/D}}$•- plots in the activation-controlled zone. The relevant data are collected in Table 15.

The standard potentials for the formation of the radical anion, $E^\circ_{\mathrm{AB/AB}}$•-, are too scattered to provide useful information and indeed some work in this direction is currently underway.[164] However, it is interesting to observe that these $E^\circ_{\mathrm{AB/AB}}$•- values are often close to those estimated for the concerted process, $E^\circ_{\mathrm{AB/A}}$•,B-. This would suggest that, at least on thermodynamic grounds, the two ET mechanisms can compete. On the other hand, the stepwise pathway is kinetically favored over the concerted reaction, even

F. MARAN, D.D.M. WAYNER AND M.S. WORKENTIN

Table 15 Dissociative ET data for the homogeneous reduction of triphenylmethyl aryl sulfides.[a]

X	$E°_{AB/AB·^-}$ [b] (V)	$E°_{AB/A·,B^-}$ [c] (V)	$\Delta G_0^{\neq}$ [d] (kcal mol⁻¹)	$\Delta G_{0,i}^{\neq}$ [e] (kcal mol⁻¹)	$\Delta G_{AB·^-}$ [c] (kcal/mol)	log k_{frag} (s⁻¹)
OMe	-1.77^f	-1.83	10.8	7.4	1.4	n.d.[g]
H	-2.16^h	-1.69	6.2	2.8	-11.5	11.9
	-1.75^f		10.1	6.7		
Cl	-1.87^i	-1.55	7.9	4.5	-7.4	> 8.30
COMe	-1.58^f	-1.38^j	8.5	5.1	-4.6	9.30
CN	-1.72^k	-1.29	6.7	3.3	-9.9	8.08
NO$_2$	-1.00^l	-1.23	n.d.[g]	n.d.[g]	5.3	5.6

[a]Data were obtained in DMF/0.1 M TBAP at 25°C[153,159,160] or in DMF/0.1 M TBABF$_4$ at 22°C.[154]
[b]From best fitting of the redox catalysis data.
[c]From the $E°_{RS·/RS^-}$ data of Table 8, BDFE$_{C-S}$ = 49.2–8.5 kcal/mol,[89,154] and equations (41) and (42).
[d]Intrinsic barrier for the solution ET.
[e]Inner reorganization barrier of a single sulfide molecule, using 3.5 kcal/mol for the sulfide self-exchange solvent reorganization barrier[159] and 3.3 kcal/mol for the donor self-exchange intrinsic barrier (see text).
[f]Reference 154. [g]Not determined. [h]Reference 153. [i]Reference 160.
[j]$E°_{RS·/RS^-}$ = 0.38 V, from $E°_{RS·/RS^-}$ = 0.076 + 0.604σ (see text).
[k]Reference 159.
[l]Reference 201.

when the stepwise mechanism involves an unusually large intrinsic barrier. The $\Delta G_0^{\neq}$ data refer to the average activation energy for ET to the sulfide by an aromatic radical anion donor. Based on the Marcus cross-relationship, we can extract the solvation contribution of both the donor and the sulfide from the total intrinsic barrier by adopting an average value of 3.3 kcal/mol for the aromatic radical anions donors[90,202,203] and 3.5 kcal/mol for the sulfide. This then allows the inner intrinsic barrier contribution pertaining to a single sulfide molecule, $\Delta G_{0,I}^{\neq}$ to be estimated (Table 15). The values are rather large, as a rule larger than the solvent reorganization term. This points to significant C—S bond elongation. Moreover, a definite substituent effect emerges: an increase of the electron-withdrawing character leads to a decrease of the inner reorganization. This contribution essentially disappears when X = NO$_2$.

The cleavage rate tends to decrease when the substituent helps to accommodate the unpaired electron by lowering the π^* orbital energy. However, the cleavage rate constants are, in general, very large, pointing to transient formation of radical anions in very shallow energy minima. Indeed, it appears that the ET to the OMe and H derivatives may be essentially concerted.[153,154] The $\Delta G_0^{\neq}$ data may be compared with the average intrinsic barrier expected for a concerted dissociative process to the sulfides. A value of 15.7 kcal mol^{-1}

was obtained by using the above donor and solvent reorganization values and 49.2 kcal mol^{-1} for the BDE of the sulfide (assumed to be essentially substituent independent).[154] The experimental barriers of Table 15 are smaller than the concerted value and thus it seems that we are facing either another case of "almost-concerted" stepwise ETs or the effect of ion–dipole interactions between the fragmented species in the solvent cage, which decrease the barrier as observed with benzyl halides.[26–28] At present, there are not enough data to sort out this issue. However, we tend to favor the first hypothesis because the latter effect should not be relevant for the two sulfides discussed here.

Going back to the inner reorganization energy, there is other heterogeneous data indicating that C—S bond elongation plays an important role as a factor slowing down the ET rate. A careful study of the kinetics of the heterogeneous reduction of the CN derivative was carried out, using convolution analysis and double-layer correction.[159] These results are particularly relevant because they provide the first example of a stepwise dissociative ET where excellent agreement exists between heterogeneous and homogeneous ET data obeying the Marcus equation. In fact, the convolution analysis provided identical $E^{\circ}_{AB/AB^{\bullet-}}$ (−1.72 V) calculated independently through best fitting of the homogeneous rate data. The electrode reduction at the Hg electrode gave an intrinsic barrier of 6.1 kcal mol^{-1} leading to an inner intrinsic barrier of $ca.$ 2.5 kcal mol^{-1} for the heterogeneous reduction. The heterogeneous reduction of the p-chloro derivative gave a double-layer corrected inner reorganization energy of 7.7 kcal/mol (Hg electrode), leading to an estimated inner reorganization barrier of $ca.$ 4 kcal/mol. The corresponding double-layer uncorrected result is $ca.$ 5 kcal/mol.[160]

The effect of the substitution on the benzyl side has been tested by comparing the data for the dissociative ET with the series PhCH$_2$-SPh,[158] Ph$_2$CH-SPh,[62] and Ph$_3$C-SPh.[153] The heterogeneous data (Hg electrode) indicate that more reorganization is involved when increasing the number of phenyl groups. The α values are 0.51, 0.47, and 0.43 and the $\log k^{\circ}_{het}$(cm s^{-1}) and $\Delta G_0^{\neq}$ (kcal mol^{-1}) values are −1.79 and 7.4, −2.08 and 7.7, and −2.35 and 8.0, respectively. In practice, the initial ET is rate determining for Ph$_3$C-SPh but some mixed ET/bond cleavage kinetic control characterizes the reduction of PhCH$_2$SPh and Ph$_2$CHSPh. It is interesting to observe that the corresponding electroreduction of PhSPh is controlled at low scan rate only by the cleavage rate.[94] The same intrinsic barrier trend comes from the homogeneous catalysis data, the intrinsic barriers now being 7.5, 8.5, and 10.1 kcal mol^{-1}.[62,154,158]

The cleavage rate seems to increase very rapidly in the same order (1.7×10^8, 5×10^8, and 8×10^{11} s^{-1}) in agreement with the electrode kinetic data. The error, however, is too large to safely rely on such a comparison, also considering some other results reported very recently on the reduction of Ph$_3$CSPh.[154] The cleavage rate constant of the radical anion of PhSPh

($E° = -2.73$ V) is much smaller, being $6 \times 10^6 \, \text{s}^{-1}$.[94] This is because the
C(aryl)S—bond (78 kcal mol^{-1}) is much stronger than the C(alkyl)S—bond
(e.g. 49.2 kcal mol^{-1} in Ph$_3$C-SPh). Assuming the role constant of the
backward reaction (to form the radical anion) is in the range
10^9–10^{10} M^{-1} s^{-1}, the free energy of the cleavage can be estimated to be
3.1–4.4 kcal mol^{-1}. This is in excellent agreement with the 4.9 kcal mol^{-1}
value that is obtained by using equation (40) together with an entropy correction of 8.5 kcal mol^{-1},[89] and $E°_{\text{PhS}^•/\text{PhS}^-} = 0.07$ V (Table 8).

The data pertaining to the corresponding *para*-nitro derivatives
(PhCH$_2$SC$_6$H$_4$NO$_2$, Ph$_2$CHSC$_6$H$_4$NO$_2$, and Ph$_3$CSC$_6$H$_4$NO$_2$) provide supple-
mentary information.[85,199–201] The $E°$s are only slightly dependent on the R
substituent of RSC$_6$H$_4$NO$_2$, being -1.09, -1.06, -1.03, and -1.00 V for
R = CH$_3$, PhCH$_2$, Ph$_2$CH, and Ph$_3$C, respectively. This indicates that a π^*
radical anion, localized on the nitro group forms. This is reinforced by similar
EPR data recorded for the various radical anions, including the diradical
dianion (4-O$_2$NC$_6$H$_4$S)$^{2-}$ (see ref. 199). This, together with the high
heterogeneous ET rates typical of the formation of radical anions with little
reorganization energy ($k°_{\text{het}} > 0.1 \, \text{cm s}^{-1}$), indicates that the C—S bond
length is essentially unaffected by the one-electron reduction. On the other
hand, the effect of the substitution on the fragmentation rate is dramatic,
which increases roughly by a factor of $10^4 \, \text{s}^{-1}$/Ph unit when going from
R = Me to R = Ph$_3$C,[85] the values being $\sim 10^{-7}$, 1.75×10^{-3}, 1.5×10^1 and
$4.1 \times 10^5 \, \text{s}^{-1}$. This cannot be rationalized in terms of different stabilization of
the starting radical anions, since the standard potentials of the three benzyl
aryl sulfides are within 60 mV (1.4 kcal mol^{-1}) of each other. On the other
hand, the fragment anion NO$_2$PhS$^-$, $E° = 0.53$ V,[162] is constant across the
series. Thus, the reactions are controlled either by the relative energy of
the radical fragment, R$^•$, and/or the intrinsic barriers. Since there is no reason
to expect that the intrinsic barriers should be significantly different, the
relative kinetics must be related to the energy of the radical products
implying that the change in the C—S bond energy of the neutral molecule
changes more dramatically than expected for the corresponding C—H bonds
in the hydrocarbons.[204] Obviously, more work is needed to understand these
reactions; in particular, careful measurement of the C—S bond energy in the
neutral molecule are required.

A similar study of the kinetics of fragmentation of $^{-•}$ArCR$_2$SPh and
PhCR$_2$SAr$^{-•}$ (Ar = 4-nitrophenyl) has been recently reported.[105] Similar to
the observations in the cleavage of ether radical anions,[82,84] it was found that
the heterolytic pathway is preferred (although the energetic preference is not
as pronounced). In this case, the $\Delta G^{\neq}$ was estimated to be 3 kcal mol^{-1} larger
for the fragmentation of PhCR$_2$SAr$^{-•}$ compared with $^{-•}$ArCR$_2$SPh. It was
suggested that the difference between the two modes of fragmentation
might be due to differences in the extent of charge delocalization in the
corresponding transition states. The transition states for the fragmentation

of $ArCR_2SPh^{-\bullet}$ have the negative charge extensively delocalized, while those for $PhCR_2SAr^{-\bullet}$ are limited to the 4-nitrothiophenyl moiety. In essence, the difference was attributed to an electronic coupling effect at the transition state, not an intrinsically higher $\Delta G^{\neq}$ as suggested in Section 3. This reasoning has some interesting implications. As mentioned in Section 3, it was argued, from a study of the heterolytic fragmentation of anion radicals of a large number of α -substituted acetophenones, that the solvent reorganization is the major contributor to the intrinsic barrier with bond stretching at the transition state playing only a minor role.[97] Solvent reorganization can only play a role if the charge distribution changes from reactants to transition state. Consequently, a change from a localized charge structure in reactants to a highly delocalized transition state (as suggested for $^{-\bullet}ArCR_2SPh$) should result in a larger intrinsic barrier compared with a reaction in which the charge does not move on going from reactants to transition state (as suggested for $PhCR_2SAr^{-\bullet}$). It is not possible to resolve this issue at this time. An obvious approach would be to study the fragmentation reactions in the gas phase where limitations due to solvent reorganization but not to electronic or structural reorganization are removed. If the simple valence bond model in Scheme 5 is correct, then the relative intrinsic barriers for homolysis versus heterolysis will be unchanged.

5 Concluding remarks

The study of the dissociative reduction of ethers, thioethers, peroxides and disulfides provides new insights into the stepwise and concerted mechanisms and reinforces some established concepts. While much of our understanding comes from studies using conventional electrochemical approaches, such as cyclic voltammetry and homogeneous redox catalysis, convolution voltammetry is particularly useful for the evaluation of the rate of heterogeneous electron transfer and the transfer coefficient over a wide range of driving forces. The combination of electrochemical data with other kinetic or thermodynamic approaches provides independent confirmation of the kinetic and thermodynamic data and allows the kinetic window to be extended both for highly exergonic and highly endergonic processes.

Results from the dissociative reduction of aryl ethers led to a number of important generalizations. These are classical stepwise systems initially forming π^*-type radical anions. In this case, the intrinsic barriers for the formation of the intermediate radical anions are dominated by solvent reorganization with only a small (sometimes negligible) contribution from internal reorganization. Thus, the ETs to these systems are properly described by Marcus theory, in which the harmonic approximation satisfactorily accounts for both outer and inner reorganization factors. On the other hand, the radical anion cleavage requires bond elongation and solvent reorganization. The inner contribution may be particularly large for these compounds. Another trend that emerges is that the magnitude of the intrinsic barrier for the fragmentation depends on whether the process is a formal homolysis or heterolysis. There is evidence to support the suggestion that for processes with similar driving forces the heterolysis pathway is preferred. This preference can be rationalized in the context of valence bond configuration mixing theory or in terms of increased electronic coupling at the transition state. More work is necessary to evaluate the generality of this trend. In addition, there is compelling evidence that the electronic configuration of the singly occupied molecular orbital plays the dominant role in determining the fragmentation kinetics, reinforcing the idea that there must be good overlap between this orbital (SOMO) and the σ^* orbital of the scissile bond. Finally, care must be taken to ensure that the kinetics are in the activation region in the assessment of intrinsic barriers. Depending on the magnitude of the intrinsic barrier, it is possible that even thermoneutral processes can be kinetically limited by escape of the fragments from the solvent cage.

In contrast to "normal" stepwise processes, a large and often dominant inner intrinsic barrier characterizes the dissociative ET to sulfides and disulfides. In these systems significant S—C or S—S bond lengthening accompanies the ET, accounting for up to two-thirds of the overall intrinsic barrier. Under these conditions, the ET cannot be described within the Marcus Model. Instead, Morse curves must be used for both AB and AB$^{\bullet-}$, as described in detail very recently.[163,165,166] Previously, it was assumed that the shape factor (β) was the same for AB and AB$^{\bullet-}$.[104] This, however, is not a reasonable assumption for systems undergoing major structural modifications. In fact, data suggest (see Section 4) that, in addition to the BDE, the force constant and the shape factor also decrease upon radical anion formation. The relationship between force constant and BDE has been discussed by Zavitsas.[197] Neglecting this aspect results in a significant error in the calculation of the inner contribution to the intrinsic barrier. For these loose radical anions, the cleavage step is thus governed by a small intrinsic barrier, although the process is often endergonic in particular with disulfides. The practical consequence is the observation of transfer coefficients that are significantly less than 0.5 and that are at times less than 0.4. Thus, an α value less than 0.4 is a necessary, but not sufficient, criterion to distinguish stepwise from concerted ET processes.

As an aside, it should be noted that a large intrinsic ET barrier does not necessarily imply an increase of the bond length upon radical anion formation. A substantial angle deformation also may contribute to the internal intrinsic barrier, $\Delta G_{0,i}^{\neq}$. This was shown in the case of the stepwise dissociative oxidation of oxalate ($^-O_2C\text{-}CO_2^- \longrightarrow {}^-O_2C\text{-}CO_2^{\bullet} + e \longrightarrow CO_2 + CO_2^{-\bullet}$), where the data suggest that the oxalate undergoes a substantial increase of the O-C-O angle upon formation of the OCO$^\bullet$ moiety.[66] Analogous additional reorganization terms may show up in concerted dissociative reductions.

Peroxides and endoperoxides in many ways behave as classical concerted dissociative systems. In fact, because of the low O–O bond energies, and thus low intrinsic barriers, studies of the kinetics of ET in these systems provide the best examples to date of the parabolic activation driving force relationships. Interestingly, the adiabatic model for dissociative ET that holds for alkyl halides does not suitably describe the kinetics for dissociative ET of O–O bonds. The data for ET to peroxides and endoperoxides can only be adequately explained if one considers the ET as non-adiabatic. Intrinsic barriers for endoperoxides are not as low as one might expect because of the very low O–O BDE, and this may be the result of other internal reorganization energy contributions associated with the formation of the distonic radical anion. The dissociative ET of the O–O bonds of perbenzoates nicely illustrates a transition between the classical concerted and stepwise processes and shows that strongly exergonic cleavages may be not barrierless.

This question of the transition from the stepwise to the concerted process continues to challenge the experimentalist. The energy diagrams in Fig. 2, as presented by Savéant and others in this area, represent the classic situation in which a π^* anion radical interacts with the surfaces for the neutral A-B and the dissociative surfaces (i.e. three interacting surfaces). The transition is then the point at which the surface for the π^* anion radical penetrates through, and then below, the avoided crossing between the neutral and dissociative curves. For σ^* radical anions it is possible to consider a transition from stepwise to concerted in which only two surfaces are required. In this case the bond length in the radical anion becomes progressively longer (and weaker) towards the dissociative limit. The electronic nature of this transition is largely unexplored. In addition, a very weakly bonded σ^* radical anion would not be distinguishable from an anion/radical complex such as that described in Section 1. In both cases, the ET kinetics will be faster than expected for a purely concerted dissociative ET, but much slower than a classical stepwise ET mechanism.

The interest in ET reactions[205] and subsequent reactions of radical anions[104,206,207] continues to increase. Over the past few years several accounts or reviews focused in detail (but sometimes from quite different perspectives) on the problem of dissociative ET.[10,11,15,16,148,208,209] Various theoretical models and theories have also been proposed to describe the concerted dissociative ET in its adiabatic or non-adiabatic and homogeneous or heterogeneous aspects.[12,13,149,210–212] Some unexplored areas still remain. One is the intramolecular dissociative ETs through well-defined rigid spacers of the D-Sp-A type, in which an electron donor (D) and electron acceptor (A) are separated by a saturated spacer (Sp) capable of keeping the exchanging centers at distances longer than a couple of sigma bonds.

Although these ETs have been the subject of several studies employing stable acceptors,[213,214] little is known pertaining to dissociative-type acceptors[64,102,150] despite the relevance of peroxides and especially disulfides in biological systems. Well-defined intramolecular systems should provide insights into the distance and stereochemical dependences. The problem of homolytic versus heterolytic is still far from settled and must be addressed with more rigorous theoretical models and experimental data.

There are other areas in which dissociative ETs may make an impact. One area still to be explored is the possible application of these radical-forming processes in surface physics and chemistry, in particular as a way to modify surfaces.[215,216] Almost nothing is known of the problem of concerted vs. stepwise dissociative ETs in both oxidative processes[66,217] and organometallic chemistry.[218,219] The activation driving force relationships for those concerted mechanisms in which there are weak interactions between the fragments in the cage, as found with benzyl chlorides and bromides[26-28] must be better understood in order to better define how one can detect a transition between the two classical mechanisms. Analogously, the transition between dissociative ET and S_N2 needs to be better defined, also in view of very recent theoretical treatments.[220,221] Significant progress has been made in our understanding of dissociative ET reactions over the last five years. With increasing interest in the area, we hope that some of the key challenges outlined in this review will be addressed in the coming years.

References

1. Chanon, M., Rajzmann, M. and Chanon, F. (1990). *Tetrahedron* **46**, 6193
2. Hush, N.S. (1957). *Elektrochem.* **61**, 734
3. Eberson, L. (1963). *Acta Chem. Scand.* **17**, 2004
4. Eberson, L. (1982). *Acta Chem. Scand.* **B36,** 533
5. Eberson, L. (1982). *Chem. Scri.* **20**, 29
6. Eberson, L. (1987). *Electron Transfer Reactions in Organic Chemistry*. Springer-Verlag, Heidelberg
7. Marcus, R.A. (1956). *J. Chem. Phys.* **24**, 966.
8. Marcus, R.A. (1977). In *Special Topics in Electrochemistry*, Rock, P.A. (ed.), pp. 161. Elsevier, New York
9. Marcus, R.A. and Sutin, N. (1985). *Biochem. Biophys. Acta* **811**, 265
10. Hush, N.S. (1999). *J. Electronal. Chem.* **460**, 5
11. Eberson, L. (1999). *Acta Chem. Scand.* **53**, 751
12. Savéant, J.-M. (1987). *J. Am. Chem. Soc.* **109**, 6788
13. German, E.D. and Kuznetsov, A.M. (1994). *J. Phys. Chem.* **98**, 6120
14. Marcus, R.A. (1998). *Acta Chem. Scand.* **52**, 858
15. Savéant, J.-M. (1994). In *Advances in Electron Transfer Chemistry*, Mariano, P.S. (ed.), vol. 4, p. 53. JAI Press, Greenwich, CT
16. Savéant, J.-M. (2000). In *Advances in Physical Organic Chemistry*, Manuscript in preparation
17. Steelhammer, J.C. and Wentworth, W.E. (1969). *J. Chem. Phys.* **51**, 1802

18. Wentworth, W.E., Becker, R.S. and Tung, R. (1967). *J. Phys. Chem.* **71**, 1652
19. Wentworth, W.E., George, R. and Keith, H. (1969). *J. Chem. Phys.* **51**, 1791
20. Savéant, J.-M. (1990). *Adv. Phys. Org. Chem.* **26**, 1
21. Savéant, J.-M. (1993). *Acc. Chem. Res.* **26**, 455
22. Antonello, S. and Maran, F. (1997). *J. Am. Chem. Soc.* **119**, 12595
23. Antonello, S. and Maran, F. (1999). *J. Am. Chem. Soc.* **121**, 9668
24. Aasmus, K.-D. (1990). *Sulfur-Centered Reactive Intermediates in Chemistry and Biology*, Chatgilialoglu, C. and Aasmus, K.-D. (eds), p. 155. Plenum Press, New York
25. Chen, E.C.M., Albyn, K., Dussack, L. and Wentworth, W.E. (1989). *J. Phys. Chem.* **93**, 6827
26. Cardinale, A., Donkers, R.L., Workentin, M.S., Wayner, D.D.M. and Maran, F. (2001). Manuscript in preparation
27. Cardinale, A., Gennaro, A. and Maran, F. (2001). Manuscript in preparation
28. Gennaro, A., Isse, A.A. and Maran, F. (2001). submitted
29. Dem'yanov, P.I., Myshakin, E.M., Boche, G., Petrosyan, V.S. and Alekseiko, L.N. (1999). *J. Phys. Chem. A* **103**, 11469
30. Bard, A.J. and Faulkner, L.R. (1980). *Electrochemical Methods, Fundamentals and Applications*. Wiley, New York
31. Galus, Z. (1994). In *Fundamentals of Electrochemical Analysis*, 2nd Edn, Ellis Horwood, New York
32. Andrieux, C.P. and Savéant, J.-M. (1986). In *Investigation of Rates and Mechanisms of Reactions*, Bernasconi, C. F. (ed.), Vol. 6, 4/E, Part 2, p. 305. Wiley, New York
33. Andersen, M.L., Mathivanan, N. and Wayner, D.D.M. (1996). *J. Am. Chem. Soc.* **118**, 4871
34. Andersen, M.L. and Wayner, D.D.M. (1996). *J. Electroanal. Chem.* **412**, 53
35. Andersen, M.L., Long, W.N. and Wayner, D.D.M. (1997). *J. Am. Chem. Soc.* **119**, 6590
36. Andersen, M.L. and Wayner, D.D.M. (1999). *Acta Chem. Scand.* **53**, 830
37. Andrieux, C.P., Hapiot, P. and Savéant, J.-M. (1990). *Chem. Rev.* **90**, 723
38. Wayner. D.D.M. and Parker, V.D. (1993). *Acc. Chem. Res.* **26**, 287
39. Nadjo, L. and Savéant, J.-M. (1973). *J. Electroanal. Chem.* **48**, 113
40. Andrieux, C.P. and Savéant J.-M. (1986). *J. Electroanal. Chem.* **205**, 43
41. Lund, T. and Lund, H. (1986). *Acta Chem. Scand.* **B40**, 470
42. Lund, H., Daasbjerg, K., Lund, T., Occhialini, D. and Pedersen, S.U. (1997). *Acta Chem. Scand.* **51**, 135
43. Pedersen, S.U. and Svensmark, B. (1986). *Acta Chem. Scand.* **A40**, 607
44. Fuhlendorff, R., Occhialini, D., Pedersen, S.U. and Lund, H. (1989). *Acta Chem. Scand.* **43**, 803
45. Occhialini, D., Pedersen, S.U. and Lund, H. (1990). *Acta Chem. Scand.* **44**, 715
46. Andrieux, C.P., Blocman, C., Dumas-Bouchiat, J.H., M'Halla, F. and Savéant, J.-M. (1980). *J. Electroanal. Chem.* **113**, 19 and references therein
47. Savéant, J.-M. and Su, K.B. (1984). *J. Electroanal. Chem.*, **171**, 341
48. Savéant, J.-M. and Su, K.B. (1985). *J. Electroanal. Chem.* **196**, 1
49. Daasbjerg, K., Pedersen, S.U. and Lund, H. (1989). *Acta Chem. Scand.* **43**, 876
50. Pedersen, S.U. and Daasbjerg, K. (1989). *Acta Chem. Scand.* **43**, 301
51. Daasbjerg, K. (1993) *Acta. Chem. Scand.* **47**, 398
52. Pedersen, S.U., Lund, T., Daasbjerg, K., Pop, M., Fussing, I. and Lund, H. (1998). *Acta Chem. Scand.* **52**, 657
53. Pedersen, S.U., Christensen, T.B., Thomasen, T. and Daasbjerg, K. (1998). *J. Electroanal. Chem.* **454**, 123

54. Andrieux, C.P., Nadjo, L. and Savéant, J.-M. (1970). *Electroanal. Chem.* **26**, 147
55. Oldham, K.B. (1972). *Anal. Chem.* **44**, 196
56. Grenness, M. and Oldham, K.B. (1972). *Anal. Chem.* **44**, 1121
57. Imbeaux, J.C. and Savéant, J.-M. (1973). *J. Electroanal. Chem.* **44**, 169
58. Savéant, J.-M. and Tessier, D. (1982). *Faraday Discuss. Chem. Soc.* **74**, 57
59. Antonello, S., Musumeci, M., Wayner, D.D.M. and Maran, F. (1997). *J. Am. Chem. Soc.* **119**, 9541
60. Savéant, J.-M. and Tessier, D. (1975). *J. Electroanal. Chem.* **65**, 57
61. Elving, P.J. (1977). *Can. J. Chem.* **55**, 3392
62. Arévalo, M.C., Farnia, G., Severin, M.G. and Vianello, E. (1987). *J. Electroanal. Chem.* **220**, 201
63. Maran, F., Roffia, S., Severin, M.G. and Vianello, E. (1990). *Electrochim. Acta* **35**, 81
64. Antonello, S. and Maran, F. (1998). *J. Am. Chem. Soc.* **120**, 5713
65. Daasbjerg, K., Jensen, H., Benassi, R., Taddei, F., Antonello, S., Gennaro, A. and Maran, F. (1999). *J. Am. Chem. Soc.* **121**, 1750
66. Isse, A.A., Gennaro, A. and Maran, F. (1999). *Acta Chem. Scand.* **53**, 1013
67. Mathivanan, N., Johnston, L.J. and Wayner, D.D.M. (1995). *J. Phys. Chem.* **99**, 8190
68. Laarhoven, L.J.J., Mulder, P. and Wayner, D.D.M. (1999). *Acc. Chem. Res.* **32**, 342
69. Laarhoven, L.J.J., Mulder, P. and Wayner, D.D.M. (1999). *NATO ASI Series C Mathematical and Physical Sciences – Advanced Study Institute*, **535**, 137.
70. Wayner, D.D.M., Lusztyk, E., Pagé, D., Ingold, K.U., Mulder, P., Laarhoven, L.J. and Aldrich, H.S. (1995). *J. Am. Chem. Soc.* **117**, 8737
71. Benson, S.W. (1976). *Thermochemical Kinetics*, 2nd edn, Wiley, New York
72. Benson, S.W. (1978). *Chem. Rev.* **78**, 23
73. Hapiot, P., Pinson, J. and Yousfi, N. (1992). *New. J. Chem.* **16**, 877
74. Bordwell, F.G. (1988). *Acc. Chem. Res.* **21**, 456
75. Maran, F., Celadon, D., Severin, M.G. and Vianello, E. (1991). *J. Am. Chem. Soc.* **113**, 9320
76. Izutzu, K. (1990). Acid-Base Dissociation Constants in Dipolar Aprotic Solvents, *Chemical Data Series No. 35*; Blackwell Scientific Publications, Oxford
77. Maercker, A. (1987). *Angew. Chem., Int. Ed. Engl.* **26**, 972
78. Azzena, U., Denurra, T., Melloni, G., Fenude, E. and Rassu, G. (1992). *J. Org. Chem.* **57**, 1444
79. Marquet, J., Cayón, E., Martin, X., Casado, F., Gallardo, I., Moreno, M. and Lluch, J.M. (1995). *J. Org. Chem.* **60**, 3814
80. Koppang, M.D., Woosley, N.F. and Bartak, D.E. (1984). *J. Am. Chem. Soc.* **106**, 2799
81. Koppang, M.D., Woosley, N.F. and Bartak, D.E. (1985). *J. Am. Chem. Soc.* **107**, 4692
82. Maslak, P. and Guthrie, R.D. (1986). *J. Am. Chem. Soc.* **108**, 2628
83. Rodriguez, J.L. (1993). PhD Thesis, Universidad de la Laguna
84. Maslak, P. and Guthrie, R.D. (1986). *J. Am. Chem. Soc.* **108**, 2637
85. Vianello, E. (1997). Personal communication
86. Amatore, C., Capobianco, G., Farnia, G., Sandonà, G., Savéant, J.-M., Severin, M.G. and Vianello, E. (1985). *J. Am. Chem. Soc.* **107**, 1815
87. Cardinale, A. and Maran, F. (2001). Manuscript in preparation
88. Arévalo, M.C., Maran, F., Severin, M.G. and Vianello, E. (1996). *J. Electroanal. Chem.* **418**, 47

89. Donkers, R.L., Maran, F., Wayner, D.D.M. and Workentin, M.S. (1999). *J. Am. Chem. Soc.* **121**, 7239
90. Kojima, H. and Bard, A.J. (1975). *J. Am. Chem. Soc.* **97**, 6317
91. Bordwell, F.G., Zhang, X.-M., Satish, A.V. and Cheng, J.-P. (1994). *J. Am. Chem. Soc.* **116**, 6605
92. Bordwell, F.G. and Cheng, J.-P. (1991). *J. Am. Chem. Soc.* **113**, 1736
93. Thornton, T.A., Woolsey, N.F. and Bartak, D.E. (1986). *J. Am. Chem. Soc.* **108**, 6497
94. Griggio, L. (1982). *J. Electroanal. Chem.* **140**, 155
95. Tanner, D.D., Chen, J.J., Chen, L. and Luelo, C. (1991). *J. Am. Chem. Soc.* **113**, 8074
96. Banerjee, A. and Falvey, D.E. (1997). *J.Org. Chem.* **62**, 6245
97. Andrieux, C.P., Savéant, J.-M., Tallec, A., Tardivel, R. and Tardy, C. (1997). *J. Am. Chem. Soc.* **119**, 2420
98. Anne, A., Fraoua, S., Moiroux, J. and Savéant, J.-M. (1996). *J. Am. Chem. Soc.* **118**, 3938
99. Maslak, P. Vallombroso, T.M., Chapman, W.H., Jr. and Narvaez, J.N. (1994). *Angew. Chem. Int. Ed. Engl.* **33**, 73
100. Shaik, S. and Shourki, A. (1999). *Angew. Chem. Int. Ed. Engl.* **38**, 586
101. Pearl, D.M., Burrow, P.D., Nash, J.J., Morrison, H. and Jordan, K.D. (1993). *J. Am. Chem. Soc.*, **115**, 9876
102. Pearl, D.M., Burrow, P.D., Nash, J.J., Morrison, H., Nachtigallova, D. and Jordan, K.D. (1995). *J. Phys. Chem.* **99**, 12379
103. Savéant, J.-M. (1994). *Tetrahedron* **50**, 10117
104. Savéant, J.-M. (1994). *J. Phys. Chem.* **98**, 3716
105. Maslak, P. and Theroff, J. (1996). *J. Am. Chem. Soc.* **118**, 7235
106. Guthrie, R.D., Patwardhan, M. and Chateauneuf, J.E. (1994). *J. Phys. Org. Chem.* **7**, 147
107. Antonello, S., Venzo, A. and Maran, F. (2001). Manuscript in preparation
108. Lawless, J.G., Bartak, D.E. and Hawley, M.D. (1969). *J. Am. Chem. Soc.* **91**, 7121
109. Andrieux, C.P., Le Gorande, A. and Savéant, J.-M. (1992). *J. Am. Chem. Soc.* **114**, 6892
110. Adam, W. and Schönberger, A. (1992). *Chem. Ber.* **125**, 2149
111. Koo, J. and Schuster, G.B. (1978) *J. Am. Chem.. Soc.* **100**, 4496
112. Schuster, G.B. (1979). *Acc. Chem. Res.* **12**, 366
113. Zupancic, J.J., Horn, K.A. and Schuster, G.B. (1980). *J. Am. Chem. Soc.* **102**, 5279
114. Schuster, G.B. (1991). In *Advances in Electron Transfer Chemistry*, Mariano, P.S. (ed.), vol. 1, p. 163, JAI Press, Greenwich
115. Takano, Y., Tsunesad, T., Isobe, H. Yoshioka, Y., Yamaguchi, K. and Saito, L. (1999). *Bull. Chem. Soc. Jpn.* **72**, 213
116. Wilson, T. (1995). *Photochem. Photobiol.* **62**, 601
117. Ando, W. (1992). *Organic Peroxides*. Wiley, New York
118. Foote, C.S., Valentine, J.S., Greenberg, A. and Liebman, J.F. (eds) (1995). *Active Oxygen in Chemistry*, Vol. 2. Blackie Academic and Professional, New York
119. Foote, C.S., Valentine, J.S., Greenberg, A. and Liebman, J.F. (eds), (1995) *Active Oxygen in Biochemistry*, Vol. 3. Blackie Academic and Professional, New York
120. Casteel, D.A. (1999). *Nat. Prod. Rep.* **16**, 55
121. Klayman, D. (1985). *Science*, **228**, 1049
122. Haynes, R.K. and Vonwiller, S.C. (1997). *Acc. Chem. Res.* **30**, 73
123. Meshnick, S.R., Taylor, T.E. and Kamchonwongpaisan, S. (1996). *Microbiological Reviews* **60**, 301

124. Bhisutthibhan, J., Pan, X.-Q., Hossler, D.J., Walker, D.J., Yowell, C.A., Carlton, J., Dame, J.B. and Meshnick, S.R. (1998). *J. Biol. Chem.* **273**, 16192
125. Posner, G.H., Cumming, J.N., Woo, S.-H., Ploypradith, P., Xie, S. and Shapiro, T. (1998). *J. Med. Chem.* **41**, 940 and references therein
126. Posner, G.H., Parker, M.H., Northrop, J., Elias, F.S., Ploypradith, P., Xie, S. and Shapiro, T.A. (1999). *J. Med. Chem.* **42**, 300
127. Wu, W.-M., Wu, Y., Wu, Y.-L., Yao, Z.-J., Zhou, C.-M., Li, Y. and Shan, F. (1998). *J. Am. Chem. Soc.* **120**, 3316
128. Wu, Y., Yue, Z.-Y. and Wu, Y.-L. (1999). *Angew. Chem. Int. Ed.* **38**, 2580
129. Workentin, M.S., Maran, F. and Wayner, D.D.M. (1995). *J. Am. Chem. Soc.* **117**, 2120
130. Workentin, M.S. and Donkers, R.L. (1998). *J. Am. Chem. Soc.* **120**, 2664
131. Donkers, R.L. and Workentin, M.S. (1998). *J. Phys. Chem.* **B102**, 4061
132. Donkers, R.L. and Workentin, M.S. (2001). *Chem. Eur. J.* in press
133. Donkers, R.L., Tse, J. and Workentin, M.S. (1999). *J. Chem. Soc. Chem. Commun.* 135
134. Grimshaw, J., Langan, J.R. and Salmon, G.A. (1994). *J. Chem. Soc. Faraday Trans.* **90**, 75
135. Andrieux, C.P., Gallardo, I., Savéant, J.-M. and Su, K.B. (1986). *J. Am. Chem. Soc.* **108**, 638
136. Savéant, J.-M. (1992). *J. Am. Chem. Soc.* **114**, 10595
137. Lund, H., Daasbjerg, K., Lund, T. and Pedersen, S.U. (1995). *Acc. Chem. Res.* **28**, 313
138. Whisman, M.L. and Eccleston, B.H. (1958). *Anal. Chem.* **30**, 1638
139. Swern, D. and Silbert, L.S. (1963). *Anal. Chem.* **35**, 880
140. Hayano, S. and Shinozuka, N. (1970). *Bull. Chem. Soc. Jpn.* **43**, 2039
141. Kjær, N.T. and Lund, H. (1995) *Acta. Chem. Scand.* **49**, 848.
142. Stringle, D.L.B., Campbell, N. and Workentin, M.S. (2001). Manuscript in preparation
143. Savéant, J.-M. and Tessier, D. (1977). *J. Phys. Chem.* **81**, 2192
144. Baldwin, A.C. (1983). In *The Chemistry of Peroxides*, Patai, S. (ed.), p. 97. Wiley, New York
145. Benassi, R. and Taddei, F. (1994). *J. Mol. Struct. (Theochem).* **303**, 101
146. Back, R.D., Ayala, P.Y. and Schlegel, H.B. (1996). *J. Am. Chem. Soc.* **118**, 12758
147. Andrieux, C.P., Savéant, J.-M. and Tardy, C. (1998). *J. Am. Chem. Soc.* **120**, 4167
148. Maletin, Y.A. and Cannon, R.D. (1998). *Theor. Exper. Chem.,* **34**, 57
149. Schmickler, W. (2000). *Chem. Phys. Lett.* **317**, 458
150. Antonello, S., Formaggio, F., Moretto, A., Toniolo, C. and Maran, F. (2001). *J. Am. Chem. Soc.* in press
151. Andrieux, C.P., Savéant, J.-M. and Tardy, C. (1997). *J. Am. Chem. Soc.* **119**, 11546
152. Pause, L., Robert, M. and Savéant, J.-M. (1999). *J. Am. Chem. Soc.* **121**, 7158
153. Severin, M.G., Farnia, G., Vianello, E. and Arévalo, M.C. (1988). *J. Electroanal. Chem.* **251**, 369
154. Jakobsen, S., Jense, H., Pedersen, S. and Daasbjerg, K. (1999). *J. Phys. Chem. A* **103**, 4141
155. Costentin, C., Hapiot, P., Médebielle, M. and Savéant, J.-M. (1999). *J. Am. Chem. Soc.* **121**, 4451
156. Andrieux, C.P., Robert, M., Saeva, F. D. and Savéant, J.-M. (1994). *J. Am. Chem. Soc.* **116**, 7864
157. Falsig, M., Lund, H., Nadjo, L. and Savéant, J.-M. (1980). *Nouv. J. Chim.* **4**, 445

158. Severin, M.G., Arévalo, M.C., Farnia, G. and Vianello, E. (1987). *J. Phys. Chem.* **91**, 466
159. Severin, M.G., Arévalo, M.C., Maran, F. and Vianello, E. (1993). *J. Phys. Chem.* **97**, 150
160. Tognato, S. (1991). Thesis, *Laurea in Chimica*, Università di Padova
161. Christensen, T.B. and Daasbjerg, K. (1997). *Acta Chem. Scand.* **51**, 307
162. Antonello, S., Benassi, R., Daasbjerg, K., Gennaro, A., Sensen, H. Maran, F. and Taddei, F. (2001). Manuscript in preparation
163. Antonello, S., Benassi, R., Gavioli, G., Maran, F. and Raddei, F. (2001). Submitted
164. Antonello, S., Arévalo, M. C., Meneses, A. B. and Maran, F. (2001). Work in progress
165. Benassi, R. and Taddei, F. (1998). *J. Phys. Chem. A* **102**, 6173
166. German, E.D. and Kuznetsov, A.M. (1998). *J. Phys. Chem. A* **102**, 3668
167. Nygaard, B. (1966). *Acta Chem. Scand.* **20**, 1710
168. Magno, F., Bontempelli, G. and Pilloni, G. (1971). *J. Electroanal. Chem.* **30**, 375
169. Hoffman, M.Z. and Hayon, E. (1972). *J. Am. Chem. Soc.* **94**, 7950
170. Persson, B.J. (1978). *Electroanal. Chem.* **86**, 313
171. Simonet, J., Carrion, M. and Lund, H. (1981). *Liebigs Ann. Chem.* 1665
172. Tagaya, H., Aruga, T., Ito, O. and Matsuda, M. (1981). *J. Am. Chem. Soc.* **103**, 5484
173. Liu, M., Visco, S.J. and DeJonghe, L.-C. (1989). *J. Electrochem. Soc.* **136**, 2570
174. Liu, M., Visco, S.J. and DeJonghe, L.-C. (1990). *J. Electrochem. Soc.* **137**, 750
175. Simonet, J. (1993). In *The Chemistry of Sulphur-containing Functional Groups, Suppl. S*, Patai, S. and Rappoport, Z. (eds), Chapter 10, p. 439. Wiley, New York
176. Ludvik, J. and Nygard, B. (1997). *J. Electroanal. Chem.* **423**, 1
177. Honeychurch, M.J. (1997). *Bioelectrochem. Bioenerg.* **44**, 13
178. Chai, C.L.L., Heath, G.A., Huleatt, P.B. and O'Shea, G.A. (1999). *J. Chem. Soc., Perkin Trans. 2*, 389
179. Shida, T. (1968). *J. Phys. Chem.* **72**, 2597
180. Griller, D. and Martinho Simões, J.A. (1990). *Sulfur-centered Reactive Intermediates in Chemistry and Biology*, Chatgilialoglu, C. and Aasmus, K.-D. (eds), p. 327. Plenum Press, New York
181. Cremonini, M.A., Lunazzi, L. and Placucci, G. (1992). *J. Chem. Soc. Perkin Trans. 2*, 451
182. Cremonini, M.A., Lunazzi, L. and Placucci, G. (1993). *J. Org. Chem.* **58**, 3805
183. Mezyk, S.P. and Armstrong, D.A. (1999). *J. Chem. Soc. Perkin Trans. 2*, 1411
184. Rossi, R.A., Pierini, A.B. and Peñéñory, A.B. (1995). In *The Chemistry of Halides, Pseudo-Halides and Azides*, Patai, S. and Rappoport, Z. (eds), vol. 24, p. 1395. Wiley, New York
185. Armstrong, D.A. (1990). In *Sulfur-centerd Reactive Intermediates in Chemistry and Biology*, Chatgilialoglu, C. and Asmus, K.-D. (eds), p. 121. Plenum Press, New York
186. Armstrong, D.A., Sun, Q. and Schuler, R.H. (1996). *J. Phys. Chem.* **100**, 9892
187. Venimadhavan, S., Amarnath, K., Harvey, N.G., Cheng, J.-P. and Arnett, E.M. (1992). *J. Am. Chem. Soc.* **114**, 221
188. Andrieux, C.P., Hapiot, P., Pinson, J., Savéant, J.-M. (1993). *J. Am. Chem. Soc.* **115**, 7783
189. Nakamura, M., Ito, O. and Matsuda, M. (1980). *J. Am. Chem. Soc.* **102**, 698
190. Ito, O. and Matsuda, M. (1983). *J. Am. Chem. Soc.* **105**, 1937
191. Jeschke, G., Wakasa, M., Sakaguchi, Y. and Hayashi, H. (1994). *J. Phys. Chem.* **98**, 4069

192. Olmstead, M.L., Hamilton, R.G. and Nicholson, R.S. (1969). *Anal. Chem.* **41**, 260
193. Benassi, R., Fiandri, G.L. and Taddei, F. (1997). *J. Mol. Struct. (Theochem)* **418**, 127
194. Göbl, M., Bonifacic, M. and Asmus, K.-D. (1984). *J. Am. Chem. Soc.* **106**, 5984
195. Bonazzola, L., Michaut, J.P. and Roucin, J. (1985). *J. Chem. Phys.* **83**, 2727
196. Bergès, J., Kassab, E., Conte, D., Adjadj, E. and Houée-Levin, C. (1997). *J. Phys. Chem. A* **101**, 7809
197. Zavitsas, A.A. (1987). *J. Phys. Chem.* **91**, 5573
198. Samide, M.J. and Peters, D.G. (1998). *J. Electrochem. Soc.* **145**, 3374
199. Farnia, G., Severin, M.G., Capobianco, G. and Vianello, E. (1978). *J. Chem. Soc. Perkin Trans.* 2, 1
200. Capobianco, G., Farnia, G., Severin, M.G. and Vianello, E. (1982). *J. Electroanal. Chem.* **136**, 197
201. Capobianco, G., Farnia, G., Severin, M.G. and Vianello, E. (1984). *J. Electroanal. Chem.* **165**, 251
202. Larsen, H., Pedersen, S.U., Pedersen, J.A. and Lund, H. (1992). *J. Electroanal. Chem.* **331**, 971
203. Jürgens, D., Pedersen, S.U., Pedersen, J.A. and Lund, H. (1997). *Acta Chem. Scand.* **51**, 767
204. McMillan, D.F. and Golden, D.M. (1982). *Ann. Rev. Phys. Chem.* **33**, 493
205. Barbara, P.F., Meyer, T.J. and Ratner, M.A. (1996). *J. Phys. Chem.* **100**, 13148
206. Maslak, P. (1993). In *Topics in Current Chemistry*, Mattay, J. (eds), vol. 168, p. 1. Springer-Verlag, Berlin
207. Gaillard, E.R. and Whitten, D.G. (1996). *Acc. Chem. Res.* **29**, 292
208. Burrow, P.D., Gallup, G.A., Fabrikant, I.I. and Jordan, K.D. (1996). *Austr. J. Phys.* **49**, 403
209. Speiser, B. (1996). *Angew. Chem., Int. Ed. Engl.* **35**, 2471
210. Matyushov, D.V. and Maletin, Y.A. (1988). *Chem. Phys.* **127**, 325
211. Koper, M.T.M. and Voth, G.T. (1998). *Chem. Phys. Lett.* **282**, 100
212. Calhoun, A., Koper, M.T.M. and Voth, G.A. (1999). *J. Phys. Chem. B* **103**, 3442
213. Closs, G.L. and Miller, J.R. (1988). *Science* **240**, 440
214. Paddon-Row, M.N. (1994). *Acc. Chem. Res.* **27**, 18
215. Allongue, P., Henry de Villeneuve, C., Pinson, J., Ozanam, F., Chazalviel, J.N. and Wallart, X. (1998). *Electrochim. Acta* **43**, 2791
216. Allongue, P., Delamar, M., Desbat, B., Fagebaume, O., Hitmi, R., Pinson, J. and Savéant, J.-M. (1997). *J. Am. Chem. Soc.* **119**, 201
217. Kanoufi, F. and Bard, A.J. (1999). *J. Phys. Chem. B* **103**, 10469
218. Maletin, Y.A., Strizhakova, N.G., Kozachkov, S.G. and Cannon, R.D. (1995). *J. Electroanal. Chem.* **398**, 129
219. Teixeira, M.G., Paolucci, F., Marcaccio, M., Aviles, T., Paradisi, C., Maran, F. and Roffia, S. (1998). *Organometallics* **17**, 1297
220. Marcus, R.A. (1997). *J. Phys. Chem. A* **101**, 4072
221. Kuznetsov, A.M. (1999). *J. Phys. Chem. A* **103**, 1239

N-Arylnitrenium Ions

MICHAEL NOVAK and SRIDHARAN RAJAGOPAL

Department of Chemistry and Biochemistry, Miami University, Oxford, Ohio

1 Introduction

Nitrenium ions are divalent nitrogen-centered cations $(R_1R_2N^+)$ that are isoelectronic with carbenes. Like carbenes, they have singlet and triplet electronic states. Calculations on the parent ion, NH_2^+, at sufficiently high levels of theory have indicated that the triplet state is more stable than the singlet by 29–36 kcal/mol.[1,2] These results cluster around the experimentally determined singlet–triplet gap of 30.1 ± 0.2 kcal/mol obtained from photo-ionization of NH_2.[3] Photochemically generated NH_2^+ exhibits singlet and triplet chemistry in aromatic solvents containing trifluoroacetic acid (TFA).[4] The singlet chemistry includes amination of the solvent, hydride transfer from toluene, and insertion into O—H bonds.[4] The triplet chemistry, revealed by inert dilution experiments and triplet-sensitized photolysis, is dominated by H· abstraction.[4a]

Calculations on N-alkyl- and N,N-dialkylnitrenium ions are complicated by the fact that in several cases the singlet states do not appear to be local minima, but correspond to saddle points on the energy surface.[2] In these cases 1,2 rearrangement to an iminium ion is calculated to occur without an energy barrier.[2] The triplet states appear to be true minima and, with the possible exception of the pyrrolidine nitrenium ion $C_4H_8N^+$, are calculated to be more stable than the singlet state, although in some cases the calculated singlet–triplet splitting is small enough to make unambiguous assignment of the ground state impossible.[2]

ADVANCES IN PHYSICAL ORGANIC CHEMISTRY
VOLUME 36   ISBN 0-12-033536-0

It is not clear whether alkylnitrenium ions are generated in solvolysis reactions of R_1R_2NX (X = Cl, $ArSO_3$, $ArCO_2$). These reactions are usually promoted by Ag^+.[5] Substitution products, often accompanied by skeletal rearrangements, and apparent H· abstraction products are observed.[5,6] These products were originally interpreted to provide evidence for discrete singlet and triplet ions.[5] Many of these reactions are retarded by O_2 and/or promoted by benzoyl peroxide and Ag(0) suggesting a homolytic origin of the reactions.[6] In other cases 1,2 migration apparently occurs simultaneously with loss of the leaving group to lead directly to an iminium ion.[7] Attempts to generate alkylnitrenium ions photochemically in aromatic solvents containing TFA have led to products similar to those observed when NH_2^+ is generated in the same solvents.[4e] These include amination products of the aromatic co-solvents, and products of apparent hydride transfer from toluene and mesitylene.[4a,e] These data should be interpreted with caution in view of the solvolysis results.

The singlet state of N-arylnitrenium ions (**1**, Scheme 1) is stabilized by interaction of the π-system of the aryl ring with the empty p-orbital of the

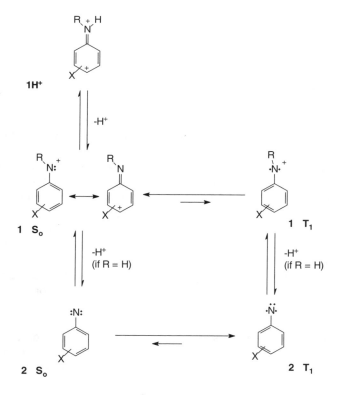

Scheme 1

(presumably) sp^2 hybridized nitrogen. Experimental data and calculations agree that most N-arylnitrenium ions are ground state singlets. Even though it is usually not the ground state, the triplet state is accessible through triplet-sensitized photolysis. Much of the chemistry of the singlet state resembles that of a highly delocalized carbenium ion, while the triplet chemistry is dominated by H· abstraction that leads to the arylamine. Singlet ions are also subject to reduction so the presence of the amine in product mixtures is insufficient evidence for the involvement of triplet ions. The chemistry of **1** is further complicated if R = H because in this case **1** is the conjugate acid of an arylnitrene (**2**, Scheme 1). This provides the opportunity to generate **1** via protonation of **2** and to study the acid–base equilibrium. It also adds to potential complications in interpretation of product data. Protonation of **1** to form the dication **1H$^+$** can also occur in acidic media.

Chemistry we now associate with N-arylnitrenium ions was first discovered by Bamberger and others in the late 19th century, but further developments in the field occurred slowly until the late 1960s when Gassman and his group began systematic investigations of the solvolysis reactions of N-*tert*-butyl-N-chloroanilines. More recently, considerable attention has been paid to N-arylnitrenium ion chemistry, in part because of the suggestion made over 30 years ago that these species may be responsible for the carcinogenicity of metabolites of arylamines.[8] This research has made it possible to distinguish singlet and triplet chemistry of N-arylnitrenium ions, to observe ions generated by laser flash photolysis, to measure their lifetimes in nucleophilic solvents, to learn a great deal about N-arylnitrenium ion reactivity and selectivity, and to show that, indeed, these species are responsible for the formation of the major DNA adducts that are the result of arylamine metabolism. This chapter will concentrate on the developments in the field of N-arylnitrenium ion chemistry made since the mid 1980s, although earlier work that impacts on current developments will be reviewed. Since we are concerned here only with N-arylnitrenium ions, we will drop the prefix and refer to these species simply as nitrenium ions unless specific comparisons are being made to other types of nitrenium ions.

2 Nitrenium ions prior to *ca.* 1990

Several reviews of the known chemistry of nitrenium ions up to the early 1980s are available.[9–11] For this reason we will only review the developments of the first 100 years of nitrenium ion chemistry that are important to understanding the more recent advances. A comprehensive review of the progress in nitrenium ion chemistry during the 1980s will be provided.

In 1894 Bamberger began reporting on the rearrangement that bears his name.[12] In its simplest form (Scheme 2) the Bamberger rearrangement is the conversion of an N-arylhydroxylamine (**3**) into the isomeric *para*-amino-

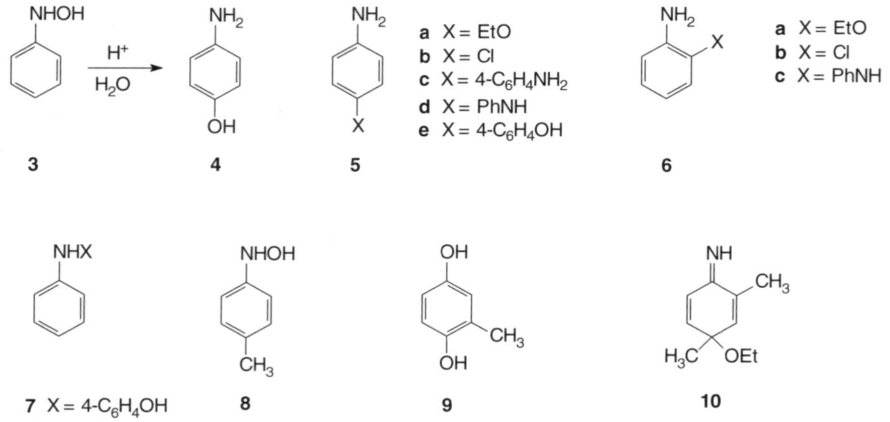

Scheme 2

phenol (**4**) that occurs in dilute aqueous acid. Bamberger recognized that this was an intermolecular process because the introduction of non-solvent species into the reaction mixture (EtOH, Cl⁻, PhNH₂, PhOH) led to incorporation of these materials into the products. *Para*-substituted products (**5**) predominated, but smaller amounts of *ortho*-substituted products (**6**) and products in which the OH was directly displaced (**7** and possibly **5d**) were also detected.[13–15] Bamberger observed that *para*-substituted hydroxylamines (**8**) often led to products (**9**) in which the *para*-substituent had migrated.[16] He showed by isolation of the intermediate **10** and its subsequent decomposition that these products were derived from hydrolysis of an iminoquinol followed by a dienone-phenol rearrangement of the resulting quinol (Scheme 3).[17] Bamberger formulated the mechanism for the formation of the iminoquinol in terms of an intermediate we now recognize as an arylnitrene (Scheme 3).[14,17,18]

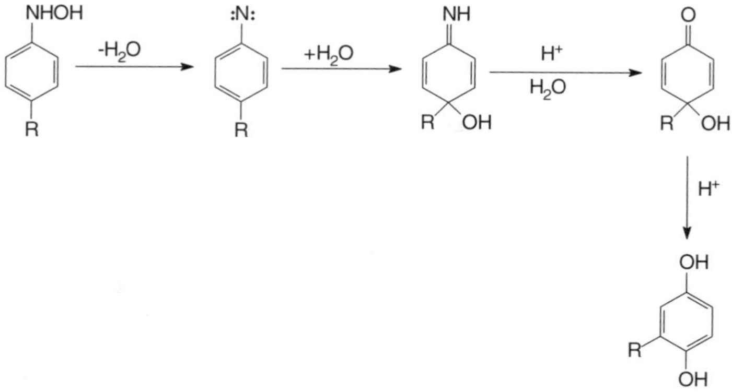

Scheme 3

In Bamberger's time the chemistry of arylnitrenes was unknown so he did not know of the characteristic reactions that could be used to preclude their intermediacy.[19] The formulation of the mechanism in terms of a nitrenium ion is due to Heller, Hughes, and Ingold who showed in 1951 that the reaction rate is proportional to the concentration of protonated hydroxylamine, reaching a constant value in sufficiently acidic solutions.[20] They also discovered that the reaction rate is independent of [Cl$^-$] in HCl solutions even under conditions in which **5b** and **6b** are major products.[20] Other workers showed through hydrolysis in ^{18}O–H$_2$O that **4** is produced in an intermolecular process, and that no ^{18}O is incorporated into **3** during the reaction.[21]

In 1981 Manabe and co-workers performed a kinetic study of the Bamberger rearrangement of a series of *meta*-substituted phenylhydroxylamines in aqueous sulfuric acid.[22] They found that, in the pH region, the observed rate constants for all compounds reached a saturation limit at pH < 1.0, but in the H$_o$ region (H$_o$ < −1.0) the rate constants again increased. They interpreted their results in terms of the mechanism of Scheme 4. They were able to measure K_a^N directly, but not K_a^O. The observed limiting rate constant, $k_o K_a^N / K_a^O$, correlated against σ_m with a ρ_m of −3.2. Based on the observed correlation of K_a^N with $\sigma_m (\rho_m = -2.6)$ and an assumed correlation of K_a^O with σ_m that has the same slope as that for the ionization of ArNHNH$_2^+$ ($\rho_m = -1.2$), they estimated ρ_m for k_o as −4.6. They concluded that this large sensitivity to the *meta*-substituent, the equivalence of k_{obs} in HCl and H$_2$SO$_4$ solutions of the same pH, and $\Delta S^{\ddagger}$ for k_{obs} ranging from 1 to 4 cal/mol-K were most consistent with an S$_N$1 mechanism involving rate-limiting formation of a nitrenium ion. They did not speculate on the mechanism of the process (k') observed in strongly acidic media.

Williams and co-workers provided solvent isotope effect data that supported the mechanism of Scheme 4.[23] The rearrangement of N-phenyl-hydroxylamine (p$K_a^N = 1.9$) in aqueous H$_2$SO$_4$ exhibits an inverse solvent isotope effect at pH > 2 and a normal solvent isotope effect of 1.5 in the plateau region at pH < 1.0. This is expected for the mechanism of Scheme 4

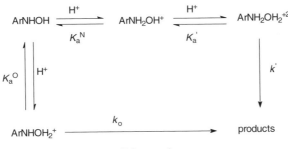

Scheme 4

because $k_{obs} \cong k_o[H^+]/K_a^O$ at pH > 2 where the rate is dependent on $[H^+]$ and $k_{obs} \cong k_o K_a^N/K_a^O$ at pH < 1.0 where the rate is independent of $[H^+]$. Since solvent isotope effects for ionization of weak acids are greater than those for strong acids and $K_a^O \gg K_a^N$, a normal solvent isotope effect would be expected at pH < 1.0, and an inverse effect would be expected in the pH range in which k_{obs} is proportional to $[H^+]$. A 4-methyl substituent increased the rate of the rearrangement by ca. 100 fold at pH 2.3, but an N-ethyl substituent only increased the rate 1.2 fold at the same pH. The authors argued that these substituent effects suggested a rate-limiting transition state in which most of the positive charge is delocalized into the ring with little charge located on N.[23]

Okamoto and co-workers noted that N-phenylhydroxylamine gave predominately diphenylamine on treatment with benzene in TFA but mostly 4-aminobiphenyl and 2-aminobiphenyl in the stronger acid trifluoromethanesulfonic acid (TFSA).[24] Similar results were obtained if benzene was replaced by toluene or anisole. The authors suggested that the reaction in TFA proceeded through O-protonated hydroxylamine either via a direct S_N2 displacement on N by the aromatic nucleophile or via attack of the aromatic compound on the N of a nitrenium ion.[24] In TFSA they favored a mechanism in which the diprotonated hydroxylamine lost water to generate an iminium-benzenium dication (**11**, Scheme 5), a protonated nitrenium ion.[24] This

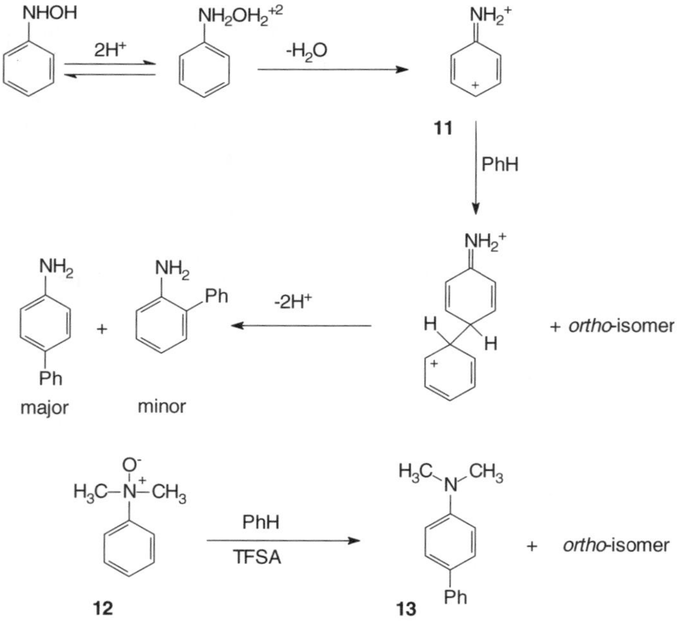

Scheme 5

dication was then envisaged to react with the aromatic nucleophile to generate the aminobiphenyl products. In support of this mechanism they showed that N,N-dimethylaniline N-oxide, **12**, which cannot form a nitrenium ion, generated N,N-dimethyl-4-aminobiphenyl, **13**, and a minor amount of its *ortho*-isomer on treatment with benzene and TFSA.[24]

Olah generated similar dicationic species upon treatment of 4-hydroxy- or 4-methoxy- nitrosobenzenes with 1:1 $HSO_3F \cdot SbF_5$ in SO_2 (Scheme 6).[25] These species were stable in the superacid media and were characterized by ^{13}C NMR spectroscopy. No nitrenium ion species were detected.[25] Although Olah was unable to detect simple monoarylnitrenium ions, a few stabilized diarylnitrenium ions were detected during cyclic voltammetry experiments on the corresponding diarylamine in CH_3CN.[26] For example, the di-*para*-anisylnitrenium ion and its conjugate acid (Scheme 7) were both observed. This ion had a lifetime of about 1 s in CH_3CN.[26]

In a series of papers beginning in 1968, Gassman and co-workers examined the solvolysis of N-*tert*-butyl-N-chloroanilines (**14**, Scheme 8) in MeOH and EtOH.[27–31] In EtOH buffered with AcOH/NaOAc, the solvolysis rate constants for **14a–f** correlated well with σ^+.[29,31] The ρ^+ for the reaction was -6.4, and the major products were the isomeric *ortho*-chloroanilines **15** and the parent anilines **16**. The unsubstituted compound **14c** also yielded some N-*tert*-butyl-4-chloroaniline (11% compared to 48% of **15c**). Only the most reactive N-chloroaniline, **14a**, yielded a significant amount (10%) of product, **17a**, derived from reaction with solvent. The yield of the reduction products **16** increased with increasing electron-withdrawing power of X from 1% for $X = 4 - Me$ to 29% for $X = 4 - CN$. The results were interpreted, in terms of an ionization, to yield a nitrenium ion–chloride ion tight ion pair that under-

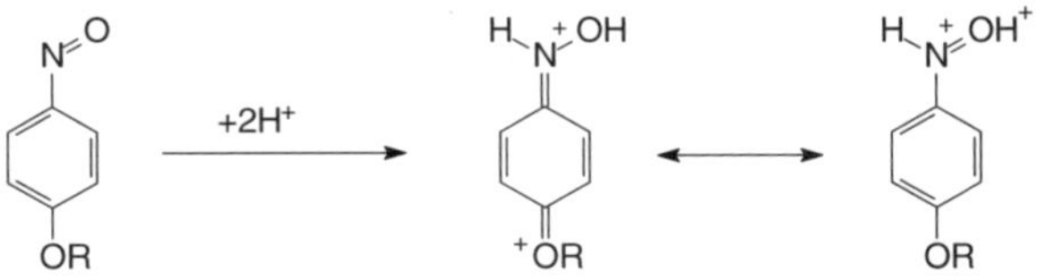

Scheme 6

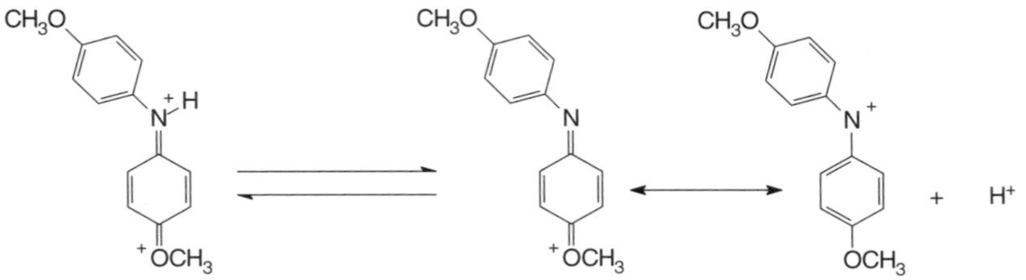

Scheme 7

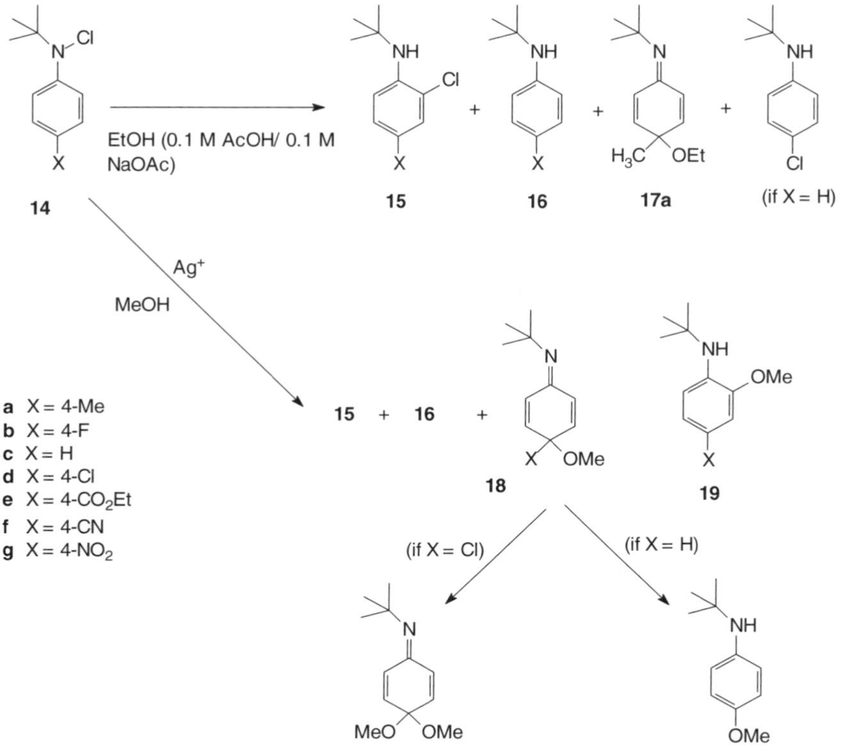

Scheme 8

went internal return to form **15**. It was suggested that the reduction products **16** might be derived from a triplet nitrenium ion that was stabilized relative to the singlet state by electron-withdrawing substituents.[31] Only the nitrenium ion with the most electron-donating substituent appeared to be stable enough to escape internal return and react with solvent.

In the more strongly ionizing and more nucleophilic solvent MeOH containing silver trifluoroacetate, a greater proportion of solvent-derived products were observed.[27,28,30] The product **18a** accounted for 70% of **14a** under these conditions, while **19c** and N-*tert*-butyl-*para*-anisidine accounted for 45% of **14c**.[30] If X was sufficiently electron withdrawing, the solvent-derived products were suppressed. Both **14e** and **14g** yielded only the rearranged products **15** and the reduction products **16**.[30]

The decomposition of aryl azides in aqueous acid was known to produce *para*-aminophenols even before Bamberger began his work on the rearrangement of N-arylhydroxylamines.[32] Bamberger recognized that N-arylhydroxylamines and aryl azides produced identical product mixtures when decomposed under the same conditions in aqueous acid, and he proposed a common mechanism involving an arylnitrene.[33] Further understanding of this reaction was hampered for many years by a lack of realization that Bamberger's experiments had indeed established a strong parallel between the two reactions.[34]

In 1981 Takeuchi and co-workers began reporting the results of their studies of the photolysis and thermolysis of phenyl azide under acidic conditions.[35] In acetic acid containing EtOH, phenyl azide decomposed to give products consistent with competing nitrene and nitrenium ion pathways (Scheme 9). Photolysis at 25°C led to a larger proportion of the apparent nitrene-derived product **20** than did thermolysis at 138°C, but both sets of conditions gave rise to all the products shown in Scheme 9.[35] Because the *ortho/para* product ratio **22/21** exceeded 1.0 under all conditions, but **24/23** was less than 0.5, and the yield of **23 + 24** was always small compared to **21 + 22** even at high EtOH concentrations, it was assumed that **21** and **22** were derived from efficient internal return of the tight ion pair **25**.[35]

In TFA and TFSA, phenylnitrene decomposes rapidly at 25°C and generates diphenylamines (**26**, Scheme 10) and smaller amounts of 2- and 4-aminobiphenyls (**27** and **28**, Scheme 10) in the presence of benzene and other aromatics.[36] The ratio **26:27:28** (X = Y = H) of 1.0:0.11:0.11 for the

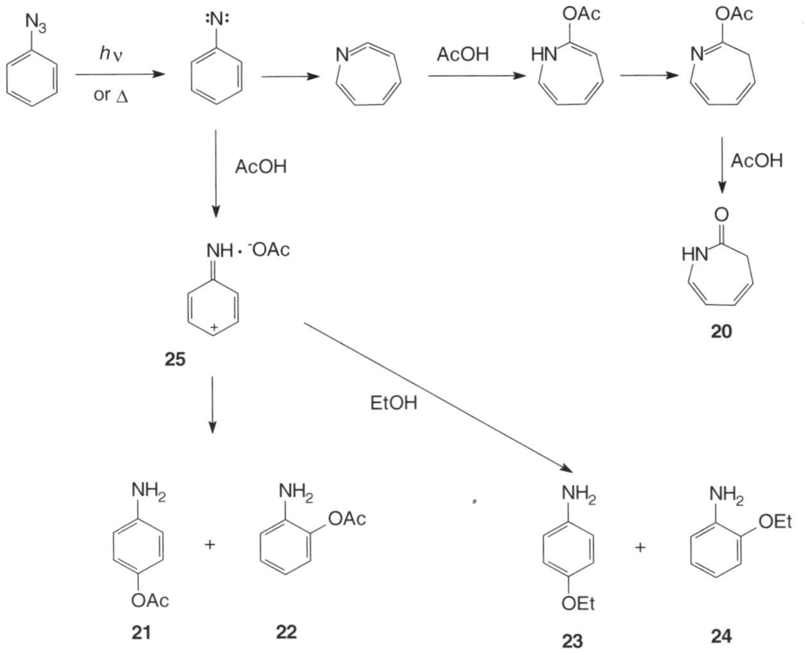

Scheme 9

reaction with benzene in TFA is nearly identical to the ratio of 1.0:0.14:0.16 previously reported for the same three products produced by the decomposition of N-phenylhydroxylamine in benzene/TFA under similar reaction conditions.[24] The partial rate factors, f_p, for the *para*-position of toluene, cumene, biphenyl, bromobenzene, and chlorobenzene for the production of the diarylamines correlated with σ^+ to give a ρ^+ of -4.5 in TFA, while the pseudo-first-order rate constant for the decomposition of phenyl azide in TFA was independent of the identity of the aromatic hydrocarbon.[36] The results suggested that the diarylamines were produced by attack of the aromatic hydrocarbon on the N of a nitrenium ion that was produced by acid-catalyzed decomposition of the azide (Scheme 10). Phenyl azide and azides substituted with electron-withdrawing groups predominately generate the N-substitution products **26**, while azides with electron-donating substituents predominately generate the C-substitution products **27** and **28**.[36] This result was rationalized in terms of the effect of the substituent on the charge densities on nitrogen and the aromatic ring of the nitrenium ion.

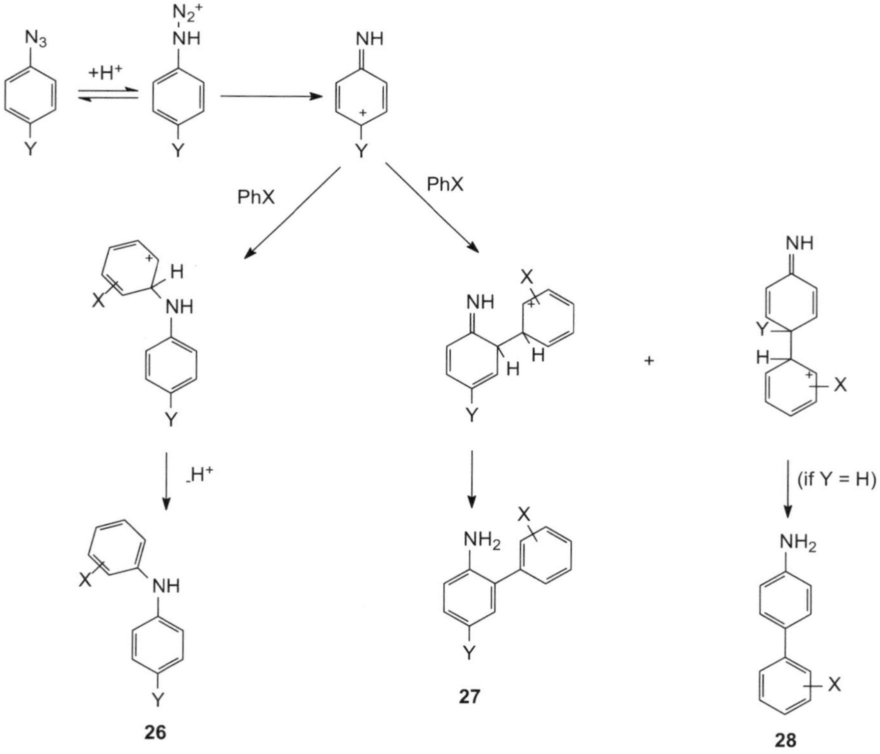

Scheme 10

The similarity of the results obtained with phenyl azide and N-phenyl-hydroxylamine in benzene/TFA indicates that both reactions proceed by similar mechanisms, but N-phenylhydroxylamine in benzene/TFSA produces a higher yield of the C-substitution products **27** and **28**.[24] As previously suggested (Scheme 5), N-phenylhydroxylamine can be doubly protonated to yield the dication **11** in strong acids, but the more weakly basic phenyl azide is less likely to be doubly protonated. The differences observed between the behavior of N-phenylhydroxylamine and phenyl azide in TFSA may be due to the inability of phenyl azide to directly generate **11**.

Phenyl azide was also found to react with alkenes in TFA (Scheme 11).[37] The reaction was assumed to go via an aziridinium ion generated from attack of the alkene on the nitrenium ion because of the overall *trans*-addition to the alkene noted in product **29**. An alternative S_N2 mechanism was disfavored because phenyl azide decomposes at 21°C in 50 vol% cyclohexene/TFA with an almost identical first-order rate constant as in 50 vol% benzene/TFA even though cyclohexene is a considerably stronger nucleophile than benzene.[37]

The apparent ability of nitrenium ions to undergo both C- and N-substitution was exploited by a number of researchers to bring about intramolecular cyclizations from aryl azide or hydroxylamine precursors (Scheme 12).[11,38,39] These reactions had some synthetic utility, but in most cases the mechanisms were not carefully investigated to show that nitrenium ions were actually involved. One exception was cyclization of **30** in aqueous sulfuric acid to generate **31** (Scheme 13).[39] This reaction occurred with nearly an identical rate constant to the Bamberger rearrangement of **32** to generate **33**. Since the cyclization of **30** occurred without any rate acceleration compared to **32**, the intramolecular attack of the hydroxyl group must occur after the rate-limiting step of the reaction, presumably formation of a nitrenium ion.[39]

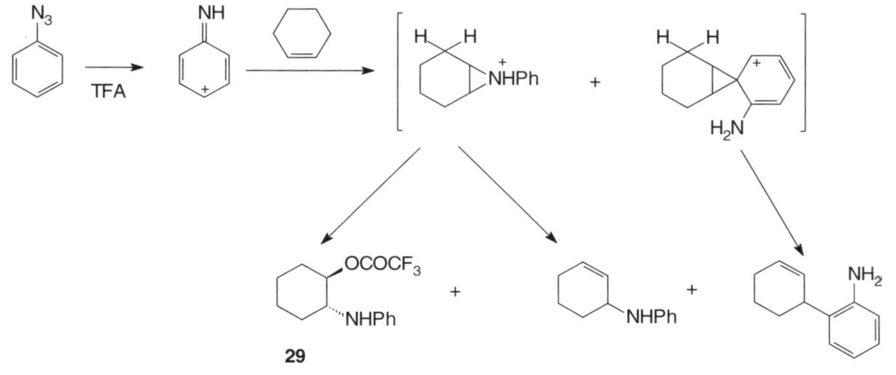

Scheme 11

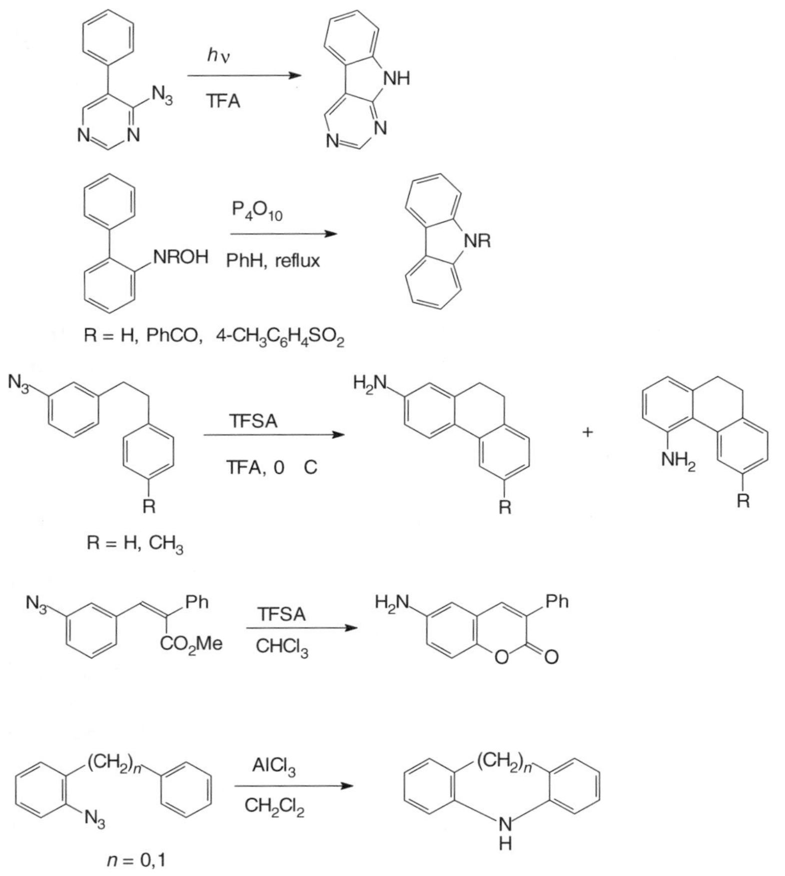

Scheme 12

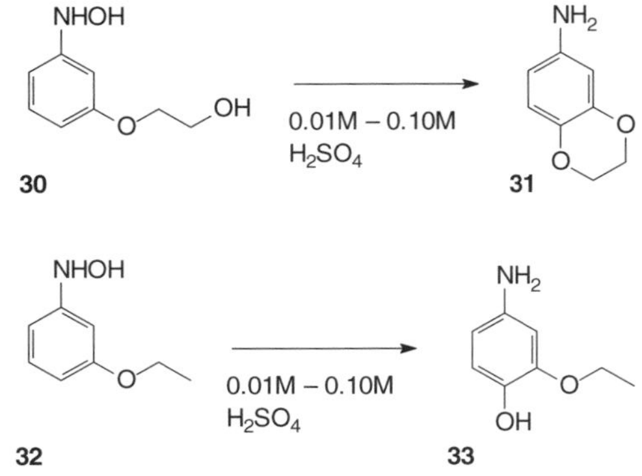

Scheme 13

Other possible sources of photochemically generated nitrenium ions were investigated. Chief among these were 3-substituted-2,1-benzisoxazoles (3-substituted anthranils) or 3-substituted-N-alkyl-2,1-benzisoxazolium salts (3-substituted N-alkyl anthranilium salts).[40–45] Photolysis of the anthranils in highly acidic media generated products apparently derived from nitrenium ions. For example, 3-methyl- and 3-phenylanthranil **34a** and **34b** underwent photolysis in concentrated HCl or H_2SO_4 to generate the products shown in Scheme 14.[40–42] Thermolysis of 2-azidoacetophenone, **35**, in concentrated H_2SO_4 led to the same products as **34a**, but in lower yield and with a different

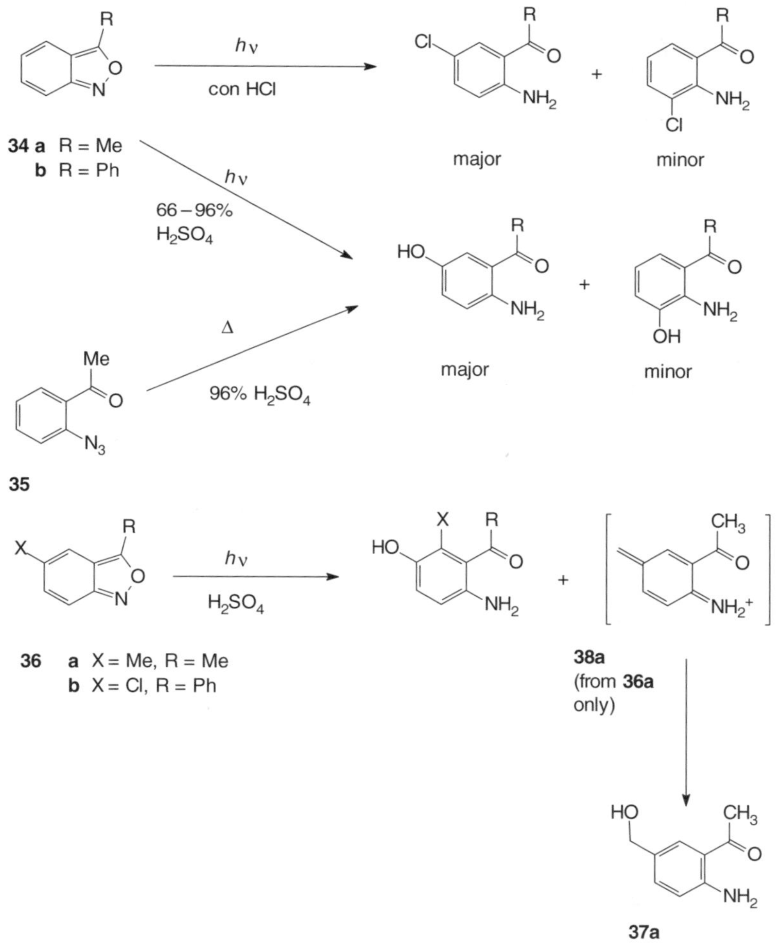

Scheme 14

product ratio.[42] If the 5-position of the anthranil was blocked by an alkyl or halogen substituent, as in **36**, products analogous to those previously observed by Bamberger in the rearrangement of 4-substituted-N-arylhydroxylamines were generated (Scheme 14).[41,42] For **36a** another pathway was revealed by the hydroxymethyl product **37a**, which is apparently generated from **38a**.[42] In the presence of aromatic compounds such as anisole both N- and C-substitution products were observed (Scheme 15).[43] Under neutral or weakly acidic conditions, photolysis of **34a** led to azepine products character-istic of arylnitrenes.[42,44] The photolysis products in concentrated acid were assumed to be generated from nitrenium ions formed by photolysis of the N-protonated anthranil (Scheme 16).[40–43] Under these strongly acidic conditions it is likely that the dication is also present and responsible for some of the products. The generation of similar product mixtures from thermolysis of appropriate aryl azides under similar conditions was strong evidence for similar or identical reaction pathways for the two reactions, but not sufficient evidence by itself to implicate nitrenium ions. Further support for the mechanism of Scheme 16 came from the observation that N-alkylated anthranilium salts gave products similar to those described

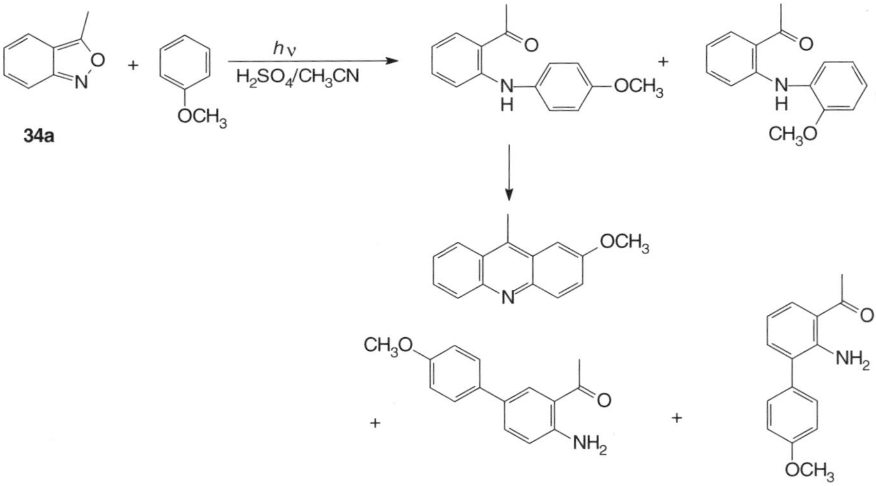

Scheme 15

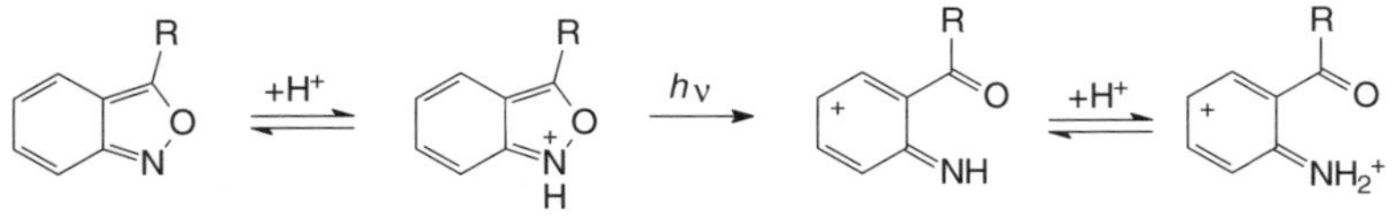

Scheme 16

above when irradiated in neutral aqueous or methanolic solutions, including incorporation of non-solvent nucleophiles into the products (Scheme 17).[45]

The photolysis of **36a** in H_2SO_4 also generates some of the reduction product 2-amino-5-methylacetophenone, as does thermolysis of 2-azido-5-methylacetophenone in H_2SO_4.[42] The authors suggested that the reduction product came from hydrogen abstraction by the triplet nitrenium ion.[42] They suggested that if nucleophilic addition to C-5 was reversible because of the methyl substituent, intersystem crossing to the triplet state might become more efficient than in cases with no substituent or a halogen substituent.[42] This explanation requires that the triplet state is the ground state of the ion, or at least of similar stability to the singlet state. Calculations described below suggest this is not likely.

During the late 1960s and early 1970s, research into aromatic amine carcinogens had established that these species were precarcinogens that required metabolic activation.[8,46] A common metabolic pathway was established.[8,46] That pathway is summarized in Scheme 18. The end product of the metabolism, a sulfuric or acetic acid ester of a hydroxylamine or hydroxamic acid, was shown to react most predominately with guanine of the four DNA bases to generate a C-8 adduct in which the nitrogen of the carcinogen became bonded to C-8 of the guanine base (Scheme 18).[47] Other minor adducts were often found, and some specific amines did not generate C-8 guanine adducts as the major carcinogen-DNA reaction products.[48] Ester derivatives of N-arylhydroxylamines or N-arylhydroxamic acids were regarded as the ultimate carcinogenic metabolites of aromatic amines and amides.[8,46,47] These structures led to the speculation that the compounds might undergo $N-O$ bond heterolysis *in vivo* to generate nitrenium ions that were the species actually responsible for the reactions with guanine residues in DNA.[8,46] The structures of the C-8 adducts are not what one would expect from reaction of guanine or the guanine residue of DNA with a cationic intermediate. In most cases in which these species are known to react with a cation via an S_N1 mechanism the site of reaction is N-7 or O-6.[49] The C-8 site is more characteristically attacked by radical intermediates.[50] The C-8 adduct could also arise from rearrangement of an initially formed adduct at N-7.

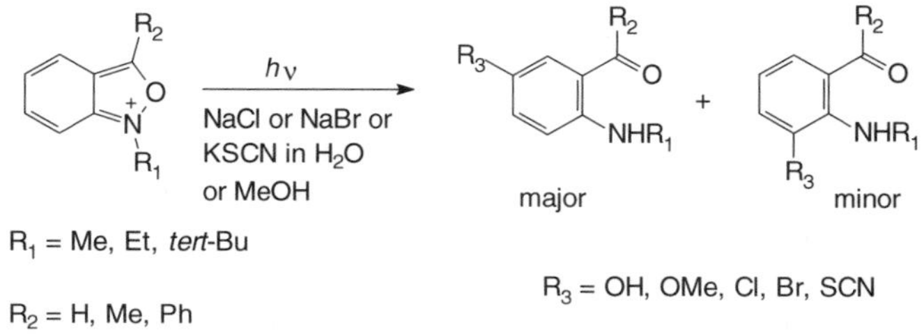

R_1 = Me, Et, *tert*-Bu

R_2 = H, Me, Ph

R_3 = OH, OMe, Cl, Br, SCN

Scheme 17

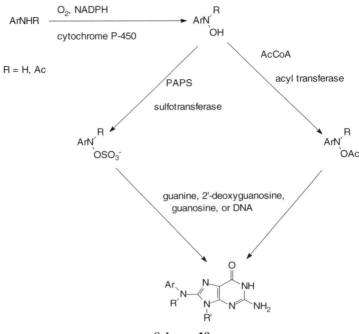

Scheme 18

In a series of papers, Scribner and co-workers sought to provide evidence for the nitrenium ion hypothesis.[51–53] The model compounds that they studied were the N-acetoxy-(carbonyl-^{14}C)-N-arylacetamides **39a–f** of the corresponding carcinogenic amines (Scheme 19). Rates of formation of water-soluble-^{14}C in the presence of citrate and methionine in 40 vol% acetone-H_2O increased in a non-linear manner with citrate or methionine concentration and levelled off at high concentrations.[51] Several of the model esters, notably **39a**, decolorized the stable free radical 2,2-diphenyl-1-picrylhydrazyl in 20% EtOH-H_2O.[52] Ascorbic acid added to solutions of **39a** containing guanosine reduced the extent of adduct formation and led to formation of the reduction product N-acetyl-2-aminofluorene.[52] These results were interpreted in terms of the mechanism of Scheme 19, the important features of which are reversible formation of the nitrenium ion–acetate ion pair and intersystem crossing of the singlet ion to the triplet state that ultimately reacts with guanosine to form the C-8 adduct.[51,52]

Unfortunately, the authors performed little detailed product analyses and did not take into account the possibility that many of the reactions they were monitoring were acyl transfer processes that led to hydroxamic acid products (Scheme 20). They also failed to maintain control of pH and ionic strength in their reactions. Underwood and co-workers showed that [18]O scrambling did not occur in carbonyl-^{18}O-labeled esters **39a,b,c,e**, and **f** during their

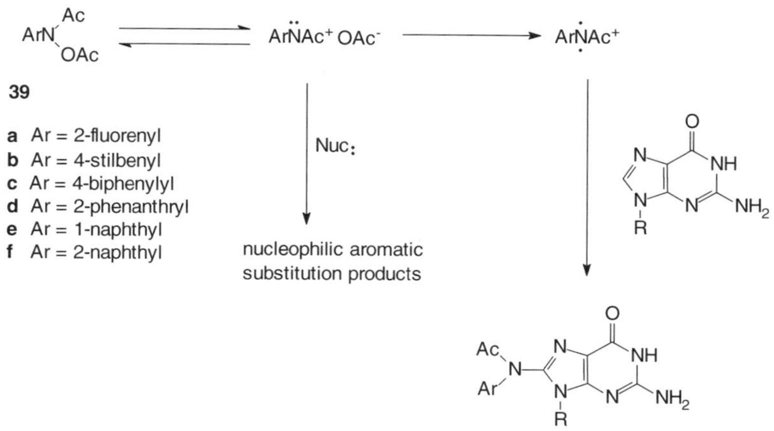

Scheme 19

Scheme 20

decomposition in 40% acetone-H_2O (**39d** was not tested).[54] The ion pairs of Scheme 19 could not have been formed reversibly. Underwood's group also found that the kinetics of decomposition of **39a,b,c,e,** and **f** in 40% acetone-H_2O were given by equation (1).[54,55]

$$k_{obs} = k_o + k_{OH}[OH^-] + k_b \text{ [buffer]} \qquad (1)$$

Product analyses showed that for all five esters, the OH^-- and buffer-dependent components generated the corresponding hydroxamic acids. The pH-independent reaction also led to the hydroxamic acid product for **39c** and **39f**, but **39a** and **39e** generated products that appeared to be derived from N—O bond heterolysis in the pH region dominated by k_o (pH < 8).[55]

Products isolated from the hydrolysis of **39a** at neutral pH included the rearranged materials **40a,b** and the phenols **41a,b** (Scheme 21).[55] Addition of a variety of reducing agents including NaI, $Na_2S_2O_3$, and hydroquinone led to formation of **42**, at the expense of the other reaction products except **40a,b**.[55] Scribner had previously shown that **39b** gave rise to **43** as the major solvolysis product in 40% acetone-H_2O at neutral pH.[53] The diol product was thought to arise from attack of H_2O on a quinone imide methide, **44**, formed by attack of H_2O on the β-carbon of a highly delocalized nitrenium ion (Scheme 22).

Underwood and Callahan found in a kinetic study of the hydrolysis of a series of N-acetoxyacetanilides, including **39a,c,** and **e**, in 40% acetone-H_2O

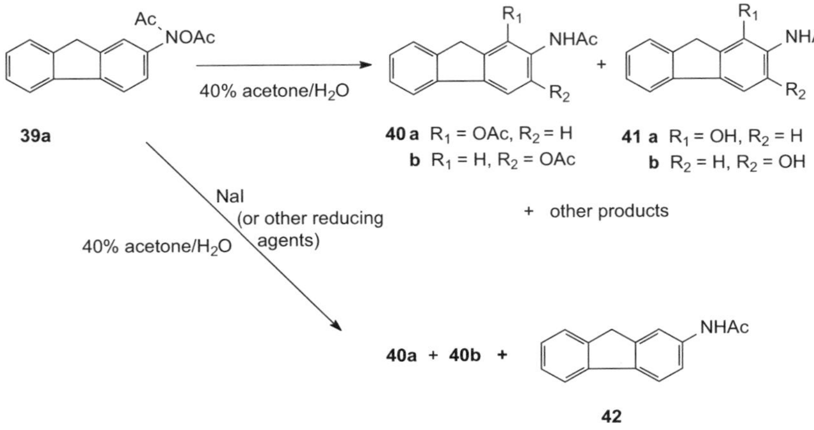

Scheme 21

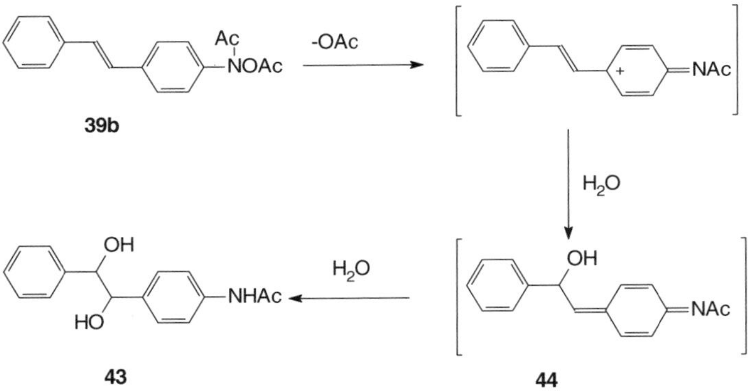

Scheme 22

that k_o for those esters with $\sigma^+ > -0.3$ was the rate constant for uncatalyzed ester hydrolysis leading to the hydroxamic acid, while for those esters with $\sigma^+ < -0.3$, k_o correlated with σ^+ with a ρ^+ of -6.2 and reaction products consistent with N—O bond cleavage were isolated.[56] For those esters that underwent hydrolysis to form the hydroxamic acid products, k_o correlated better with σ to give a ρ of $+1.5$.[56]

In 1984 Gassman and Granrud, and Novak and co-workers, published their results on reactions of similar esters of hydroxamic acids.[57,58] Gassman and Granrud showed that the rearrangement of the methanesulfonate esters **45a–g** in $CDCl_3$ (Scheme 23) occurred in a first-order fashion and that k_{obs} correlated with σ^+ with a slope, ρ^+, of -9.2.[57] Novak and co-workers showed that the pH-independent first-order rate constants for hydrolysis in 5 vol%

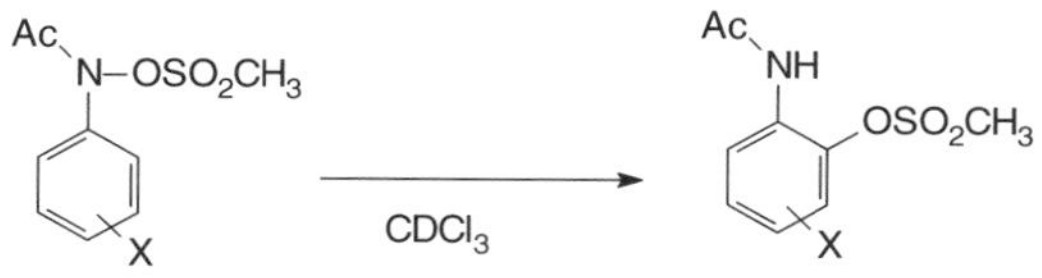

Ac
  \
   N–OSO₂CH₃ → (CDCl₃) →   Ac
                                \
                                 NH
                                     \
                                      OSO₂CH₃

45 a X = 3-Cl
   b X = 4-CO₂CH₃
   c X = 3-CF₃
   d X = 3-CN
   e X = 4-CF₃
   f X = 4-CN
   g X = 4-NO₂
   h X = 4-CH₃

Scheme 23

CH_3CN-H_2O of the N-sulfonatooxyacetanilides **46a–f** (Schemes 24 and 28) correlated with σ^+ with a slope of -4.5 at 25°C.[58] Products derived from the hydrolysis reactions of **46a–d** and the related ester **47** are summarized in Scheme 24.[58–63] These products, and those observed by others,[53,55,57] show that esters of N-arylhydroxamic acids can undergo N—O bond cleavage, but the alternative acyl or sulfonyl transfer reaction cannot be over-looked.[54,55,56,64] Solvent composition is often critical to the outcome of the reaction. For example, **46b** and **46c** undergo S—O bond cleavage to generate the corresponding hydroxamic acids in EtOH,[58] and **39b** acetylates the ribose of adenosine and guanosine in 0.1 M phosphate buffer in 50% acetone-water, but alkylates the base of the same two nucleosides in the absence of the phosphate.[64]

Scheme 24 presents a mechanism that was consistent with available data. Heterolytic cleavage of the N—O bond is indicated by the substituent effects, as well as by the rearrangement and other products noted in Schemes 21–24. The addition of non-solvent nucleophiles does not increase the rate of disappearance of the esters even though the nucleophiles are incorporated into the products, so S_N2 mechanisms were not considered. A tight ion pair, **48**, that is not attacked by solvent or other reagents is assumed to be the first intermediate formed because the yield of the rearranged product **49** cannot be reduced by addition of I^- even though this halide can completely suppress the solvent-derived products at sufficiently high concentrations.[58–61] The yield of **49** was substituent dependent, ranging from negligible for **47** to 40% for **46c**, and greater than 50% for **46e** and **46f**.[58–63] This is consistent with Gassman and co-workers observations of the substituent-dependent yields of the rearranged product **15** (Scheme 8) produced during the methanolysis of the N-*tert*-butyl-N-chloroanilines, **14**.[30] The tight ion pair can separate to a solvent-separated ion pair, **50**, or a free nitrenium ion (the issue could not be decided with available data) that is subject to attack by solvents or non-

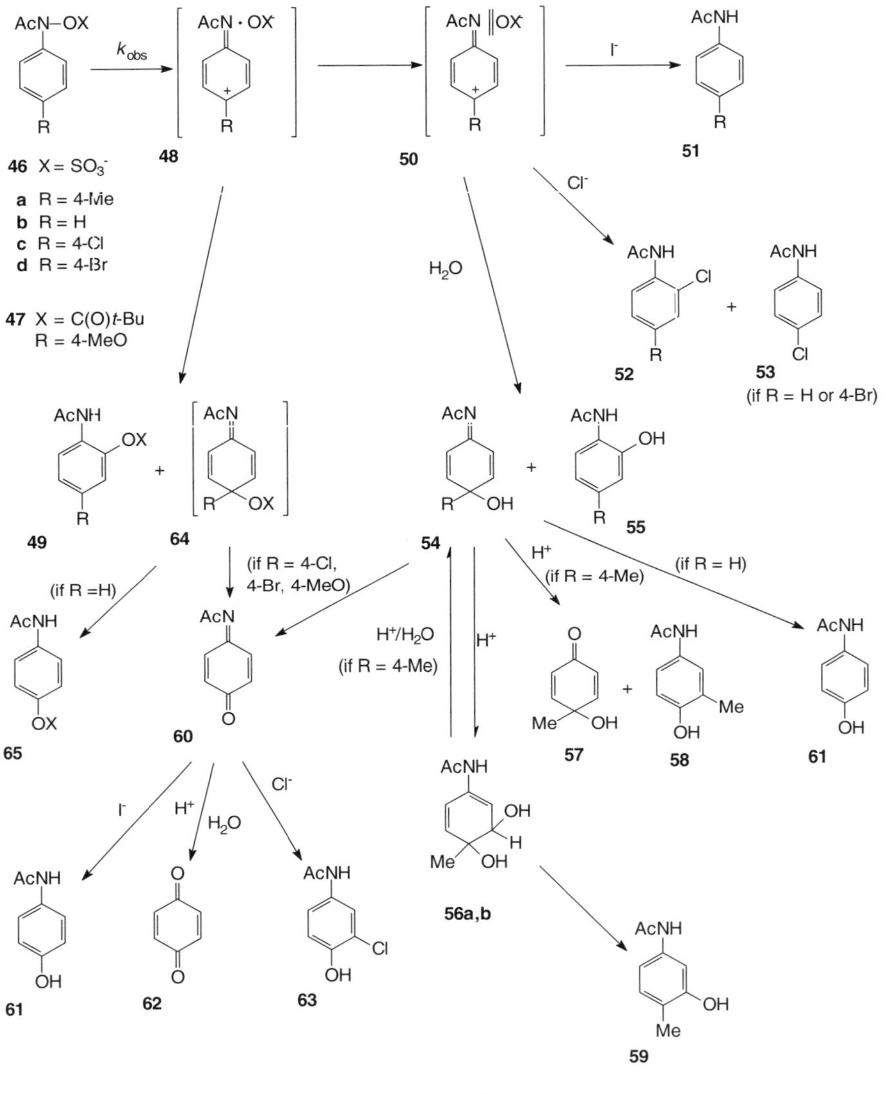

Scheme 24

solvent species. The halide I^- always generates the reduction product **51**.[58–61]
So do several other reducing agents including Br^-, SCN^-, $S_2O_3^=$ and
$FeCl_2$.[58,61] All of these species are less effective than I^- at causing reduction,
and at least one of them (Br^-) also behaves as a nucleophile in the reaction.[61]
Since the spin trap PBN and the radical trap 4-OH-TEMPO had no effect on
the I^- mediated reduction, it appears that a triplet nitrenium ion or other

radical species is not involved. Yields of I_2 were equivalent to the yields of reduction product, and the saturation yields of the reduction product accounted for all of the starting material except for the rearrangement products.[58,61] The mechanism of Scheme 25 was favored for the reduction.[61] It was argued that the "soft" base I^- would prefer to attack at the softer nitrogen rather than the hard acid carbons of the aromatic ring.[61] It was noted that no products of nucleophilic attack of I^- on the aromatic ring could be detected.[61] This mechanism has precedent in the reactions of hydroxylamine-O-sulfonate.[65] The ester **46d** also exhibited halogen exchange in Cl^- or Br^- (Scheme 24 and 26). The latter process was detected with $^{79}Br^-$ enriched KBr. The isotope exchange data show that this process accounts for 29% of the reduction of **46d** in 0.5 M KBr solutions. The majority of the reduction occurs without isotope exchange, apparently by a mechanism similar to that shown in Scheme 25.[61] Although I^- and Br^- acted either exclusively or primarily as reducing agents, Cl^- behaved exclusively as a nucleophile.[58-61] For most esters the *ortho*-substituted product **52** was the major Cl^- adduct, but if R = H (**46b**), *para*-chloroacetanilide, **53**, was the major Cl^- adduct.[58]

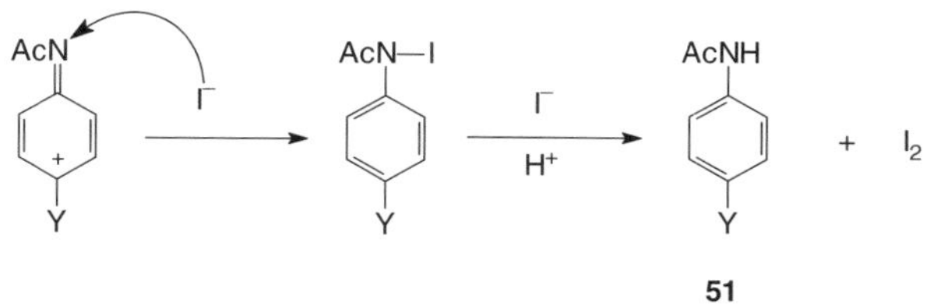

Scheme 25

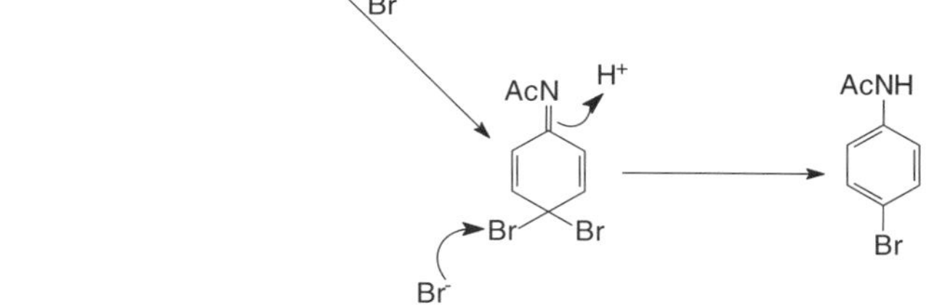

Scheme 26

Attack of the solvent led primarily to the N-acetyliminoquinol **54** and lesser amounts of the *ortho*-acetamidophenol, **55**. The intermediate **54** was detected by HPLC, UV and ^{1}H NMR if R = 4-CH$_3$, but it decomposed to generate **57**, **58**, and **59** as shown in Scheme 24.[59] The diastereomeric diols **56a,b** were also detected, and the kinetics of their decomposition showed that they were formed reversibly from **54**.[59] The methoxy analogues of **54** and **56a,b** were isolated and characterized by Gassman and Granrud during the methanolysis of **45h**.[66] These species decomposed into the methoxy analogues of **58** and **59**.[66]

For the other esters **54** was not directly detectable, but its existence could be inferred from its decomposition products **60** or **61**. N-acetyl-*para*-benzoquinone imine, **60**, was detected during the hydrolysis of **47**.[62] Its decomposition products, **62** and **63**, accounted for >90% of **47**, and about 30% of **46c** in buffers from pH 3.0 to 8.0 containing 0.5 M KCl.[58,62] The identity of **60** was confirmed by the equivalence of its decomposition kinetics and reaction products (**61–63**) observed in solutions of **47**, or its 4-ethoxy analogue, to that of authentic **60** throughout the pH range 1.0 to 8.0.[62,63] It was not possible to directly detect **60** in the hydrolysis of **46c** and **46d**, but its characteristic decomposition products were detected.[58,61]

The presence of **61** (15%) in the hydrolysis of **46c** in 0.5 M KI, conditions that completely suppress the solvent-derived products of hydrolysis of **46c**, revealed another pathway for production of **60** that appears to account for

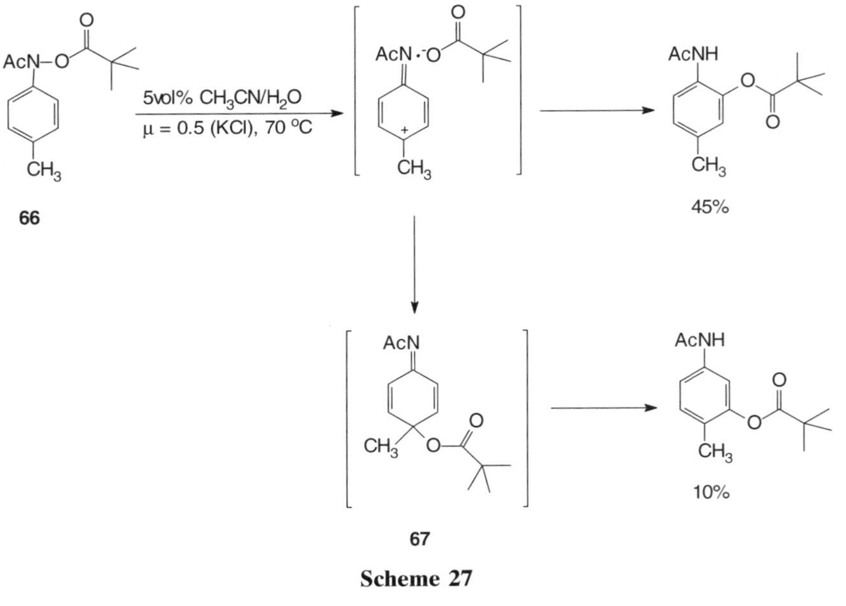

Scheme 27

about 50% of **60** generated from **46c**.[58] This pathway appears to proceed through the sulfonated N-acetylquinol imine, **64**.[58] This pathway was also substantiated for **46b** because **65** accounts for 7% of the hydrolysis product of that ester.[58] The observation that the hydrolysis of N-(pivaloyloxy)-*para*-acetotoluidide at 70°C (**66**, Scheme 27) leads to both 2-(pivaloyloxy)-4-methylacetanilide (45%) and 3-(pivaloyloxy)-4-methylacetanilide (10%) also supports the existence of an intermediate **67** similar to **64** during the hydrolysis of this pivalic acid ester analogue of **46a**.[60]

Although the rate constants for decomposition of the more reactive esters **46a-d** and **47** show no pH dependence in the pH range 1–8,[58–63] the less reactive **46e** and **46f** (Scheme 28) exhibit pH-dependent decomposition kinetics in this pH range.[58] At 80°C the first-order hydrolysis rate constant, k_{obs}, for **46e** was found to fit equation (2).[67]

$$k_{obs} = k_H[H^+] + k_o + k_{OH}[OH^-] \tag{2}$$

The magnitude of the rate constants were such that **46e** exhibited a U-shaped pH-rate profile with a broad pH-independent region from pH 3.5 to 7.0 in which $k_{obs} \approx k_o$.[67] Reaction products isolated within this pH range were consistent with those previously observed for **46a-d**, and Cl$^-$ and I$^-$ had effects on product distribution and identity similar to those discussed above for **46a-d**. It was concluded that the pH-independent reaction involved N—O bond heterolysis to yield nitrenium ion intermediates as in Scheme 24.[67]

The acid- and base-dependent hydrolysis of **46e** led to the deacetylated products shown in Scheme 28. These products could not have been derived primarily from hydrolysis of the corresponding amides because the authentic amides do not undergo significant hydrolysis under the reaction conditions within the time frame of the product study experiments.[67] The rearranged products, the solvent-derived products, and, particularly, *meta*-bromoaniline produced in the presence of I$^-$ suggested that the sources of these materials are the deacetylated nitrenium ion pairs **69e** and **70e** (Scheme 28).[67] The products of the Bamberger rearrangement of N-(3-bromophenyl)hydroxyl-amine at pH 1.0 in the presence of 0.5 M Cl$^-$ or I$^-$ are, with the exception of the rearranged products shown in Scheme 28, consistent with the product distributions obtained for **46e** at pH 1.0 or 7.8 in the presence of 0.5 M Cl$^-$ or I$^-$.[67]

Inverse solvent isotope effects for k_H (0.79 ± 0.07) and k_{OH} (0.85 ± 0.12) for **46e** are consistent with acid and alkaline hydrolysis of acetanilides.[67] It was concluded that the H$_3$O$^+$ and OH$^-$ dependent reactions observed for **46e** and **46f** were hydrolysis reactions that generated the deacetylated esters **68e** and **68f** (Scheme 28). Since HPLC data show that all reaction products derived from **46e** are generated in a first-order fashion with rate constants equivalent to those for the disappearance of **46e**, **68e** must decompose with a

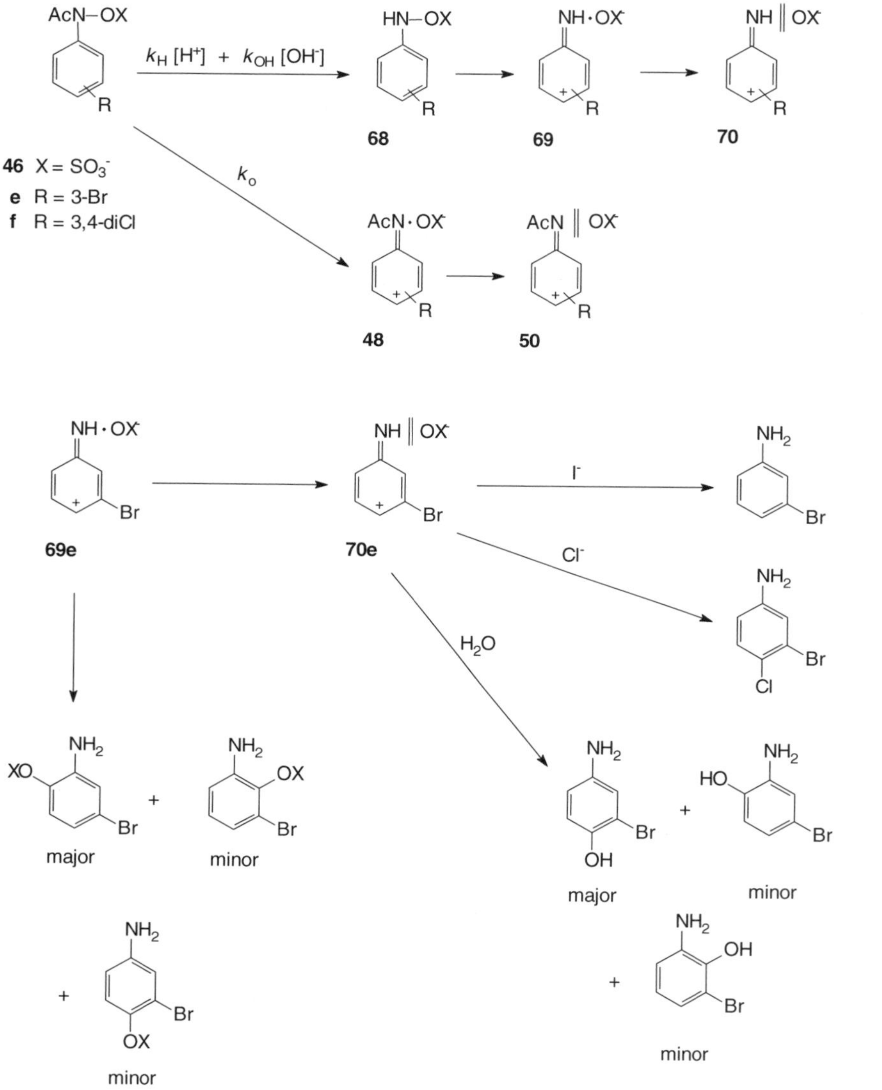

Scheme 28

rate constant significantly larger than the rate constant for its formation.[67] The pH-dependent decomposition of N-sulfonoxyacetanilides is only observed at pH 1–8 in cases in which the ring is sufficiently electron withdrawing that k_o is smaller than *ca.* $10^{-4}\,\text{s}^{-1}$ at 80°C or *ca.* 10^{-7}s^{-1} at 20°C.[58,67]

Although **68e** could not be prepared, the less reactive pivalic acid ester analogues **71a–d** (Scheme 29) were synthesized.[68] Hydrolysis rate constants at 40°C were pH independent from pH 1.0 to 7.0 and k_{obs} correlated with σ^+ to give a ρ^+ of −6.0.[68] The products derived from **71a–c** are summarized in Scheme 29. These products are consistent with a nitrenium ion mechanism. In particular, the products and product ratios derived from the *meta*-bromo ester **71b** were consistent with those previously reported for **68e** and the Bamberger rearrangement of N-(3-bromophenyl)hydroxylamine, with the exception of the rearrangement products.[67] The rearrangement products **72** appear to be derived from intramolecular aminolysis of **73**. These

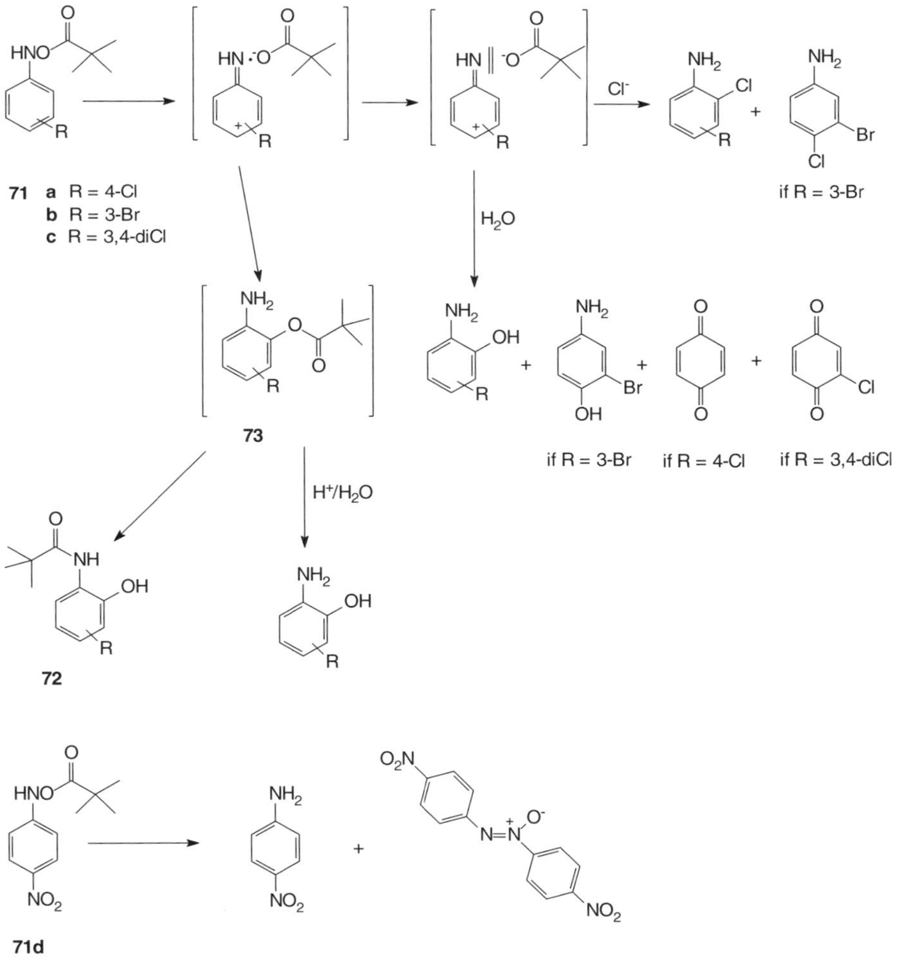

Scheme 29

intermediates were not isolated, but **73a** was generated *in situ* from a precursor, **74a**, (Scheme 30) and was shown to give products consistent with those observed during the hydrolysis of **71a**.[68] It was possible to detect **73a** by HPLC at early reaction times (<60 s) during the hydrolysis of **74a**. The same HPLC peak was observed at early reaction times during the hydrolysis of **71a**.[68]

The *para*-nitro ester **71d** generated only 4-nitroaniline (70%) and 4,4′-dinitroazoxybenzene (10%) when it underwent decomposition (Scheme 29). These products could have been derived from either a triplet nitrene or a triplet nitrenium ion precursor.[68] Homolysis of the N—O bond to generate radical intermediates was ruled out because of the nearly quantitative yield of pivalic acid derived from **71d**. The pivaloxy radical would have undergone rapid decarboxylation to generate CO_2 and the *tert*-butyl radical under these conditions.[68] Since no rearrangement product was observed, it was tentatively concluded that this ester underwent direct decomposition to 4-nitrophenylnitrene without the intermediacy of a nitrenium ion.[68]

The esters **71a–d** were susceptible to reduction to the corresponding amine by Fe^{2+}.[68,69] The reduction did not proceed through a nitrenium ion intermediate because it was accompanied by rate accelerations as large as 10^4 in 10^{-3} M Fe^{2+} over the rate in the absence of Fe^{2+}.[68] The reaction was hindered by complexation of Fe^{2+} by CN^-, and produced pivalic acid as a by-product.[68] Reduction was promoted more effectively by Cu^+ than by Fe^{2+}, and N-aryl-hydroxylamines added to the reaction mixture were oxidized to nitroso

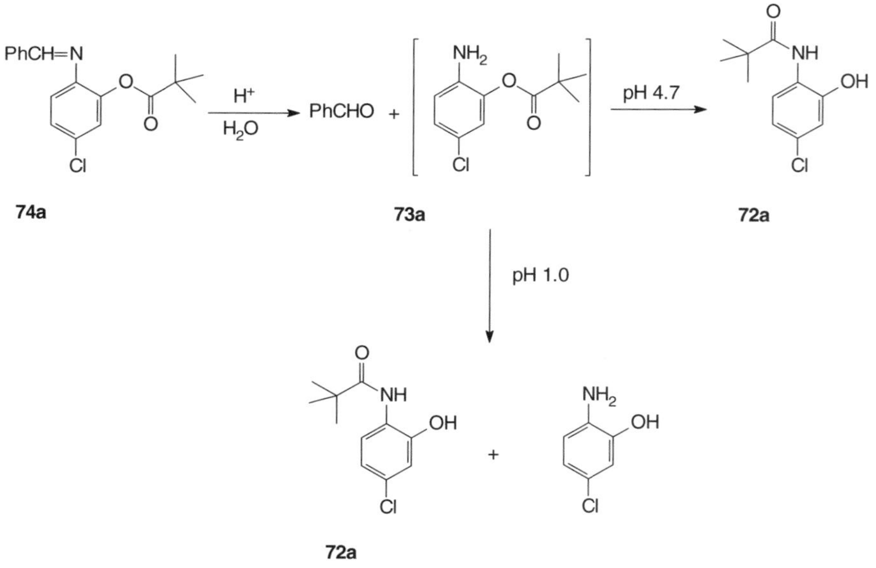

Scheme 30

compounds, apparently by single electron transfer from an arylamino radical or radical cation.[69] A mechanism was proposed in which single electron transfer from Fe^{2+} to the ester occurred within a complex.[68,69] The resulting arylamino radical or its conjugate acid could then be reduced to the amine by a second Fe^{2+} or another species capable of electron or H· transfer. N-acylated esters such as **46a–f** and **47** do not undergo reduction by Fe^{2+} with accompanying rate accelerations.[58,68] Apparently the N-acylated materials are not able to efficiently complex with Fe^{2+}.[68]

The nature of the rearrangement reaction was probed by Heesing and co-workers who examined the extent of ^{18}O scrambling in O-alkyl or O-arylsulfonyl-N-benzoyl-N-phenylhydroxylamines during their rearrangement to the isomeric O-alkyl or O-arylsulfonyl-*ortho*-benzamidophenols (Scheme 31).[70] The results of scrambling in esters with the ^{18}O label at the ester oxygen and sulfonyl oxygens are complementary so only the results for

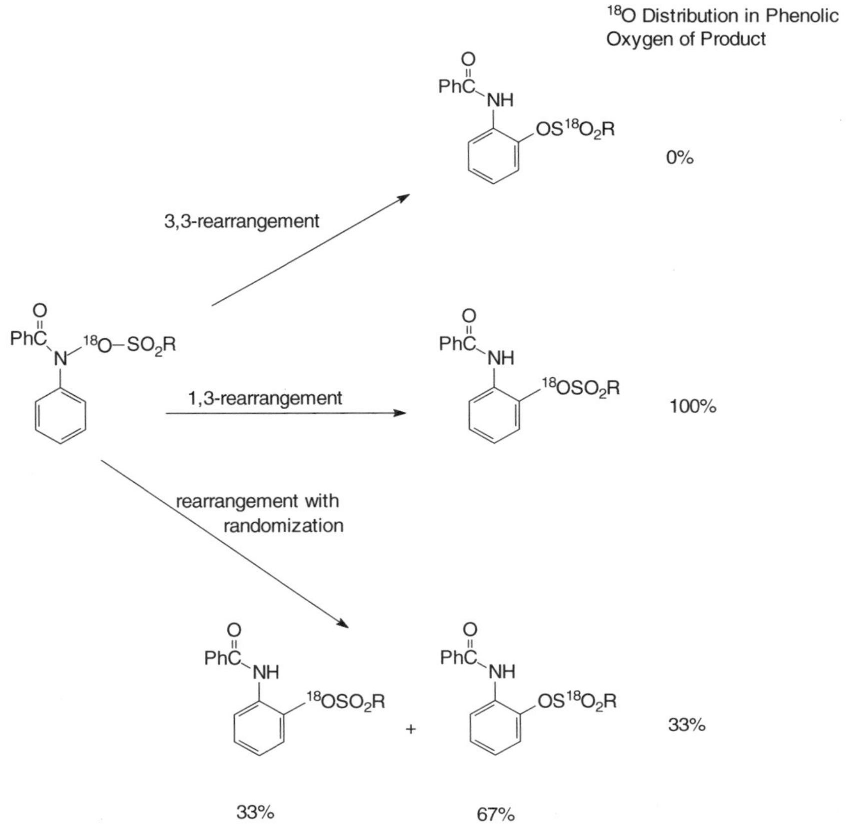

Scheme 31

esters labelled in the ester oxygen are shown in Scheme 31. Three possible outcomes that can be characterized by the % of the ^{18}O label in the phenol oxygen of the product are shown. Rearrangement of the *para*-tosyl ester in a series of non-hydroxylic solvents at 0–20°C proceeded with a label distribution in the phenol oxygen of the product that ranged from 20% in dioxane, 25% in ether, and 29% in pyridine, to 33% in acetonitrile.[70a] This corresponds to label randomization ranging from 61% in dioxane to 100% in acetonitrile. The scrambling increases to that expected for complete randomization as the solvent polarity increases. The label distribution was not changed by performing the reaction under UV irradiation, so radical processes were not considered. The authors favored a mechanism involving a short-lived ion pair that, in low polarity solvents, collapsed to products before complete randomization of the ^{18}O label could occur. The results could also be explained by a solvent-dependent combination of an ion pair mechanism with complete randomization and a 3,3-concerted rearrangement that is favored by solvents of low polarity.

Rearrangement of the same ester in MeOH surprisingly led to a distribution of the label in the phenol oxygen of the product of 43%.[70b] This is consistent with 85% of rearrangement proceeding via a process leading to randomization and 15% by the equivalent of a 1,3-rearrangement. It was suggested that the protic solvent may slow down rotation of the sulfonate ion through H-bonding interactions which prevent complete randomization of the label.[70b] Underwood found similar labelling results in the rearrangement products **40a** formed during the hydrolysis of **39a**.[55] These results could be interpreted in terms of short-lived ion pairs in which label randomization is incomplete, or in terms of a concerted mechanism in competition with an ion pair mechanism in which randomization is complete.

The first serious attempt to calculate the properties of N-arylnitrenium ions occurred in 1981 when Ford and Scribner published their results of a semi-empirical molecular orbital study at the MNDO level.[71] The MNDO calculations predicted that the ions **75a–l** (Scheme 32) are all ground state singlets by between 18 kcal/mol and 43 kcal/mol. The calculations showed that both the singlet and triplet states of these ions were stabilized relative to NH_2^+ by electron donation from the aromatic ring, but the stabilization of the singlet state was considerably larger. Calculated bond lengths for the singlet state were consistent with considerable contributions from the canonical structures shown in Scheme 32. In particular, the bond between the ring carbon and nitrogen in all twelve cases was calculated to be between 1.29–1.30 Å, considerably shorter than the 1.42 Å calculated for aniline by the same method.[71] The charges calculated for nitrogen in the cations were between 0.00 and −0.22 in all cases indicating again that the quinoid canonical structures of Scheme 32 were dominant contributors.

Free energy profiles for the reaction of **75b** with H_2O at the 2-, 3-, and 4-positions of the aromatic ring, and at N in both the gas phase and in

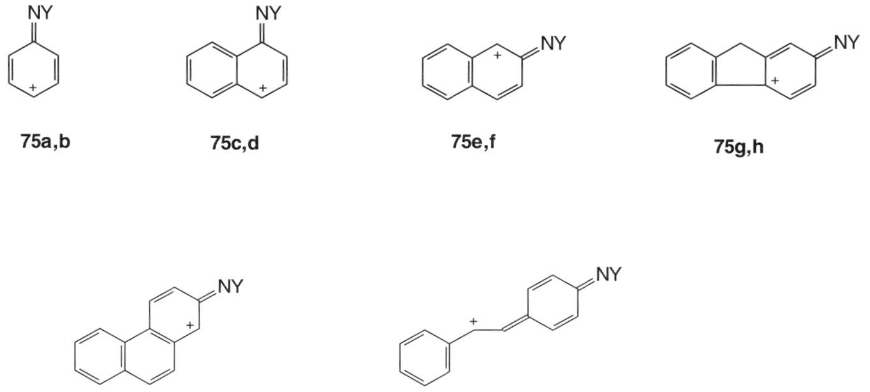

75a,b 75c,d 75e,f 75g,h

75i,j 75k,l

a,c,e,g,i,k Y = H
b,d,f,h,j,l Y = Ac

Scheme 32

aqueous solution, were calculated. The latter calculations relied on empirically estimated free energies of hydration.[72] The calculations showed that attack at C-4 and C-2 followed relatively low energy paths in both the gas phase and in aqueous solution, while the transition state for attack at N appeared to be disfavored by greater than 20 kcal/mol in both the gas phase and in solution.[71] Attack at C-3 did not result in a stable adduct at the MNDO level. Attack at C-2 was favored over attack at C-4 by *ca.* 1–2 kcal/mol in aqueous solution, but the accuracy of the method was insufficient to make any definitive predictions.[71] Experimentally, **46b** generates a yield of 39% of the *para*-product **61**, but only 2% of the *ortho*-product **55b** at 40°C in solutions containing 0.5 M Cl^- (Scheme 24).[58]

By the late 1980s it was clear that a significant number of thermal and photochemical reactions of arylhydroxylamines and their derivatives, N-chloroanilines, aryl azides, anthranilium salts, and other compounds could be explained in terms of nitrenium ions or transition states that resembled nitrenium ions. Since no monoarylnitrenium ion had been directly observed, and data on the lifetimes and quantitative reactivity/selectivity of these species were not available, it was not possible to assess whether the reactions that had been observed were due to free ions, or ion pairs, or preassociation processes. In many cases S_N2 reactions could not be ruled out because appropriate kinetics experiments had not been performed. Most authors had attributed the presence of reduction products in thermal and photochemical reactions to triplet ions, but calculations suggested that the triplet species may not be accessible in thermal processes. It was clear that singlet ions could be reduced under certain conditions, so the presence of the reduction product was not a reliable indicator of the presence of triplet ions. Some reduction reactions of the parent compounds did not involve nitrenium ions at all so the presence of reduction products was not a reliable indicator of either singlet or triplet nitrenium ions.

Since differences were often reported in product yields from photochemical and thermal reactions, it was not clear that the same intermediate was generated in both cases. This issue was complicated by the fact that the temperatures under which the two experiments were run were usually quite different. The acid–base chemistry of nitrenium ions was largely unexplored so it was not known under what conditions these species could be protonated or deprotonated. It had also not been demonstrated that nitrenium ions played any role in the biological activity of mutagenic and carcinogenic esters of N-arylhydroxylamines or hydroxamic acids, particularly in their reactions with the DNA bases. Over the next decade these issues would be resolved but many questions about nitrenium ion chemistry would remain unanswered.

3 Nitrenium ion chemistry since *ca.* 1990

REACTIONS WITH N_3^- AND SOLVENT

The results of product and kinetics studies employing Cl^- and I^- had provided evidence for an S_N1 mechanism during the Bamberger rearrangement of certain N-arylhydroxylamines and the hydrolysis of ester derivatives of N-arylhydroxylamines and N-arylhydroxamic acids.[20,22,54–63,67–69] In general, Cl^- was not a very efficient trap for nitrenium ions. While I^- was a more efficient trap, the mechanism of the process that led to reduction was far from clear. Since the absolute magnitude of the microscopic rate constants for Cl^- or I^- trapping was not known, it was not possible to use these trapping data to estimate the lifetime of nitrenium ions in aqueous solution.

Jencks and Richard, and others, had pioneered the use of the "azide clock" to quantitatively assess the lifetime of carbenium ions generated under solvolytic conditions.[73] The method relies on the use of product yield data collected at varying $[N_3^-]$ to determine the N_3^-/solvent selectivity, expressed as the ratio of the second-order rate constant for trapping of the ion by N_3^- and the pseudo-first-order rate constant for trapping of the ion by solvent: k_{az}/k_s. The assumption is made that k_{az} is diffusion limited at *ca.* $5 \times 10^9 \, M^{-1} \, s^{-1}$.[73] This assumption allows k_s to be estimated, and $1/k_s$ provides the lifetime of the ion in the solvent in the absence of added nucleophiles. McClelland and Steenken showed by direct measurement of k_{az} for a series of diarylmethyl and triarylmethyl carbocations that k_{az} is approximately constant at $(5–10) \times 10^9 \, M^{-1} \, s^{-1}$ for ions with $k_s \geqslant 10^5 \, s^{-1}$.[74] The magnitude of the diffusion-limited rate constant was slightly dependent on cation structure, (the diarylmethyl cations had an apparent limit *ca.* 1.6 times that of the triarylmethyl cations) and solvent composition in CH_3CN/H_2O mixtures, but the assumption of a diffusion-limited reaction of carbocations with N_3^- appears to be valid for moderately to highly reactive ions with $k_{az}/k_s \leqslant 5 \times 10^4 \, M^{-1}$.[74]

The application of the azide clock methodology to nitrenium ions was made by Fishbein and McClelland who showed that N_3^- trapped a reactive intermediate identified as the nitrenium ion **75m**, during the Bamberger rearrangement of N-(2,6-dimethylphenyl)hydroxylamine (Scheme 33).[75] Kinetic studies showed that the N_3^--solvent partitioning occurred after the rate-limiting step of the reaction so an S_N2 process could be eliminated. The selectivity ratio, k_{az}/k_s, was determined to be $7.5 \, M^{-1}$. Assuming that k_{az} is diffusion limited, k_s is $7 \times 10^8 \, s^{-1}$, and the approximate lifetime of the ion in H_2O is 1.5 ns.[75] The ion is short lived, but does survive long enough in H_2O to react with non-solvent nucleophiles, albeit inefficiently.

If nitrenium ions derived from metabolites of the carcinogenic aromatic amines also had lifetimes in the ns range, the hypothesis concerning their involvement in amine carcinogenicity might be incorrect because they would not survive long enough to react efficiently with DNA. Novak and co-workers showed that the biphenylyl ions **75n** and **75o** (Scheme 34) exhibit significantly larger k_{az}/k_s of $2.9 \times 10^5 \, M^{-1}$ and $1.0 \times 10^3 \, M^{-1}$, respectively.[76] The extended π-conjugation provided by the distal phenyl ring has a large effect on the kinetic lability of these two ions, while the N-acetyl group of **75o** has remarkably little effect compared to **75n**. Based on an estimated k_{az}/k_s of $1.0 \, M^{-1}$ for N-phenylnitrenium ion, **75a**,[77] the *para*-phenyl group kinetically stabilizes a nitrenium ion by *ca.* 2900-fold. The small 3-fold destabilizing effect of the N-acetyl group of **75o** is in sharp contrast to the *ca.* 10^5-fold decrease in hydrolysis rate constant that it exerts.[76]

The isolated reaction products are summarized in Scheme 34. The assumed structure of the major initial product of attack of H_2O, **78**, was based on the

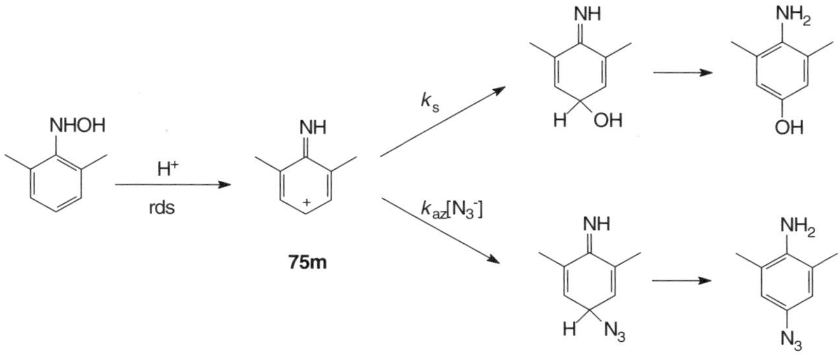

Scheme 33

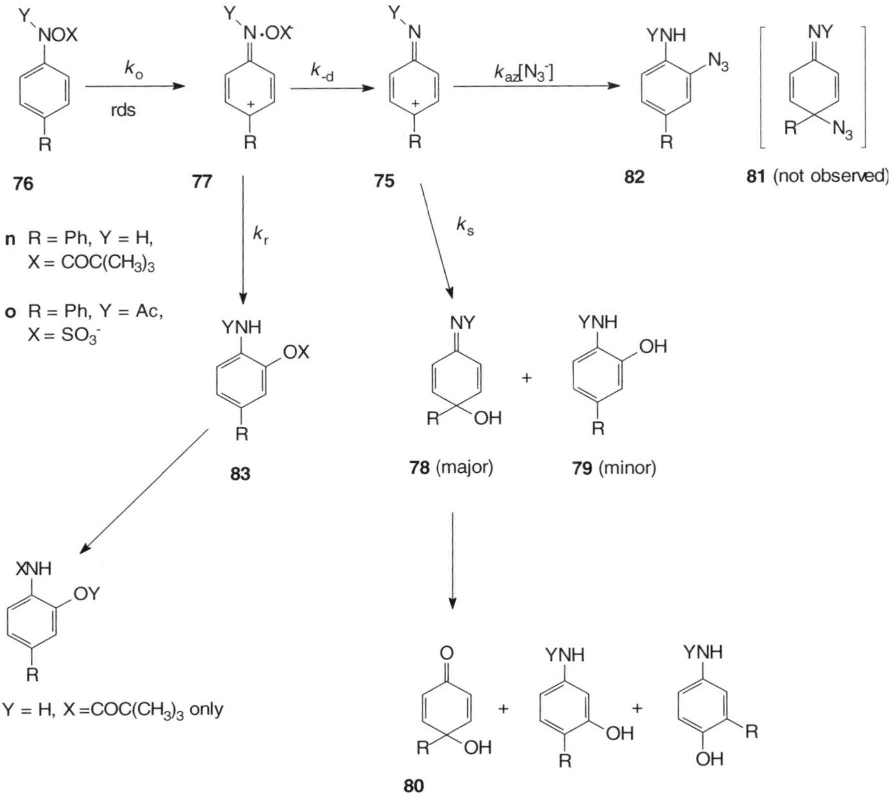

Scheme 34

structures of the stable hydrolysis products. In one case (**78n**) the kinetics of decomposition were slow enough compared to the hydrolysis of the parent ester that the intermediate could be detected by HPLC and its decomposition into **80** could be monitored.[76] The difference in the regioselectivity of N_3^- and H_2O was subsequently observed for other cases in which a *para*-alkyl or *para*-aryl substituent was present. The difference appears to be due to the fact that **78** is stable to loss of OH^- (or H_2O) under the neutral to mildly acidic conditions of this study, but **81** can lose N_3^- readily. If the reaction of **75o** and **75n** with N_3^- is diffusion limited, **81**, would simply be converted into **82** without returning to the free nitrenium ion.

The lifetimes of **75n** and **75o** are calculated to be *ca.* 0.6 μs and 0.2 μs, respectively, if $k_{az} \approx 5 \times 10^9 \, M^{-1} \, s^{-1}$. These are remarkably long lifetimes in comparison with the 4-phenylcumyl cation and the 1-(4-biphenylyl)ethyl cation, which have estimated lifetimes of *ca.* 0.5 ns and 0.1 ns, respectively, in 1/1 TFE-H_2O based on linear free energy correlations found in the literature.[73] The N-acetyl-N-(2-fluorenyl)nitrenium ion, **75h**, was also found to have a large value of k_{az}/k_s of $6.2 \times 10^4 \, M^{-1}$ by azide clock methodology.[78] This corresponds to a lifetime of *ca.* 12 μs if the assumption concerning k_{az} is valid.

McClelland and co-workers subsequently made direct measurements of k_{az} and k_s on these three ions and **75g** generated by laser flash photolysis methods that will be described later.[78,79] Their results are summarized in Table 1. For all four ions, k_{az} was in the range $(4-5) \times 10^9 \, M^{-1} \, s^{-1}$ at ionic strength 0.5. This validated the assumption of diffusion control for k_{az} for nitrenium ions in this range of selectivity. Azide/solvent selectivities determined from directly measured k_{az} and k_s values ranged from $8.6 \times 10^2 \, M^{-1}$ for **75o** to $1.2 \times 10^5 \, M^{-1}$ for **75g**, and were within 15% of the values measured by the azide clock method in the three cases in which comparison was possible. The good agreement was used as one piece of evidence that both experiments were measuring properties of the same intermediates. Lifetimes of these cations were, indeed, in the μs range as predicted by the azide clock measurements.

Azide/solvent selectivity data in predominately aqueous solution have been collected for over 30 nitrenium ions either by the azide clock method or by direct measurement of k_{az} and k_s on ions generated by laser flash

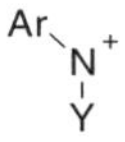

Ar
  \
   N$^+$
   |
   Y

75

84

p Ar = 4'-MeO-4-biphenylyl, Y = H
q Ar = 4'-Me-4-biphenylyl, Y = H
r Ar = 4'-F-4-biphenylyl, Y = H
s Ar = 3'-Me-4-biphenylyl, Y = H
t Ar = 3'-MeO-4-biphenylyl, Y = H
u Ar = 4'-Cl-4-biphenylyl, Y = H
v Ar = 3'-Cl-4-biphenylyl, Y = H
w Ar = 2,5-diMephenyl, Y = H
x Ar = 2-tolyl, Y = H
y Ar = 4-tolyl, Y = H
z Ar = 4-tolyl, Y = Ac
aa Ar = 4-tolyl, Y = Me
bb Ar = 4-biphenylyl, Y = Me
cc Ar = 4-MeOphenyl, Y = H
dd Ar = 4-EtOphenyl, Y = H
ee Ar = 4-EtOphenyl, Y = Ac
ff Ar = 4'-Br-4-stilbenyl, Y = H
gg Ar = 3'-Me-4-stilbenyl, Y = H
hh Ar = 4'-Me-4-stilbenyl, Y = H
ii Ar = 4'-NMeCOCH$_3$-4-stilbenyl, Y = H
jj Ar = 4'-MeO-4-stilbenyl, Y = H
kk Ar = 4-Clphenyl, Y = H
ll Ar = 4-Clphenyl, Y = Ac

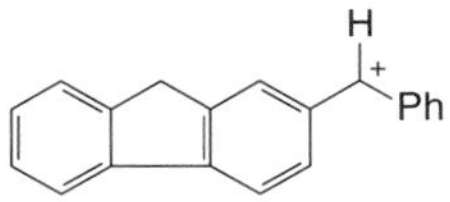

Scheme 35

photolysis.[75–87] These data are presented in Table 1. Where they have been measured, k_{az} and k_s data are given along with the logarithm of the azide/solvent selectivity, $\log S$, where S is defined as the observed azide adduct/hydration product concentration ratio extrapolated to $1\,M\ N_3^-$. For $\log S \geqslant 2.0$, $\log S$ is functionally equivalent to $\log (k_{az}/k_s)$, but for ions with $\log S < 2.0$, N_3^- trapping includes contributions from ion pair and pre-association processes.[87] The deviation between $\log S$ and $\log(k_{az}/k_s)$ is small until $\log S$ approaches 0.[87] The identities of all ions included in Table 1 are described in Schemes 32 through 35. The selectivity data for ions with $\log S < 2.0$ were collected by the azide clock method, while data for those ions with $\log S \geqslant 2.0$ were obtained by both methods.

Several observations can be made from examination of the data:

(1) The values of k_{az} cluster around $5 \times 10^9\,M^{-1}\,s^{-1}$ at ionic strength 0.5 and around $1 \times 10^{10}\,M^{-1}\,s^{-1}$ at ionic strength 0.0. Only the most selective ions such as **75p** and **75jj** deviate significantly from this trend and even these ions have k_{az} within a factor of 2 of the apparent diffusion limits. It appears that the assumption that k_{az} is diffusion limited is valid as long as $k_s > 10^4\,s^{-1}$ or $k_{az}/k_s < 5 \times 10^5\,M^{-1}$.

(2) The N-acetyl substituent decreases $\log S$ by a small amount, which varies from about 0.2 to 0.95. This small effect is consistent with a cation structure in which the positive charge is primarily located on the *para*-carbon of the aromatic ring and the C—N bond is nearly a fully formed double bond so that the N-acetyl substituent has very little interaction with the positive charge.[81]

(3) In general, nitrenium ions are several orders of magnitude longer lived in aqueous solution than are carbenium ions of analogous structure. The lifetimes of the 4-biphenylylnitrenium ions, **75n** and **75o**, and analogous carbenium ions have already been discussed. A similar observation has been made for the 2-fluorenyl ions **75g** and **75h** that are 100- to 200-fold less reactive with H_2O in aqueous solution than **84**, in spite of the substantial stabilizing effect of the phenyl substituent of **84**.[78] Even the highly reactive unsubstituted ion **75a** appears to be about 20-fold more kinetically stable in H_2O than is the 1-phenylethyl carbocation.[77,80] This long lifetime has been attributed to the kinetic barrier associated with the loss of aromatic resonance that must occur when nitrenium ions suffer attack by solvent at the ring carbons (see Schemes 34 and 36). Since benzylic carbocations undergo nucleophilic attack at the benzylic carbon, no similar kinetic barrier can exist for the carbocations.[78]

(4) Effects of aryl and vinyl substituents on cation stability are quite large. The biphenylyl ions **75n** and **75o** have *ca.* 10^3-fold longer lifetimes in aqueous solution than do their 4-tolyl counterparts, **75y** and **75z**. The 4-stilbenyl ions **75k** and **75l** have lifetimes that are *ca.* 300-fold longer than the corresponding 4-tolyl ions.

Table 1 Rate constants and selectivity data for reactions of nitrenium ions with N_3^- and solvent.[a]

Ion	$10^{-9} k_{az}$ ($M^{-1} s^{-1}$)	k_s (s^{-1})	$\log S$
75a			0.02^b
75b			-0.15^c
75d			-0.15^d
75f			0.18^d
75g	4.0	3.4×10^4	5.07^e
75h	4.2	7.7×10^4	4.74^f
			4.79^f
			4.76^g
75k	7.9	6.3×10^6	3.10^h
75l	5.3	1.6×10^7	2.52^i
			2.45^j
75m			0.88^k
75n	5.0	1.8×10^6	3.44^e
	9.6	2.7×10^6	3.55^l
			3.46^m
75o	5.1	5.9×10^6	2.94^f
			3.00^m
75p	6.1	1.6×10^3	6.59^l
75q	9.2	2.7×10^5	4.53^l
75r	9.4	1.3×10^6	3.85^l
75s	9.2	1.5×10^6	3.79^l
75t	7.9	2.5×10^6	3.50^l
75u	10.0	2.5×10^6	3.60^l
75v	10.2	1.3×10^7	2.89^l
75w			0.47^b
75x			0.37^b
75y			0.49^g
75z			0.04^g
75aa			1.66^g
75bb			4.15^g
75cc	5.4	1.8×10^6	3.48^n
75dd	5.3	1.1×10^6	3.68^n
75ee			2.73^g
75ff	7.8	6.5×10^6	3.08^h
75gg	7.8	4.6×10^6	3.23^h
75hh	7.4	1.5×10^6	3.69^h
75ii	6.5	5.6×10^5	4.06^h
75jj	4.2	6.1×10^4	4.83^h
75kk			1.38^o
75ll			0.46^p

[a] Conditions: 5% CH_3CH-H_2O, $\mu = 0.5$ ($NaClO_4$), $T = 20°C$, unless otherwise indicated. If k_{az} and k_s are reported, the rate constants were directly measured from photochemically generated ions. If only $\log S$ is reported, the selectivity was measured by the azide clock procedure. S is the observed [azide adduct]/[hydration product] ratio extrapolated to 1 M N_3^-.
[b] Reference 80: H_2O at 25°C, $\mu = 1.0$. This value is derived from Br^- trapping, but it appears that $k_{Br} \approx k_{az}$.
[c] Ref. 81: at 50°c. [d] Ref. 82. [e] Ref. 79. [f] Ref. 78. [g] Ref. 81. [h] Ref. 83: 20% CH_3CN-H_2O, $\mu = 0.0$. [i] Ref. 83. [j] Ref. 84. [k] Ref. 75: H_2O at 40°C, $\mu = 1.0$. [l] Ref. 85. 20% CH_3CN-H_2O, $\mu = 0.0$. [m] Ref. 76. [n] Ref. 86: H_2O. [o] Ref. 87. [p] Ref. 87: at 50°C.

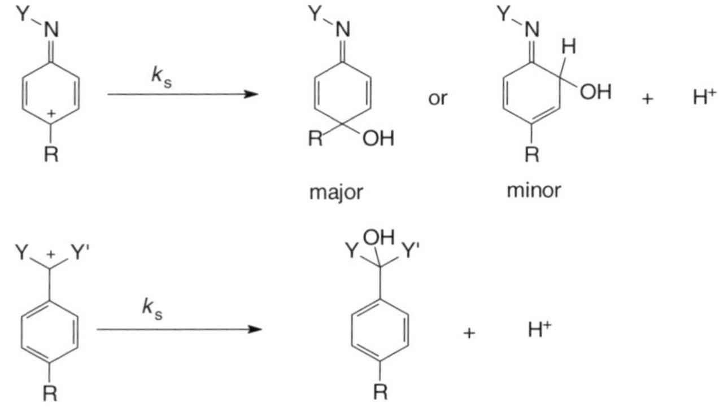

Scheme 36

In general, $\log(k_{az}/k_s)$ or $\log k_s$ for 1-arylethyl, cumyl, diarylmethyl and triarylmethyl carbocations correlate well with σ^+ or σ^{c+}.[73,74] The plots of $\log k_s$ vs. σ^+ for diarylmethyl and triarylmethyl carbocations are curved, but not highly scattered.[74] The curvature is such that π-donor substituents stabilize the cations to a greater extent than predicted by σ^+ correlation for substituents that are not π-donors.[74] The plots become linear when σ^+ is replaced by σ^{c+}, a scale based on ^{13}C NMR chemical shifts of cumyl cations.[74,88] The data presented in Fig. 1 show that the rate constants for hydrololysis of ester precursors of ArNAc$^+$ correlate with σ^+ with $\rho^+ \approx -8$, but $\log S$ for the same nitrenium ions shows essentially no correlation with σ^+. A similar scatter plot is observed for ArNH$^+$. Since k_{az} is diffusion limited throughout the series of nitrenium ions listed in Table 1, the failure of these correlations is due to the failure of $\log k_s$ to correlate with σ^+. Apparently the transition states for generation of the nitrenium ions from ester precursors resemble those for the solvolysis of cumyl chlorides, the reaction upon which the σ^+ scale is based. This correlation suggests that a significant amount of positive charge builds up on N in the transition state for N—O bond cleavage. This is in accord with the large rate decrease caused by the N-acetyl substituent. On the other hand, the substituent effects measured by the σ^+ scale fail to predict the rate of subsequent reaction of the nitrenium ion with H_2O. This is not particularly surprising because the reaction of nitrenium ions with solvent does not resemble that of arylcarbenium ions (Scheme 36). For carbenium ions, k_s is the rate constant for essentially the reverse of the reaction for which the σ^+ scale was developed, while k_s for nitrenium ions is the rate constant for a process that does not resemble the defining reaction for the σ^+ scale.

Since the σ^+ scale lacks predictive value for the reactions of nitrenium ions with solvent, attempts have been made to develop other correlations.[81,83,85,89] Novak and co-workers have shown that there is a correlation between $\log S$

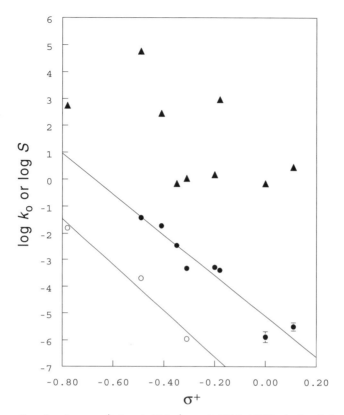

Fig. 1 Log S or $\log k_{\mathrm{o}}$ vs. σ^+ for ArNAc$^+$ or ArN(Ac)OX. ▲: $\log S$ for ArNAc$^+$, ●: $\log k_{\mathrm{o}}$ for ArN(Ac)OSO$_3^-$, ○: $\log k_{\mathrm{o}}$ for ArN(Ac)OC(O)C(CH$_3$)$_3$. Lines are determined from non-weighted least-squares fits.

and ΔE calculated at the RHF 6–31G*/3–21G level for the isodesmic reaction of Scheme 37.[81,89] Figure 2 shows such a correlation for 22 of the ions of Table 1. There is very little scatter in the data considering that the calculations include 1-naphthyl, 2-naphthyl, 4-biphenylyl, 2-fluorenyl, 4-stilbenyl and various monocyclic nitrenium ions. Except for the least selective ions, (**75a,b,f**) and the 4′-methoxy-4-biphenylyl ion (**75p**) there is a good linear correlation between $\log S$ and ΔE. Since k_{az} is diffusion limited for these ions, the correlation implies a direct proportionality between $-\log k_{\mathrm{s}}$ and ΔE. The slope of the correlation line calculated from 18 of the 22 points (0.19 ± 0.02) shows that about 25% of $\Delta(\Delta E)$ is observed in the transition states for cation hydration at 20°C.[81,89]

The remarkable lack of scatter indicates that the overriding factor in determining the kinetic lability of these ions in aqueous solution is their thermodynamic stability toward hydration.[89] The levelling off of $\log S$ at

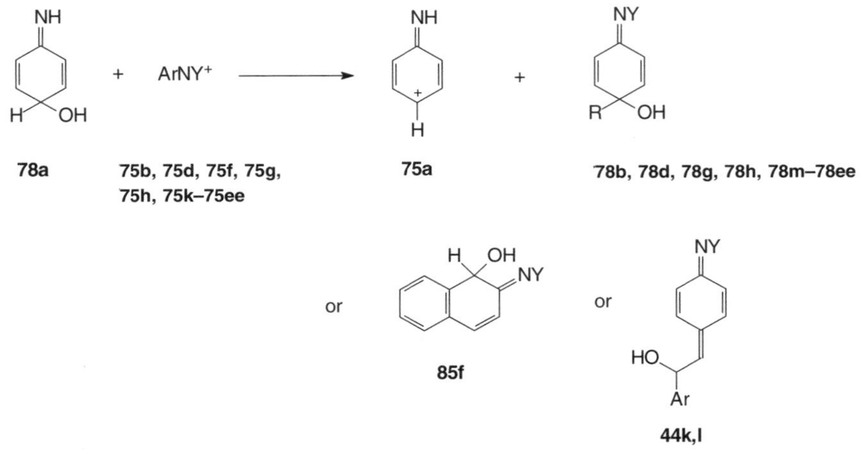

Scheme 37

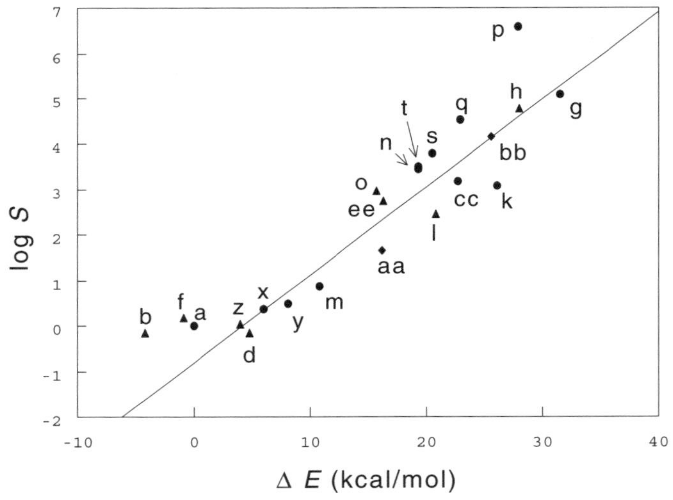

Fig. 2 Log S vs. ΔE of Scheme 37. The individual ions **75** are identified. The least-squares line is determined from all data points except those for **75a**, **75b**, **75f** and **75p**.

$ca.$ 0 for the three least selective ions is probably caused by the onset of preassociation trapping for these ions.[87] The extrapolated values for k_s for these ions, based on the correlation line and the assumption that $k_{az} = 5 \times 10^9 \, M^{-1} s^{-1}$, are $3.2 \times 10^{10} \, s^{-1}$ for **75a**, $2.1 \times 10^{11} \, s^{-1}$ for **75b** and $4.8 \times 10^{10} \, s^{-1}$ for **75f**.[89] These ions are predicted to react with solvent H_2O too rapidly for efficient trapping by non-solvent nucleophiles, so other ineffi-cient trapping mechanisms such as preassociation can compete. The transition to preassociation trapping appears to occur at $k_s \approx 10^{10}\,s^{-1}$. A similar transition has been observed for N_3^- trapping of carbenium ions at $k_s \approx 10^{10}\,s^{-1}$.[73]

The substituent effects calculated for ΔE show that aromatic and vinylic π-donors in the *para*-position have a stabilizing effect on the nitrenium ions that is much larger than is seen in σ_p^+. For example, σ_p^+ for Me, MeO, and Ph are -0.31, -0.78, and -0.18, respectively, while ΔE for **75y** (Ar = 4-tolyl), **75cc** (Ar = 4-MeOphenyl) and **75n** (Ar = 4-biphenylyl) are 8.1 kcal/mol, 22.7 kcal/mol, and 19.3 kcal/mol, respectively.[89] The calculations and experimental data show that a *para*-phenyl substituent is about as stabilizing for a nitrenium ion as is a *para*-methoxy substituent.[89] This unusual stabilization is the major reason that correlations of $\log S$ vs. σ^+ are so scattered for nitrenium ions. Substituent effects at N are relatively small. Replacement of NH by NAc destabilizes the ion toward hydration by $4.5 \pm 1.0\,kcal/mol$.[89] Based on the correlation line, at 20°C this amounts to a predicted increase in k_s by a factor of 4 to 11 when NH is replaced by NAc. The experimentally observed range of 1.5 to 9.0 (Table 1) is very close to this prediction. These calculated substituent effects on the thermodynamics of hydration and the calculated geometries of nitrenium ions (discussed in another section) indicate that for most nitrenium ions the canonical structure **II** of Scheme 38 is dominant.[81,89]

If this is the case, substituent effects in the distal ring of a 4-biphenylyl-nitrenium ion should resemble those of a benzylic carbenium ion. Ren and McClelland showed that substituent effects on $\log k_s$ for a series of distally substituted 4-biphenylylnitrenium ions (**75n, 75p–v**) were carbenium-ion-like.[85] A plot of $\log k_s$ vs. σ^+ was not highly scattered but was non-linear and similar to those previously described for diarylmethyl and triarylmethyl

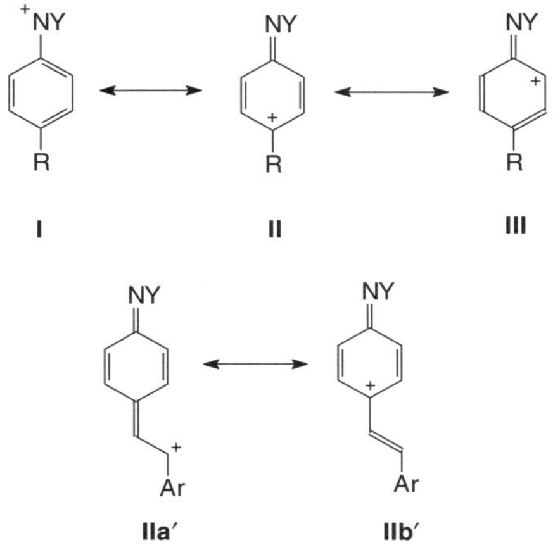

Scheme 38

carbocations.[74] The data could be satisfactorily fit to the Yukawa–Tsuno equation (equation 3), where k_s^0 is the rate constant for the unsubstituted ion.[90]

$$\log(k_s/k_s^0) = \rho[\sigma + r^+(\sigma^+ - \sigma)] \tag{3}$$

Yukawa–Tsuno parameters for correlations of $\log k_s$ for 1-arylethyl cations, mono-substituted triarylmethyl cations, and the 4-biphenylylnitrenium ions are provided in Table 2. The results show that the 4-biphenylylnitrenium ions are intermediate between the 1-arylethyl and triarylmethyl carbocations, both in absolute reactivity and in sensitivity to resonance effects of the substituents. These distally substituted 4-biphenylylnitrenium ions react with H_2O very much like substituted benzylic carbocations.[85] McClelland and co-workers found that distally substituted 4-stilbenylnitrenium ions (**75k, 75ff–75jj**) show similar behavior.[83] $\log k_s$ for the 4-biphenylylnitrenium ions has a linear correlation with $\log k_s$ for similarly substituted 4-stilbenylnitrenium ions with a slope of 1.6.[83] The lower sensitivity of the 4-stilbenyl ions to substituents in the distal ring was attributed to greater delocalization of the charge away from the distal ring due to the availability of the canonical structure **IIb'** (Scheme 38).[83]

The mechanism of Scheme 34 quantitatively explains the yields of rearrangement, solvent-derived and N_3^--derived products of hydrolysis of hydroxylamine or hydroxamic acid esters that yield selective nitrenium ions ($\log S \geqslant 2$).[87] One of the characteristics of these hydrolysis reactions is the lack of sensitivity of the yield of the rearrangement product **83** to N_3^- at concentrations sufficient to reduce the yield of the solvent-derived products to less than 10% of their yield in the absence of N_3^-. This occurs because the tight ion pair **77** has insufficient lifetime to react efficiently with non-solvent nucleophiles. The diffusional separation of the ion pair occurs with a rate constant $k_{-d} \geqslant 10^{10}\,s^{-1}$ in H_2O, so the maximum lifetime of **77** is less than 100 ps.[91] The rearrangement process governed by k_r will further reduce the lifetime of **77**. Consider an ion with $\log S = 2$, $k_{-d} = 10^{10}\,s^{-1}$, $k_{az} = 5 \times 10^9\,M^{-1}\,s^{-1}$ and N_3^- trapping of the ion pair with the same rate

Table 2 Yukawa–Tsuno parameters for the reaction of carbocations and nitrenium ions with H_2O.[a]

Cation type	ρ	r^+	k_s^0, s^{-1}
1-arylethyl	2.7	2.3	$\sim 1 \times 10^{11}$
triarylmethyl	1.3	3.6	1.5×10^5
4-biphenylylnitrenium	1.8	2.8	2.7×10^6

[a]Source: ref. 85.

constant. An N_3^- concentration of 0.1 M traps >90% of **75**, but because of the rapid diffusional separation of **77**, the same concentration of N_3^- would trap less than 5% of **77** and the yield of any rearrangement product would be largely unaffected by N_3^- up to 0.1 M. More selective ions would exhibit even less trapping of the ion pair by N_3^- because lower concentrations of N_3^- would be sufficient to trap **75** to >90%.

This behavior breaks down as the ion becomes less selective, in large part because higher concentrations of N_3^- must be used to trap **75** in N_3^--solvent selectivity experiments and these concentrations allow other trapping mechanisms to be observed. If $\log S = 1$, $[N_3^-] > 0.5\,M$ would be necessary to trap >90% of **75** and, under these conditions, trapping of the ion pair and preassociation must be considered even though they are inefficient processes.[92] An expanded hydrolysis mechanism that includes these processes is given in Scheme 39. The inclusion of preassociation will not change the N_3^- independent hydrolysis kinetics if N_3^- does not provide assistance to the ionization within the diffusional complex **86** so that $k_o' \approx k_o$.

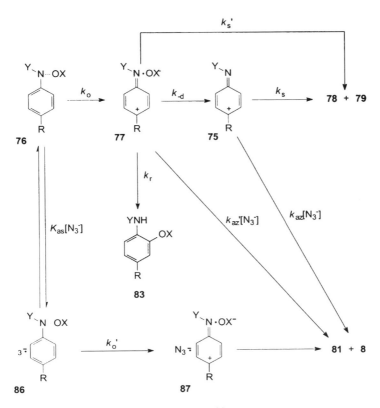

Scheme 39

Trapping of **77** will be a significant process in a narrow range of reactivity with the solvent: $5 \times 10^7 \, \mathrm{s}^{-1} < k_s \approx k'_s < 10^{10} \, \mathrm{s}^{-1}$. If $k_s \approx k'_s < 5 \times 10^7 \, \mathrm{s}^{-1}$ almost all trapping occurs at the free ion, **75**, as discussed above. If $k_s \approx k'_s > 10^{10} \, \mathrm{s}^{-1}$ the lifetimes of both **75** and **77** will be too short for any non-solvent nucleophile to trap to an appreciable extent. Under these conditions the very inefficient preassociation process becomes dominant, provided that the ternary complex **87** goes to products faster than it diffuses apart. Since the reactions of N_3^- with **75a–75ll** are at or near the diffusion limit, it is likely that this is the case, particularly for the less selective ions for which the preassociation process may become important.

An example of a case in which all three processes contribute to the N_3^- trapping is provided in Scheme 40 and Fig. 3. The significant decrease in the yield of the rearrangement product in the N_3^- concentration range required to trap most of the solvent-derived products indicates that N_3^- trapping must occur at some other point in the mechanism in addition to the free ion. The theoretical curves of Fig. 3 were obtained from fitting the experimental product yield data to the mechanism of Scheme 39 with

$$k_r = 4.5 \times 10^9 \, \mathrm{s}^{-1}, \ k_{-d} = 10^{10} \, \mathrm{s}^{-1}, \ k_s = k'_s = 2.1 \times 10^8 \, \mathrm{s}^{-1},$$
$$k_{az} = 5 \times 10^9 \, \mathrm{M}^{-1} \mathrm{s}^{-1}, \ k'_{az} = 7 \times 10^9 \, \mathrm{M}^{-1} \mathrm{s}^{-1}, \ \text{and} \ K_{as} = 0.3 \, \mathrm{M}^{-1}.^{[87]}$$

The diffusional association constant K_{as} was assumed to be equivalent to the value obtained for benzylic carbocation precursors.[73,92] The parameters k_{-d}, k_{az} and K_{as} were fixed and the other parameters were adjusted to optimize the fit.[87] The data could be fitted to a mechanism in which preassociation was left out, but this required k'_{az} to be $1.3 \times 10^{10} \, \mathrm{M}^{-1} \mathrm{s}^{-1}$, more than twice the diffusion limit observed for nitrenium ion-N_3^- reactions under these

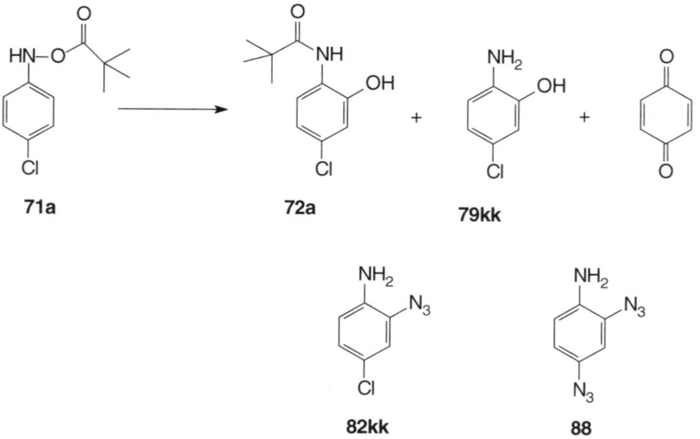

Scheme 40

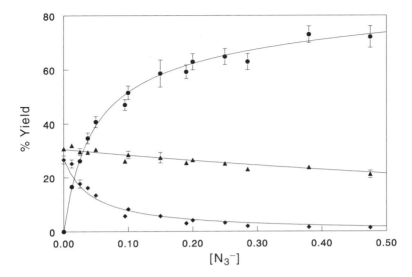

Fig. 3 Yields of reaction products for **71a** as a function of $[N_3^-]$. ●: combined yield of **82kk** and **88**, ▲ yield of **72a**, ◆: yield of **79kk**. Lines are derived from a fit to the mechanism of Scheme 39 using the rate constants given in the text.

conditions. At 0.475 M N_3^-, the calculated contributions to the N_3^- trapping by the free ion, ion pair, and preassociation are 68%, 22%, and 17%, respectively. In the range of k_s in which ion pair trapping can be a major contributor to the N_3^- trapping it will always be accompanied by trapping of the free ion, or preassociation trapping.

Scheme 41 and Fig. 4 provide an example of a case in which preassociation can account for all of the observed N_3^- trapping. In this case trapping by N_3^- amounts to only 13% of reaction products at 0.475 M N_3^-. The calculated value of k_s of $2.1 \times 10^{11}\,\mathrm{s}^{-1}$ for **75b**, obtained from the correlation of $\log S$ with ΔE described above, was used in the fit. It was assumed that the k_s' had the same value, and k_{-d} was fixed at $10^{10}\,\mathrm{s}^{-1}$. Since the fit had very little dependence on k_{az} or k_{az}', these were also fixed at $5 \times 10^9\,\mathrm{M}^{-1}\,\mathrm{s}^{-1}$. The only adjustable parameters were k_r ($2.8 \times 10^{11}\,\mathrm{s}^{-1}$) and K_{as} ($0.25\,\mathrm{M}^{-1}$).[87] Rearrangement and reaction with solvent are so rapid that N_3^- trapping of the ion pair or free ion cannot compete.

The hydrolysis of other esters that show similar low selectivity for trapping by N_3^-, Cl^- or Br^- most likely proceeds through preassociation. This includes **46e**, **46f**, **71b**, and **71c**, (Schemes 28 and 29) and ester precursors of **75e** and **75f** (Scheme 32).[58,67,68,82,89] Fishbein and McClelland showed that a large proportion of the Br^- and Cl^- trapping that occurs during the Bamberger rearrangement of N-phenylhydroxylamine can be accounted for by preassociation.[80] They estimated k_s of $8 \times 10^9\,\mathrm{s}^{-1}$ for **75a** if preassociation is

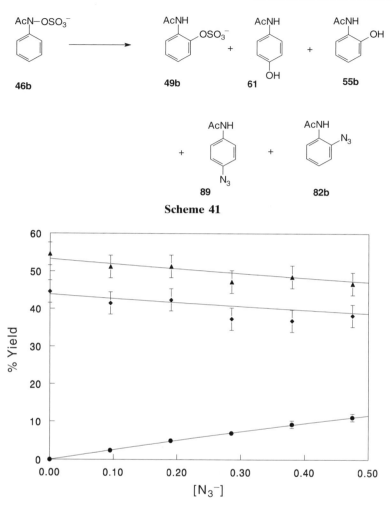

Scheme 41

Fig. 4 Yields of reaction products for **46b** as a function of $[N_3^-]$. ●: combined yield of **82b** and **89**, ▲: yield of **49b**, ◆: combined yield of **55b** and **61**. Lines are derived from a fit to the mechanism of Scheme 39 using the rate constants given in the text.

included in the hydrolysis mechanism.[80] This is within a factor of 4 of the value calculated from the correlation line of Fig. 2.[89]

Fishbein and McClelland examined the roles of ion pairs in the decomposition of O-aroyl-N-acetyl-N-(2,6-dimethylphenyl)hydroxylamines (**90**, Scheme 42).[93] These esters give rise to a nitrenium ion that has an estimated lifetime of *ca.* 0.25–0.50 ns based on the lifetime of **75m** (1.5 ns) and an assumed 3- to 6-fold decrease in that lifetime caused by substituting NAc

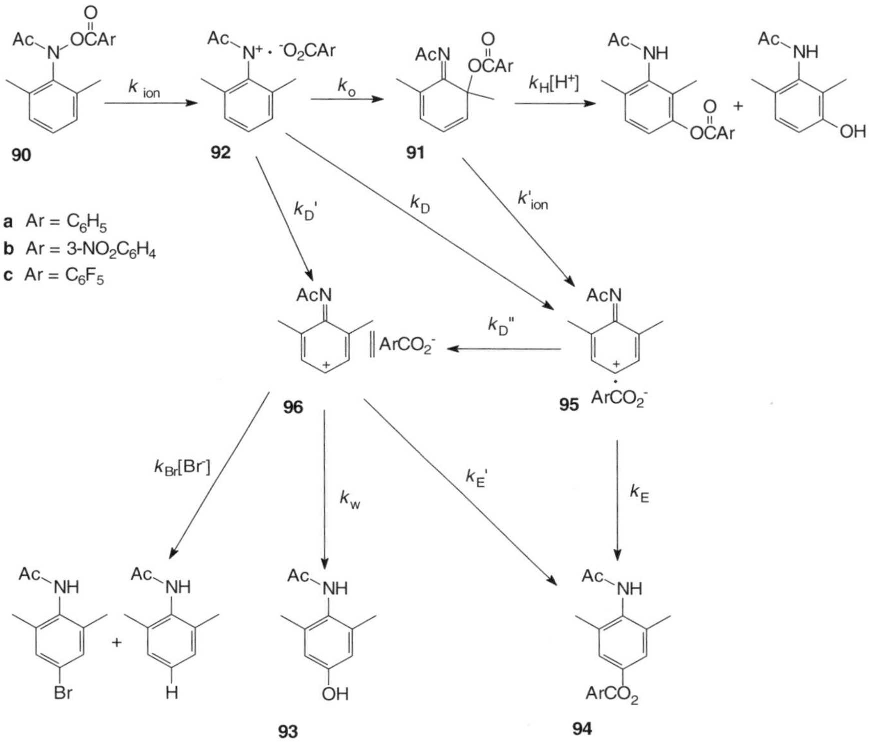

Scheme 42

for NH. This estimate is within the range of lifetimes for ions that exhibit ion pair and preassociation trapping by non-solvent nucleophiles.[87] The hydrolysis of these esters also gives rise to isolatable cyclohexadiene intermediates **91** that yield *meta*-substitution products in H^+ catalyzed processes and *para*-substitution products in uncatalyzed processes.[94]

The lack of effect of Br^- on the yield of the *meta*-substitution products up to 1.0 M Br^- suggests that the ion pair derived from ionization of the ester (**92**, Scheme 42) is too short-lived for trapping by non-solvent nucleophiles. On the other hand, H^+ can decrease the yield of the *meta*-substitution products substantially in $HClO_4$ solutions ranging from 0.1 M to 1.0 M.[93] Since protonation of carboxylates by H^+ occurs with a rate constant about 10-fold larger than that for the diffusion-controlled reaction of a carbocation or nitrenium ion with a non-solvent nucleophile,[91a] it is possible for H^+ to trap **92** under conditions in which Br^- cannot. The magnitude of the H^+ trapping of **92c** led to an estimated lifetime for this species of about 11 ps.[93]

Although Br^- did not effectively trap the intermediates leading to the *meta*-products it did affect the yields of the *para*-products, although to different extents. The yield of the *para*-phenol, **93**, was reduced more effectively by

Br⁻ than was the yield of the *para*-ester, **94**. The differential effects of Br⁻ on the yield of these two products led to consideration of the mechanism of Scheme 42, in which three ion pair intermediates are invoked.[93] Variation in the yields of the *para*-products as a function of [H⁺] and [Br⁻] led to estimates of the lifetimes for **95c** of *ca.* 21 ps and for **96c** of 0.25–0.5 ns.[93] The estimated lifetimes suggest that both **92** and **95** should be thought of as tight ion pairs while **96** appears to be a solvent-separated ion pair.[93] Internal return of **96** to the *para*-ester, **94**, amounts to about 20% of the fate of **96** in the absence of Br⁻, according to the fitting procedure, so this is apparently not an insignificant path for this ion pair. Curiously, **96** has about the same lifetime one would expect for the free ion, and it is not clear what role, if any, the free ion plays in this reaction. The authors did not include a preassociation path which would have accounted for some of the Br⁻ derived products.

The mechanisms proposed by both of these groups to explain the details of the chemistry of esters that give rise to short-lived nitrenium ions are not the only mechanisms that could fit these data. Further developments in this area will require application of picosecond spectroscopic methods to ion pairs generated by laser flash photolysis.

The regioselectivity of the reaction of nitrenium ions with H_2O is of interest. Attack at either the *ortho-* or *para*-position is possible, (Scheme 43) and other sites of attack are possible if R extends the π-conjugation of

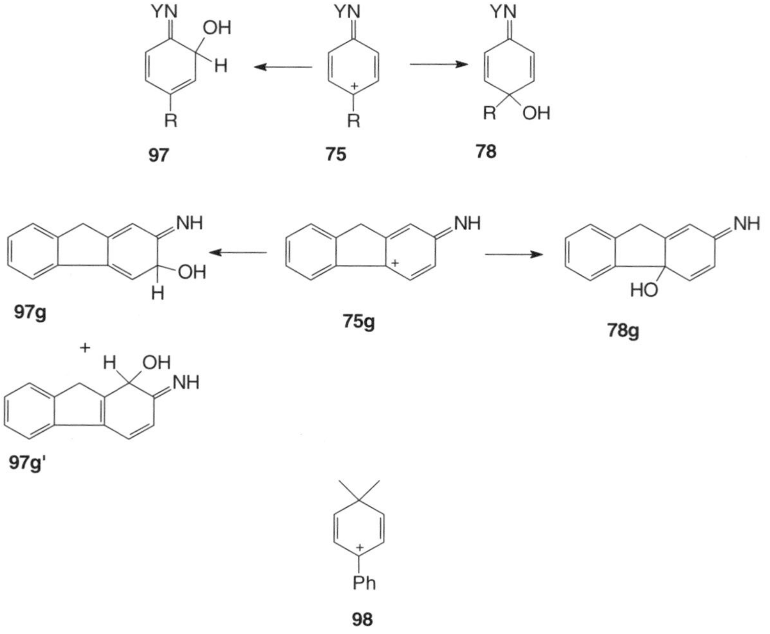

Scheme 43

the ion. Attack at N is also possible, but there is no evidence that this ever happens for H_2O. With a few notable exceptions (Scheme 37), attack at the *para*-position is favored over any other site by a factor of at least 10/1 and typically by >50/1.[89] Since **78** and **97** are not generally isolatable, the thermo-dynamic stability of these two products is not known, but calculations suggest that in most cases the two products are within 3 kcal/mol of each other.[71,89] An exception to this generalization is **75g**, in which the possible *ortho*-products **97g** and **97g′** are stabilized relative to the *para*-adduct **78g** by 6–7 kcal/mol due to ring strain in **78g**.[89] Even in this case the *para*-product is the predominant product of attack of H_2O.[89] Thermodynamic stability of the product does not govern the regioselectivity of this reaction.

The 6,6-dimethyl-3-phenylbenzenium ion, **98**, has a lifetime in H_2O that is similar to that of **75n**: *ca.* 150 ns for **98** and 300 ns for **75n** under similar conditions.[95] Attack at the *ortho*-position of **98** is kinetically favored over attack at the *para*-position by a factor of 10, and the *ortho*-product is also the thermodynamically favored product ($K = 290$).[95] The nitrenium ion has the opposite kinetic preference even though calculations suggest that **97n** is the thermodynamically favored product.[89,95] It has been suggested that this unique regioselectivity of the nitrenium ions is due to positive charge localization at the *para*-carbon or, alternatively, to the larger magnitude of LUMO coefficients at the *para*-position of the nitrenium ion.[71,89,95] The underlying reason for the differentiation of the *ortho*- and *para*-positions of the nitrenium ions is the C-N dipole that destabilizes positive charge at the *ortho*-positions.

The exceptions to the general rule of preference for *para*-attack are cases in which, according to calculations, the *para*-product is destabilized relative to the observed *ortho*-product (**85f**) by at least 35 kcal/mol, or the observed conjugated product of attack on the β-carbon of a 4-stilbenyl ion (**44k,l**) is stabilized by *ca.* 5 kcal/mol relative to the product of *para*-attack.[89] In the latter case calculations at the RHF/6-31G*//3-21G level suggest that attack of H_2O on the β-carbon may be facilitated by the large magnitude of the LUMO coefficient at that carbon.[89]

The initial products of attack of H_2O on the nitrenium ion are not stable in aqueous solution, although they have been isolated or observed in several cases and detailed kinetic studies of their decomposition have been made.[59,66,76,83,84,96–98] The intermediate **85f** undergoes rearomatization, while **44k** and **44l** are attacked by a second H_2O to generate diols as in Scheme 22.[83,84] Both **44k** and **44l** can be observed during laser flash photolysis experiments and the kinetics of their decomposition in H_2O have been monitored.[83] The usual fate of the imino quinol products **78** include hydrolysis of the imine functionality, dienone-phenol rearrange-ment, an addition–elimination pathway that leads to net *meta*-substitution of H_2O on the nitrenium ion, or generation of benzoquinone imines if R is a good leaving group.[59,62,66,76,96] These paths have been summarized in

Schemes 24 and 34. Not all specific examples follow these generalized pathways. Although **78h** does decompose predominately into **99** (Scheme 44) at neutral pH,[97] evidence suggests that it may not do so via an addition–elimination mechanism.[98] This intermediate is detectable in reaction mixtures, but it has never been isolated due to its high reactivity.[97] The N-benzoyl analogue **78h′** has been prepared by anodic oxidation of N-benzoyl-2-aminofluorene and has been shown by [18]O labeling experiments to generate **99′** by an intramolecular pathway presumably involving the intermediate **100′**.[98]

In most cases the only isolated product of N_3^- attack on a nitrenium ion is the *ortho*-substitution product **82**.[76,78,87] The *para*-product **81** has never been directly observed but its existence can be inferred in a few cases because of unusual N_3^- adducts that have been isolated.[87] The likely pathways for decomposition of **81**, based on the structures of isolated products, are summarized in Scheme 45.

REACTIONS WITH CARBON, NITROGEN AND SULFUR NUCLEOPHILES

A wide variety of products had been isolated over the years, beginning with Bamberger's own research, that could be thought of as arising from nucleophilic attack of a neutral electron-rich aromatic on either the N or *ortho*- and *para*-carbons of a nitrenium ion (Schemes 2, 10, 12, 15).[13–15,24,36,38,43] In most

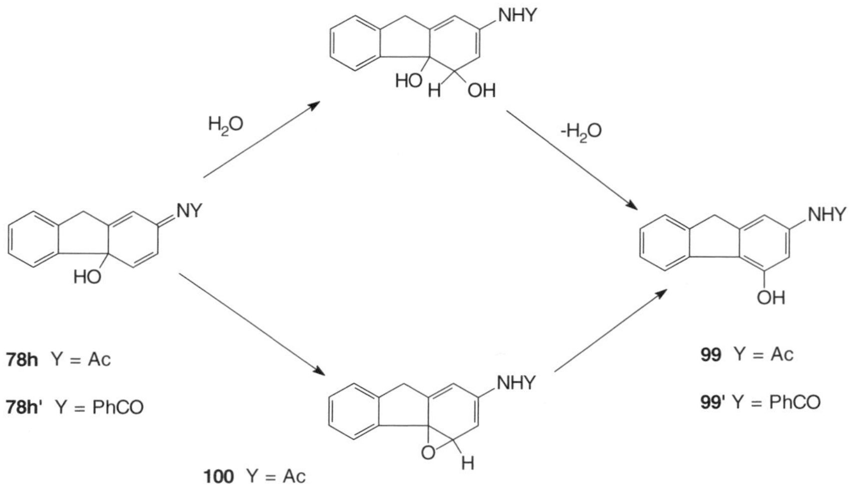

78h Y = Ac

78h′ Y = PhCO

100 Y = Ac

100′ Y = PhCO

99 Y = Ac

99′ Y = PhCO

Scheme 44

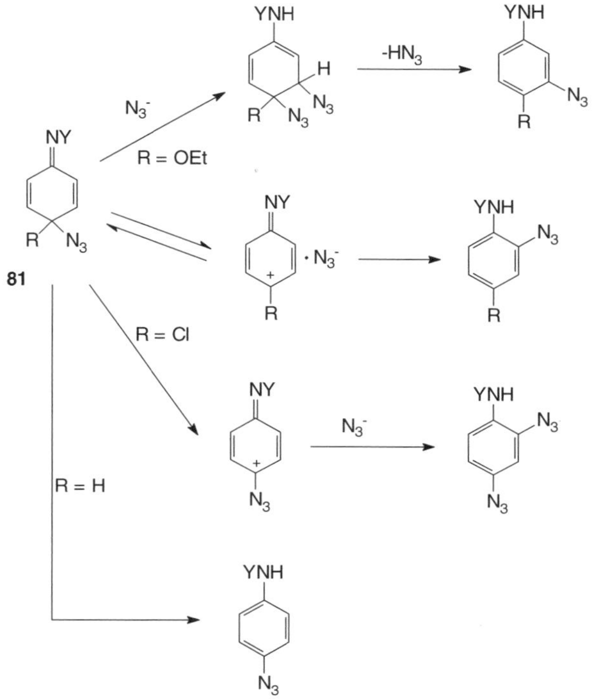

YNH
-HN₃ →
YNH

N₃⁻
R = OEt

NY

R   N₃

81

R = Cl

R = H

NY

YNH

NY · N₃⁻ →

YNH

NY

N₃⁻ →

YNH

YNH

Scheme 45

of these cases the necessary kinetics experiments to distinguish the possible nitrenium ion mechanism from S_N2 or other mechanisms had not been performed.

The Boche and Novak groups had shown that aromatic amines could react with ester derivatives of hydroxylamines through an S_N2 mechanism.[99,100] This could happen even in a polar solvent such as MeOH with an ester (**76n**) that generates a selective nitrenium ion.[100] Scheme 46 summarizes the products of the kinetically bimolecular reactions of **76n** and **76y** with aniline and N,N-dimethylaniline in MeOH that occur in competition with the apparently S_N1 solvolysis of both esters in MeOH.[100] Although the products were formed in a kinetically bimolecular process, the transition states appear to have cationic character at the aromatic ring of the N undergoing substitution. Rate constants for the solvolysis in MeOH of a series of ring-substituted esters including **76n** and **76y** correlated with σ^+ with a ρ^+ of −8.5, while the second-order rate constants for reaction with either amine correlated with σ^+ with a ρ^+ of −3.0.[100]

The biphenylyl ester **76o** and the 2-fluorenyl esters **76h** and **76h′** react with aniline and N,N-dimethylaniline in MeOH in a kinetically unimolecular

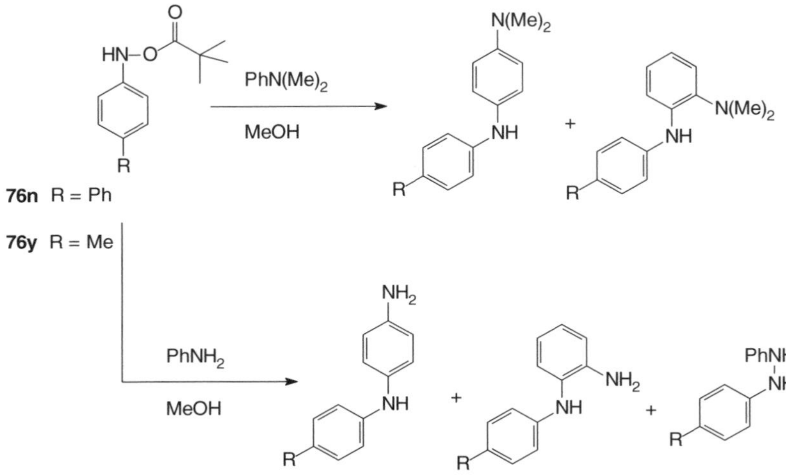

Scheme 46

process that shows characteristics similar to N_3^- trapping in H_2O.[101] The reaction products of aromatic amine trapping of the nitrenium ion are summarized in Scheme 47. There are a greater variety of structures than those observed in the S_N2 reactions, including products derived from attack of either the *para*-carbon or N of the amine on the *ortho*- and *para*-positions of the nitrenium ion as well as the N of the nitrenium ion. The reactions are relatively efficient since 0.1 M amine is sufficient to completely suppress the solvolysis products except for the rearrangement products that appear to be produced from internal return of a tight ion pair.[101] The reduction products are only generated in the presence of N,N-dimethylaniline and they appear to be produced by a single electron transfer from the amine to the nitrenium ion. The by-product of that reduction, generated in equimolar quantities with the reduction product, is **101**, a known product of the decomposition of the N,N-dimethylaniline radical cation in the presence of excess N,N-dimethylaniline.[102] The change in mechanism appears to be caused by steric hindrance to the approach of the aromatic amine in an S_N2 attack at N by the N-acetyl group.

Takeuchi and co-workers showed that the ratio of N- to C-substitution on the apparent intermediate **75a** by a series of aromatics in arene/TFA mixtures was sensitive to the structure of the precursor to **75a** (phenyl azide, N-phenylhydroxylamine or O-trifluoroacetyl-N-phenylhydroxylamine) even though the decomposition rates of these precursors were unaffected by the identity of the arene.[103] This result is consistent with the characterization of **75a** from N_3^- and Br^- trapping studies as a short-lived intermediate that will usually react through ion pair or preassociation processes that may be leaving-group dependent.[80,81,87,89]

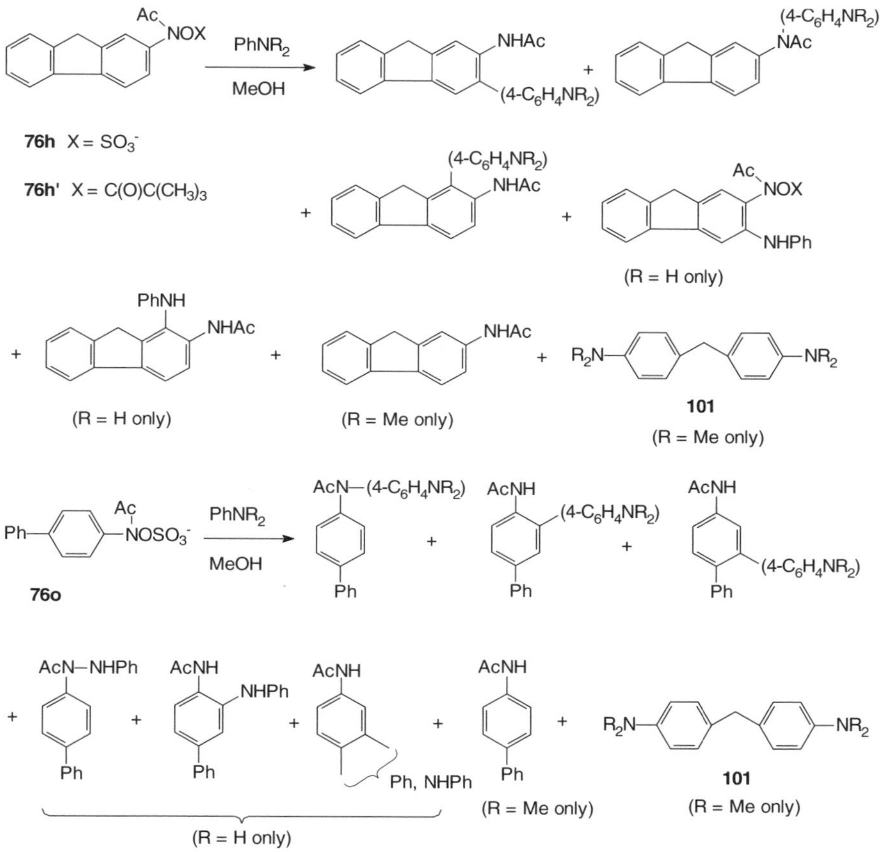
Ac
NOX
PhNR2
MeOH
NHAc
(4-C6H4NR2)
+
(4-C6H4NR2)
NAc
76h X = SO3-
76h' X = C(O)C(CH3)3
(4-C6H4NR2)
NHAc
Ac
NOX
NHPh
(R = H only)
PhNH
NHAc
NHAc
R2N
NR2
(R = H only)
(R = Me only)
101
(R = Me only)
Ac
NOSO3-
Ph
PhNR2
MeOH
76o
AcN—(4-C6H4NR2)
AcNH
(4-C6H4NR2)
AcNH
(4-C6H4NR2)
Ph
AcN—NHPh
AcNH
NHPh
AcNH
Ph, NHPh
AcNH
R2N
NR2
101
(R = Me only)
(R = Me only)
(R = H only)

Scheme 47

The structures of the N-substitution products are reminiscent of the C-8 adduct that is the major product of the reaction of 2-fluorenyl-, 4-biphenylyl- and other N-arylhydroxylamine and hydroxamic acid esters with 2′-deoxyguanosine, (d-G) 2′deoxyguanosine-5′-phosphate (d-GMP), guanosine, (G) or DNA in an aqueous environment.[47,104] The mechanism of this reaction was not seriously investigated for many years because of the mistaken impression that the reaction was inefficient and could not compete with the hydrolysis of these esters.[47,104,105] It was thought that the reaction could not occur efficiently without intercalation of the ester, or possibly the nitrenium ion, into the DNA helix.[47,105]

Novak and co-workers showed that the reaction with d-G can be highly efficient for 2-fluorenyl and 4-biphenylyl esters.[106,107] The hydrolysis of **76n**, **76o**, and **76h** in the presence of low concentrations of d-G ($\leqslant$10 mM) proceeds without rate acceleration, but with 75% to 99% conversion of the ester into **102** (Scheme 48).[106,107] Kinetics experiments with **76n** demonstrate that the trapping occurs with the same rate constant as the disappearance of the ester, and is not associated with the slower disappearance of the intermediate **78n**.[107] The reaction shows the same characteristics as trapping of nitrenium ions by N_3^-.[106,107] The ratio $k_{d\text{-}G}/k_s$ for trapping of the nitrenium ions **75n**, **75o**, and **75h** is pH independent in the pH range 3.5 to 7.5 and is only 2.5- to 7-fold smaller than k_{az}/k_s for the same ions.[106,107]

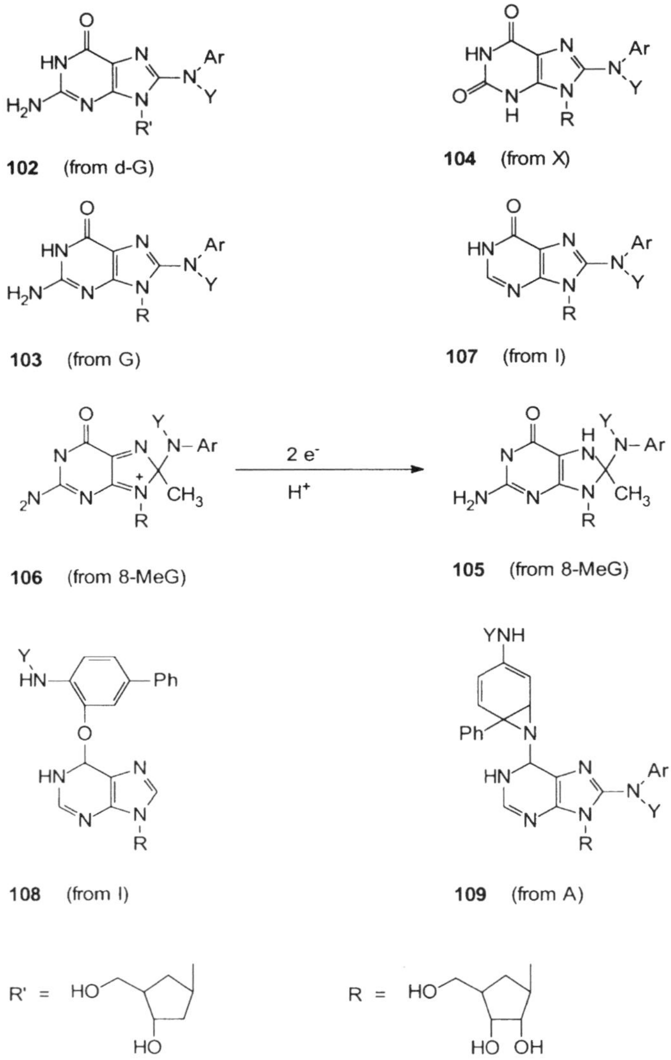

Scheme 48

Other purine nucleosides including guanosine (G), 8-methylguanosine (8-MeG), adenosine (A), inosine (I), and xanthosine (X) also trap **75n** and **75o**.[107] All show pH-independent trapping in the pH range 3.5 to 7.5, except X. The plot of observed k_x/k_s vs. pH is consistent with trapping by X and its conjugate base X^-.[107] The more basic purines with pK_a N^7-H^+ $\geqslant 2.0$ (d-G, G, 8-MeG, and X^-) generate the C-8 adduct exclusively with **75n** and **75o** (Scheme 48) and have selectivity ratios that are very similar (Table 3). The 8-MeG adduct **105** is the reduction product of the initial C-8 adduct **106** that was detected, but not isolated.[107]

The less basic purines generate different adducts. Both a C-8 adduct **107** and an O-6 adduct **108** are produced in the presence of I, while the exclusive product of the reaction of A with **75n** and **75o** is the unique benzene imine **109**.[107] These purines also exhibit lower selectivity for trapping of the nitrenium ions (Table 3). The pyrimidine nucleosides thymidine (T), uridine (U), and cytosine (C) showed negligible reactivity with these two nitrenium ions.[107] The selectivity ratios for T, U, and C given in Table 3 are upper limits based on the decrease in the yield of the hydrolysis products at high nucleoside concentration (*ca.* 50 mM).[107] Since no adducts were isolated it is not clear that these selectivities represent nucleophilic trapping by the pyrimidines.

Rate constants for the reaction of each purine nucleoside, k_{nuc}, were estimated based on the known values of k_s for **75n** and **75o** that had previously been determined under identical solvent and temperature conditions. The results indicate that k_{nuc} levels off at *ca.* 2.0×10^9 M^{-1} s^{-1} for the most reactive purine nucleosides (Table 3). It was suggested that this was the approximate diffusion-controlled limit for reaction of these ions with purine nucleosides.[107]

McClelland and co-workers verified the absolute magnitude of the $k_{d\text{-}G}$ values for **76h**, **76n**, and **76o** from measurements of the effect of d-G on the rate constants for disappearance of these ions that had been generated by laser flash photolysis.[108–110] They provided additional data, included in Table 3, for **75g** and **75p–75v**. Their results confirm that $k_{d\text{-}G}$ reaches an apparent diffusion-controlled limit of *ca.* 2.0×10^9 M^{-1} s^{-1} for the 4-biphenylyl ions with $k_s \geqslant 10^6$ s^{-1}.[109] McClelland also showed that carbocations with lifetimes similar to **75g**, **75h**, **75n** and **75o** did not exhibit significant reaction with d-G in aqueous solution. In the less nucleophilic solvent trifluoroethanol, $k_{d\text{-}G}$ for carbocations in this stability range is *ca.* 10^6–10^7 M^{-1} s^{-1}.[109] The high selectivity of the 2-fluorenyl- and 4-biphenylylnitrenium ions is not true for all nitrenium ions. The *para*-ethoxyphenylnitrenium ions **75dd** and **75ee** have upper limits for the rate constant for their reaction with d-G of *ca.* 2–4×10^7 s^{-1} (Table 3).[86,111] These ions have lifetimes in H_2O that are quite similar to **75n** and **75o** (Table 1), and they do generate C-8 adducts from their reaction with d-G,[104] but they are *ca.* 60- to 70-fold less selective toward d-G than their 4-biphenylyl counterparts. It has

Table 3 Rate constants and selectivity data for reactions of nitrenium ions with nucleosides.[a]

Ion	Nucleoside	k_{nuc} ($M^{-1} s^{-1}$)	k_{nuc}/k_s (M^{-1})
75g	d-G	7.6×10^{8} [b]	2.9×10^{4}
	G	7.2×10^{8} [b]	2.8×10^{4}
	d-GMP	9.2×10^{8} [b]	3.5×10^{4}
	GMP	9.3×10^{8} [b]	3.6×10^{4}
	d-I	9×10^{5} [b]	35
75h	d-G	6.2×10^{8} [c]	8.0×10^{3}
	d-G	5.6×10^{8} [d]	7.3×10^{3}
	d-G	4.1×10^{8} [b]	3.2×10^{3}
	G	4.3×10^{8} [b]	3.3×10^{3}
	d-GMP	4.5×10^{8} [b]	3.5×10^{3}
	GMP	4.9×10^{8} [b]	3.8×10^{3}
	d-I	1.8×10^{6} [b]	14
	d-A	3.2×10^{6} [b]	25
75n	d-G	1.9×10^{9} [e]	1.1×10^{3}
	d-G	2.0×10^{9} [d]	1.1×10^{3}
	d-G	2.0×10^{9} [b]	7.4×10^{2}
	G	1.2×10^{9} [e]	6.8×10^{2}
	d-GMP	1.9×10^{9} [b]	7.0×10^{2}
	GMP	2.4×10^{9} [b]	8.9×10^{2}
	8-MeG	1.8×10^{9} [e]	1.0×10^{3}
	X⁻	2.2×10^{9} [e]	1.2×10^{3}
	I	1.2×10^{8} [e]	65
	A	3.1×10^{7} [e]	17
	X	1.5×10^{8} [e]	85
	T	$\leqslant 8 \times 10^{6}$ [e]	$\leqslant 4.3$
75o	d-G	1.9×10^{9} [e]	3.1×10^{2}
	d-G	2.0×10^{9} [d]	3.4×10^{2}
	G	2.1×10^{9} [e]	3.6×10^{2}
	8-MeG	1.7×10^{9} [e]	2.9×10^{2}
	X⁻	1.4×10^{9} [e]	2.5×10^{2}
	I	1.8×10^{8} [e]	31
	A	1.4×10^{8} [e]	24
	X	3.5×10^{7} [e]	6
	T	$\leqslant 7 \times 10^{6}$ [e]	$\leqslant 1.2$
	U	$\leqslant 6 \times 10^{6}$ [e]	$\leqslant 1.0$
	C	$\leqslant 9 \times 10^{6}$ [e]	$\leqslant 1.6$
75p	d-G	3.6×10^{7} [b]	2.3×10^{4}
75q	d-G	1.5×10^{9} [b]	5.6×10^{3}
75r	d-G	1.9×10^{9} [b]	1.5×10^{3}
75s	d-G	1.9×10^{9} [b]	1.3×10^{3}
75t	d-G	1.9×10^{9} [b]	7.6×10^{2}
75u	d-G	2.2×10^{9} [b]	8.8×10^{2}
75v	d-G	1.8×10^{9} [b]	1.4×10^{2}
75dd	d-G	$\leqslant 2 \times 10^{7}$ [f]	$\leqslant 18$
75ee	d-GMP	$\leqslant 4 \times 10^{7}$ [g]	$\leqslant 4.5$

[a]Conditions: 5% CH_3CN-H_2O, $\mu = 0.5$, $T = 20°C$, unless otherwise indicated.
[b]Ref. 109: 20% CH_3CN-H_2O, $\mu = 0$. Direct measurement.
[c]Ref. 106. Competition kinetics. [d]Ref. 109. Direct measurement.
[e]Ref. 107. Competition kinetics. [f]Ref. 86. Direct measurement.
[g]Ref. 111. Competition kinetics.

been suggested that the positive charge in *para*-alkoxyphenylnitrenium ions is so highly localized at the *para*-carbon that there is insufficient cationic property at N for reaction with d-G.[86] This charge-localization also appears to affect the regioselectivity of reaction of **75ee** with N_3^-.[87] High selectivity for reaction of nitrenium ions with d-G requires a combination of relatively long lifetime in the aqueous environment ($\geqslant 5 \times 10^{-8}$ s) and sufficient delocalization of the charge so that some cationic character remains on N.

Detailed mechanistic proposals for the formation of the C-8 adducts have centered around mechanisms A and B of Scheme 49.[107,110] Earlier mechanistic proposals are at odds with currently available data, and will not be discussed here.[107,112] The two mechanisms differ with respect to the initial site of attack of d-G on the nitrenium ion.

Mechanism A proposes initial attack by N-7 of d-G on the nitrenium ion to generate the N-7 adduct **110**, followed by an intramolecular rearrangement to form the cationic C-8 intermediate **111**. The evidence for the mechanism includes the precedent of other electrophiles, including carbocations, that usually react at N-7 of d-G,[49] and the reported isolation of **113** (Scheme 50) and its reduction with NaBH$_4$ into **114**.[112] Novak and co-workers were not able to isolate an adduct similar to **113** from the reaction of **76n** and **76o**

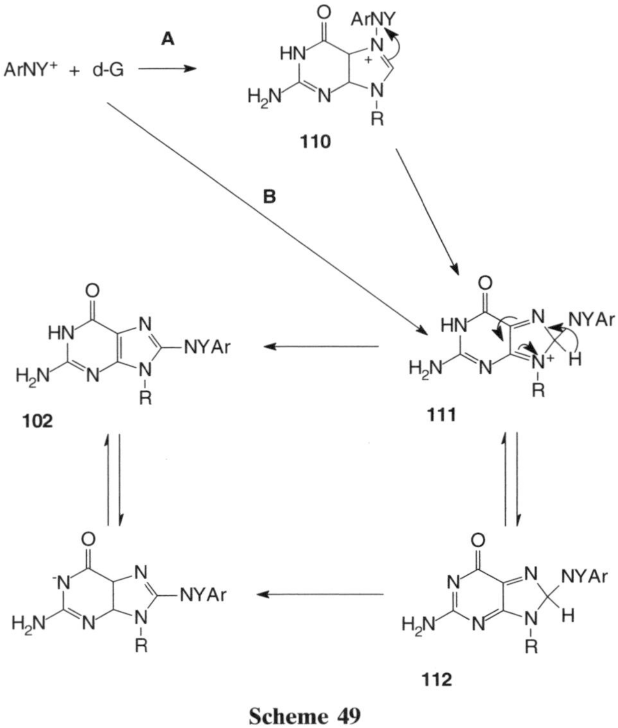

Scheme 49

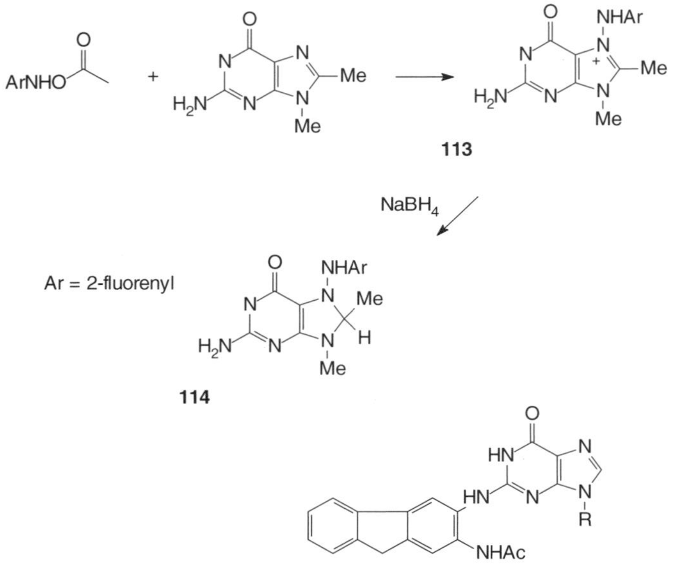

113

114

Ar = 2-fluorenyl

115

Scheme 50

with 8-MeG, but they did detect **106** (Ar = 4-biphenylyl, Y = H or Ac) as a mixture of two diastereomers and they showed that **106** was slowly reduced under the reaction conditions into **105**, as a separable mixture of two diastereomers.[107] The intermediate **106** is analogous to the proposed intermediate **111** common to both mechanisms. In spite of their inability to detect **110**, the Novak group favored mechanism A because the rate constant for formation of C-8 adducts from A, I, X, X⁻, G, d-G, and 8-MeG appeared to depend on the pK_a of N-7 of the nucleoside with a β_{nuc} of 0.7 for those nucleosides with $pK_a < 2$ and to level off at the diffusion-controlled limit for those nucleosides with $pK_a \geqslant 2$.[107]

McClelland and co-workers identified the initial adduct detected in laser flash photolysis experiments involving the reaction of **75g** with d-G as **111** (Ar = 2-fluorenyl, Y = H, R = 2′-deoxyribose).[110] This identification was based on the absorption spectrum of the intermediate, which extends out to 400 nm suggesting a highly conjugated species, by the observed pK_a of 3.9 of the intermediate, which is consistent with deprotonation of **111** to form **112**, by the lack of dependence of the rate constant for decomposition of the intermediate on the nature of Ar for the intermediates derived from **75g**, **75n**, **75p**, and **75q**, and by the kinetics of the decomposition of the intermediate into the stable C-8 adduct **102**, which includes a pH-rate profile that showed both ionization states were reactive, buffer catalysis of decomposition of the intermediate, and a large H/D kinetic isotope effect of *ca.* 6–7 at all pH from 3.0 to 7.6 for the decomposition of the intermediate derived from 8-deuterio-d-G.[110]

Although these results cannot rule out the intermediacy of **110** in the formation of **111**, **110** would have to be very short lived because **111** is formed with a pseudo-first-order rate constant identical to the rate constant for disappearance of **75g** at all [d-G] examined.[110] The McClelland group favor mechanism B on the basis of the inverse H/D kinetic isotope effect of 0.88 observed for the activation-limited (Table 3) reaction of **75p** with 8-deuterio-d-G.[110] The inverse effect is expected for a reaction in which the carbon bearing the isotope is undergoing a change in hybridization from sp^2 to sp^3. McClelland and co-workers pointed out that **111** is a highly stabilized cation with a rate constant for deprotonation by H_2O of $1.7 \times 10^3 \, s^{-1}$.[110] This makes the cation more stable to deprotonation than the 6,6-dihydro-1,3,5-trimethoxybenzenium ion by over two orders of magnitude. This stabilization may make the transition state for formation of **111** directly from the nitrenium ion and d-G energetically favorable, but this stabilization would also occur for all electrophiles, most of which do not react at C-8. The high selectivity of nitrenium ions for reaction with C-8 is not explained by this argument.

Novak and Kennedy have recently shown that the self-complementary oligomer d-ATGCAT also reacts with **76h** via the nitrenium ion **75h**.[113] The reactivity of the oligomer with **75h** could be separated into components due to the single-stranded and double-stranded forms. The trapping of **75h** by the single-stranded oligomer was *ca.* 30% as efficient as trapping by monomeric d-G, while trapping by the double-stranded oligomer was undetectable within the error limits of the method. Small amounts of trapping by the double-stranded form would have been difficult to detect because of the efficient trapping by the single-stranded oligomer. The reactivity of the double-stranded super-coiled plasmid pUC19 with **75h** was also examined. At 0°C k_{pUC19}/k_s, the average selectivity ratio per d-G moiety in pUC19, was $260 \, M^{-1}$, about 2% of the magnitude of $k_{d\text{-}G}/k_s$ at that temperature.[113]

On average, d-G residues in double-stranded DNA do not efficiently trap DNA. The d-G residues within pUC19 do not have identical chemical environments, and there must be a range of reactivities toward **75h**, but most of the d-G residues within pUC19 have very little reactivity with **75h**. The tertiary structure of double-helical DNA inhibits the formation of the C-8 adduct. This inhibition of C-8 adduct formation may explain why native DNA reacts with **76h** and related compounds to generate ca. 5–20% of the minor N-2 adduct **115** in addition to the C-8 adduct, while the N-2 adduct is undetectable in studies involving monomeric d-G.[47,48,104,106,107]

The high regioselectivity of the reaction of nitrenium ions with d-G is not typical of carbon nucleophiles. More typical are the reactions of **75h** and **75n** with N,N-dimethylaniline and aniline. Both nucleophiles generate a mixture of N- and C-substitution products (Scheme 47) with no single product accounting for more than *ca.* 35% of the overall yield of substitution products.[101] Aniline also behaves as an ambident nucleophile generating 35–60% of its substitution products via attack of the NH_2 group.[101] Falvey and co-workers investigated the factors that controlled the regiochemistry of the reactions of electron-rich alkenes with photolytically generated diphenylnitrenium ion **116** in CH_3CN.[114] Their results for reaction of **116** with a silyl ketene acetal are illustrated in Scheme 51. Products **117** and **119** are obtained from attack of the alkene on the *para*-carbon and N, respectively, of **116**. The regiochemistry of **118** indicates that this product is formed by an initial attack at the *ortho*-carbon of **116** followed by an intramolecular process.[114] The N-substitution product was only observed for the most electron-rich alkenes, the silyl ketene acetals. All other alkenes generated only *ortho*- and *para*-substitution products. The *para/ortho* ratio varied from 1.4 to 9.7 and did not appear to be related to the nucleophilicity of the alkene. The regiochemistry of the reactions did not appear to be strongly influenced by calculated charge densities or LUMO coefficients of **116**.[114] Absolute rate constants for reactions of the alkenes with **116** did correlate with the oxidation potentials of the alkenes, so that the more easily oxidized alkenes reacted more rapidly.[114] The rate constants for all alkenes examined fell in the range 10^9–10^{10} M^{-1} s^{-1}.[114]

A series of alkyl sulfides react with phenyl azide in TFA and TFSA to produce 2- and 4-aminophenyl alkyl sulfides **120** and **121** (Scheme 52).[115] Kinetics results appeared to rule out S_N2 reactions, and the ortho-product **120** predominated in most cases, so the reaction was originally thought to proceed through an azasulfonium ion, **122**, produced by attack of the sulfide on a nitrenium ion.[115] Azasulfonium salts had been isolated previously from

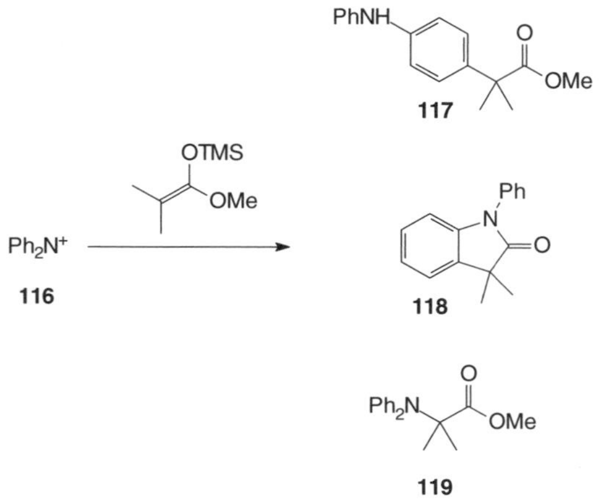

Scheme 51

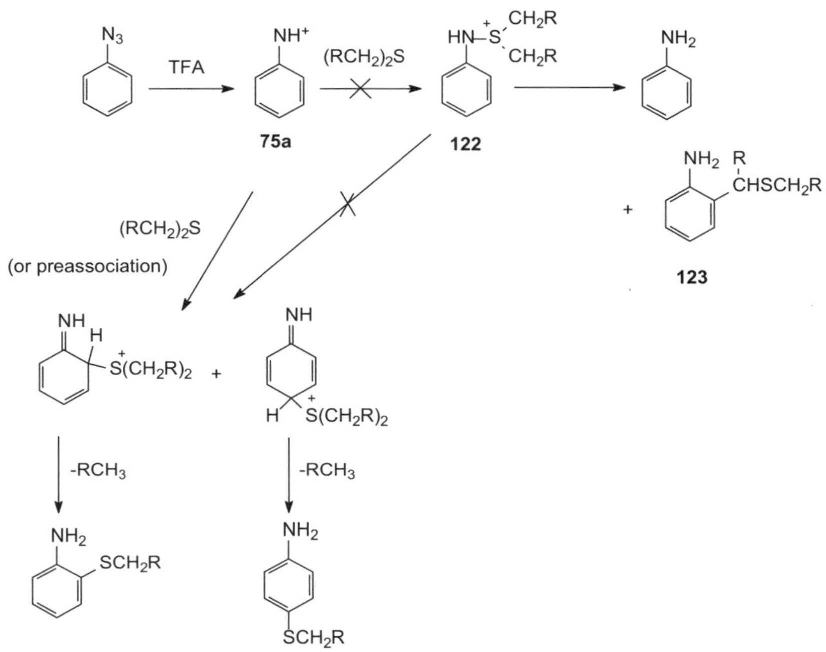

Scheme 52

the reaction of N-chloro-N-*tert*-butylanilines with dimethyl sulfide, and these intermediates had been shown to undergo thermolysis at 100°C to generate products with structures analogous to **120** and **121**, along with the parent N-*tert*-butylaniline.[116] Recently it was shown that authentic **122** (R = H, n-propyl) decomposed in TFA to give aniline and the apparent Sommelet–Hauser rearrangement product **123** as the exclusive reaction products.[117] This rules out the intermediacy of **122** in the reactions that generate **120** and **121**. The predominance of the *ortho*-product **120** is difficult to explain in terms of a free nitrenium ion reacting with the sulfide, but a preassociation process in which the sulfide interacts strongly with the N of the incipient cation might explain the unusual regioselectivity of this reaction. The short lifetime of **75a** is consistent with such a possibility.

The reactions of the selective nitrenium ions **75h** and **75o** with glutathione (GSH) in H_2O exhibit different characteristics from those described above.[118] Scheme 53 illustrates the products and reaction mechanism deduced for the reaction of **75o** with GSH.[118] Product yield data taken at varying pH showed that the reactive form of GSH was its conjugate base GS⁻. The rate constant

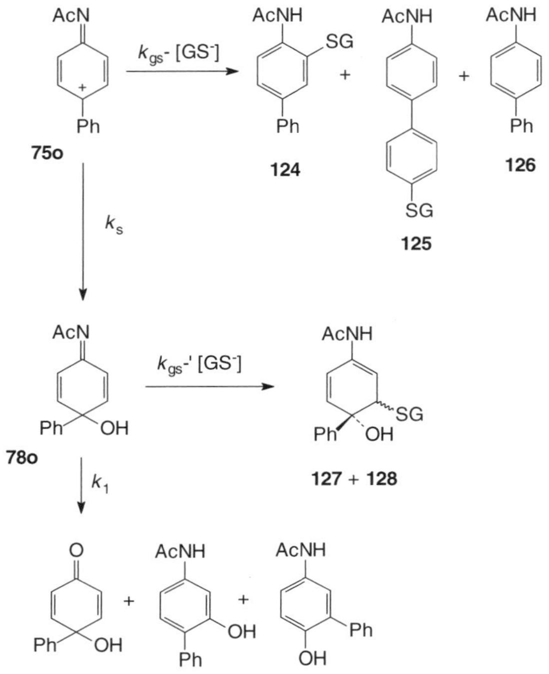

Scheme 53

for trapping of **75o**, k_{gs^-}, obtained from competition kinetics, was $1.8 \times 10^9 \, M^{-1} \, s^{-1}$.[118] The competition experiments showed that **124**, **125**, and **126** were produced from a common intermediate **75o**, but the yields of the diastereomeric products **127** and **128** decreased with increasing [GS$^-$].[118] These products appear to be derived from GS$^-$ trapping of **78o** produced from the original partitioning of **75o**. Even at the lowest concentrations of GS$^-$ used (0.5 mM) it was impossible to detect the normal hydrolysis products of **78o**, so it was concluded that $k'_{gs^-}/k_1 > 5 \times 10^4 \, M^{-1}$.[118] The reduction product **126** was assumed to be produced by GS$^-$ attack on an initially formed adduct **129** (Scheme 54). If this is so, the *ortho*-product **124** cannot also be generated by rearrangement of **129** because the yields of **124** and **126** increase with [GS$^-$] in the same manner.[118] The product of attack on the distal ring of **75o**, **125**, is quite unique. No other nucleophile has been shown to react at the distal ring of **75o**. Since very similar products, including a product of attack on the distal ring, were generated from **75h** it appears that these reactions with GS$^-$ are common to selective nitrenium ions.[118] The rate constant k_{gs^-} for **75h** was determined to be $6.3 \times 10^8 \, M^{-1} \, s^{-1}$ from competition kinetics experiments.[118]

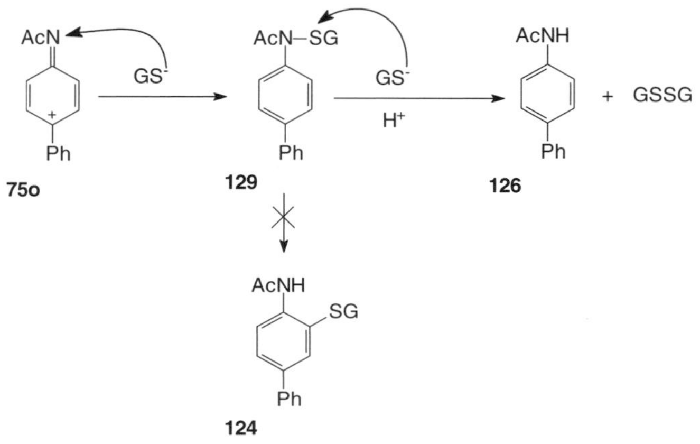

Scheme 54

DIRECT OBSERVATION OF NITRENIUM IONS: ACID–BASE CHEMISTRY AND
SINGLET–TRIPLET CHEMISTRY

Until 1993 the only nitrenium ions that had been directly observed were highly stabilized diarylnitrenium or 4-biphenylylnitrenium ions substituted with electron-donating groups that were detected during cyclic voltammetry experiments in CH_3CN.[26,119] Attempts to generate nitrenium ions in superacids had led only to dicationic species.[25] Generation of short-lived nitrenium ions (ca. 100 ns) by laser flash photolysis (LFP) , and their direct observation by UV absorption spectroscopy was first reported by Anderson and Falvey.[120] Subsequently, Falvey and McClelland have explored nitrenium ion chemistry employing ions generated by LFP of a variety of precursors. This work has led to advances in the following areas:

(1) Rate constants and mechanisms for reaction of the ions with nucleophiles.
(2) Acid–base chemistry.
(3) Singlet–triplet chemistry.
(4) Structure of the ions.

The first of these areas has been extensively discussed elsewhere in this chapter. The others will be considered here.

Falvey and co-workers used the N-*tert*-butyl-3-methylanthranilium salts **130a–h** as photoprecursors to the nitrenium ions **131a–h** (Scheme 55). The unsubstituted **130a** and related anthranilium salts and anthranils had previously been investigated as photoprecursors for nitrenium ions, but no attempts had been made to directly detect transient ions.[40–45] Transients identified as **131b–f** were detected by UV spectroscopy as products of the

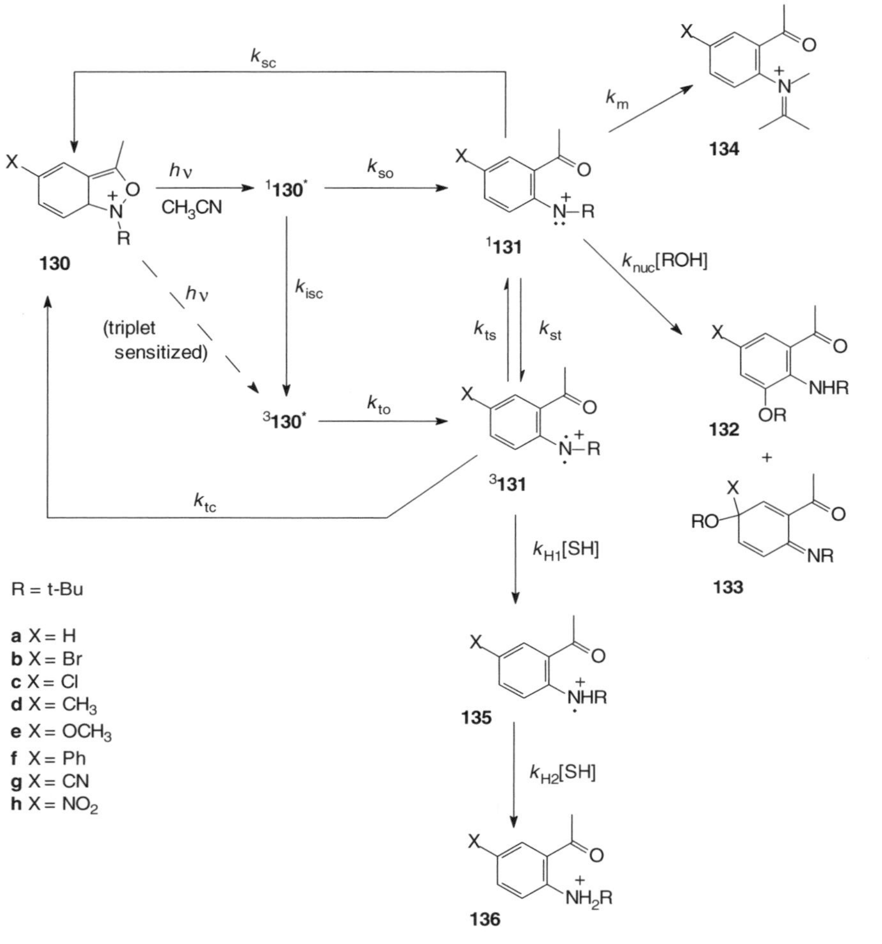

Scheme 55

LFP of **130b–f** in CH_3CN.[120–122] The transients were identified as singlet nitrenium ions based on several observations:[120–122]

(1) The pseudo-first-order rate constants for decay of the transients were dependent on the concentrations of added alcohols or H_2O according to the equation $k_{obs} = k_o + k_{nuc}[ROH]$, with k_{nuc} in the range 10^4–$10^8 \, M^{-1} \, s^{-1}$ depending on the identity of the alcohol and the cation. The products of these reactions were the expected *ortho*- and *para*-substitution products **132**, and **133**, or products derived from their

further decomposition. The values of k_{nuc} for ROH followed the reactivity order $k_{MeOH} > k_{EtOH} > k_{i-PrOH} \sim k_{H_2O} \gg k_{t-BuOH}$ previously observed for reactive diphenylcarbenium ions.[123]

(2) Effects of the aryl substituents X on k_{nuc} for alcohols and H_2O were different from those expected for arylcarbenium ions, but were very similar to those deduced for k_s from azide-clock experiments on similarly substituted nitrenium ions generated by solvolysis reactions in H_2O.[81,87]

(3) The lifetimes of the transients in CH_3CN were independent of O_2 or n-Bu$_3$SnH concentrations. These observations rule out the possibility that the transient spectra are due to triplets or radicals.[120,121]

In the absence of added nucleophiles these ions have lifetimes in CH_3CN ranging from 100 ns to 600 μs.[120–122] These lifetimes are governed by the rearrangement process (k_m) that leads to the iminium ion 134, and by thermal reversion to the parent anthrinilium ion (k_{sc}). The latter process was detected by the increase in quantum yield for the photolysis as a function of added [ROH] from ca. 0.1 in the absence of alcohol or H_2O up to a saturation limit of ca. 0.8. The quantum yield and product yield data made it possible to estimate k_m and k_{sc} for these ions.[121] The magnitude of k_{sc} ranges from ca. 2.0×10^3 s^{-1} for 131e to 1.0×10^7 s^{-1} for 131c and 131d, while k_m ranges from $<10^2$ s^{-1} for 131e to ca. 8×10^5 s^{-1} for 131b and 131c.[120–122] To a first approximation, the substituent effects for k_m and k_{sc} mirror those for k_{nuc}. Products consistent with ^{1}131a and ^{1}131g were isolated from photolysis of 130a and 130g, but transients were not detected.[122,124] It was concluded that 131a and 131g had lifetimes too short to be detected ($\leqslant$10 ns).[122,124]

Direct irradiation of 130a–c and 130f led to modest yields of 136a–c and 136f.[121,122,124] The yields of the amine could be reduced by the addition of the triplet quencher TMDD.[124] Triplet sensitized photolysis led to increased yields of the amine, even in cases in which the reduction product was not found in direct irradiation experiments.[120,124,125] Triplet sensitized photolysis always led to some of the singlet products 132,133, and/or 134.[124,125]

The generation of 136 was most consistent with intersystem crossing of the singlet excited anthranilium ion ^{1}130* to ^{3}130* (k_{isc}), or direct formation of ^{3}130* by sensitized photolysis, followed by ring opening of ^{3}130* to ^{3}131 (k_{to}). The triplet ion could then undergo hydrogen abstraction to generate 136 or intersystem crossing (k_{ts}) to the singlet ion. The non-zero yields of singlet products under triplet sensitization conditions indicates that k_{ts} is significant in most cases. The results were most consistent with a ground-state singlet ion ^{1}131. No evidence requiring intersystem crossing from ^{1}131 to ^{3}131 (k_{st}) could be found for 131a–g.

Photolysis of 130h in CH_3CN containing MeOH or H_2O led to considerably different results.[126] No products of nucleophilic attack by MeOH or H_2O on ^{1}131h could be detected. Only 134h and 136h were observed. The presence of O_2 decreased the proportion of **136h**, while triplet sensitized photolysis led exclusively to **136h**.[126]

Addition of triphenylmethane (Ph_3CH) to photolysis mixtures led to an increase in the product ratio **136h/134h** from *ca.* 1.3 in the absence of Ph_3CH to *ca.* 9 at $[Ph_3CH] > 0.15$ M.[126] The dimeric product **137** (Scheme 56) was isolated in these experiments, but no Ph_3COH was detected. The generation of **137** is consistent with formation of $Ph_3C\cdot$, but not Ph_3C^+.

A transient identified as ^{3}**130h*** was detected following LFP of **130h**. The identification was based on the fact that the lifetime of the transient was reduced from *ca.* 300 ns in N_2-purged CH_3CN to *ca.* 100 ns in the presence of saturated O_2, and that CH_3OH had no effect on the transient lifetime, nor did Ph_3CH. The latter two observations rule out ^{1}**131h** and ^{3}**131h**, respectively, as the transient. No longer-lived transients were detected in the absence of trapping agents, but in the presence of Ph_3CH, the radical Ph_3C was observed. This species grows in much more slowly than the transient identified as ^{3}**130h*** disappears, and the kinetics of its formation are governed by two pseudo-first-order rate constants, both of which are dependent on $[Ph_3CH]$. The derived second-order rate constants for the growth of $Ph_3C\cdot$ are 1.8×10^6 M^{-1} s^{-1} and 1.8×10^5 M^{-1} s^{-1}, and the contributions of the two reactions to the total absorbance by $Ph_3C\cdot$ are equal.

It was assumed that **134h** was derived from ^{1}**131h**, while **136h** was derived from ^{3}**131h**. The exclusive formation of **136h** in triplet sensitized photolysis experiments indicates that k_{ts} is insignificant in this system. The reduced yield of **136h** in the presence of O_2 was attributed to quenching of ^{3}**130h***. The increased yield of **136h** in the presence of Ph_3CH in direct irradiation experiments requires that some process must compete with hydrogen abstraction by ^{3}**131** via k_{H1}. This cannot be k_{ts}, but the data are consistent with a process (k_{tc}) that leads back to the starting anthranilium ion **130h**. This may involve ring closure to ^{3}**130h*** followed by decay to the ground state, but this is not required by the results.[126]

The kinetic analysis of Ph_3CH trapping requires a significant lifetime for ^{3}**131h** of *ca.* 2 μs.[126] This relatively long lifetime, coupled with the negligible

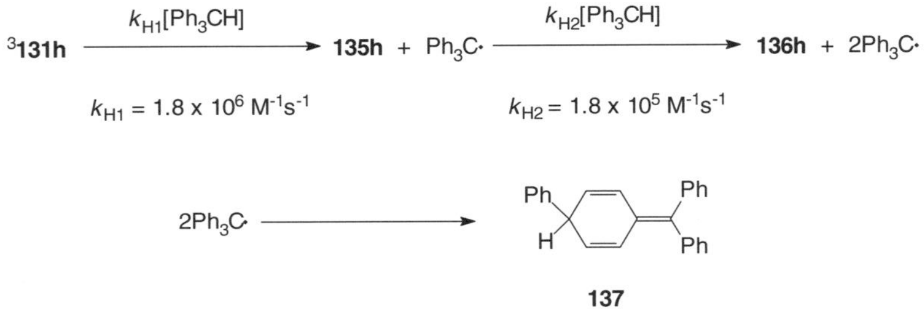

Scheme 56

value of k_{ts}, suggests that the triplet state is the ground state of **131h**. Unfortunately, although the kinetics of Ph$_3$CH trapping indicate a long lifetime for ^{3}**131h**, this species was not directly detected. The singlet state of arylnitrenium ions should be stabilized by the interaction of filled π-orbitals of the aromatic ring with the empty p-orbital on N. Electron-withdrawing groups, such as NO$_2$, lower the energy of the π-orbitals on the aromatic ring and weaken the interaction between the π-orbitals and the empty p-orbital. This will have the effect of destabilizing the singlet state relative to the triplet state.[127] The experimental observations described above are consistent with this argument.

The interpretation of the biphasic kinetics of formation of Ph$_3$C· is provided in Scheme 56. The critical feature of Scheme 56 is sequential H· transfer to ^{3}**131h** with the intermediacy of the radical cation **135h**.[126] Long-wavelength absorption, consistent with this species, is observed during the Ph$_3$CH trapping experiments.[126]

In general, Falvey and co-workers' data and conclusions, concerning the stabilization of triplet ions by electron-withdrawing groups, were in agreement with the conclusions previously reached by Gassman and co-workers in their study of the substituent effects on product distributions in the alcoholysis of **14a–g** (Scheme 8).[27–31] It is likely that the low yields of reduction products observed by Gassman for the cases with electron-donating substituents are due to impurities that cause reduction of the singlet ion, or processes that do not involve nitrenium ions, but the substantial yields of reduction products observed for **14e** and **14g** (X = 4-CO$_2$Et and X = 4-NO$_2$) may very well be due to singlet to triplet intersystem crossing of the nitrenium ions derived from those two compounds and subsequent H· abstraction from the solvent by the triplet ions.

Abramovitch and Takeuchi had explored the use of N-aminopyridinium ions as precursors to nitrenium ions in both photolysis and thermolysis reactions, but had not attempted to use these precursors under flash photolysis conditions.[4b–e,128,129] Moran and Falvey demonstrated that the LFP of **138** in CH$_3$CN (Scheme 57) generated a short-lived intermediate (1.5 μs) that had characteristics similar to the ions ^{1}**131b–f**.[130] The transient was identified as the singlet ion ^{1}**116**.[130] Evidence from product analysis and spectrophotometric detection of the cation radical Ph$_2$NH·$^+$ as a long-lived intermediate was initially thought to indicate that there were parallel path-

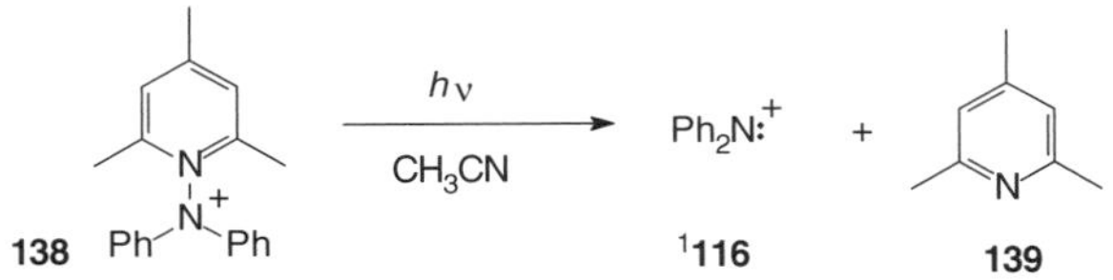

Scheme 57

ways leading to both the singlet and triplet nitrenium ion.[130a] Subsequently it was determined that the $Ph_2NH\cdot^+$ was produced from photolysis of initially formed photoproducts that accumulate during the experiment.[130b] Although [1]116 is quenched by several H atom donors to yield Ph_2NH, this reaction is not accompanied by formation of $Ph_2NH\cdot^+$ and the rate constants for trapping correlate with the hydride affinities of the donors, not with their bond dissociation energies.[130b] It was concluded that [3]116 is not produced in these photolysis experiments. The N-amino-2,4,6-trimethylpyridinium salts were subsequently used as precursors to other nitrenium ions in LFP experiments.[131–133]

The ions 141a–e were generated by photolysis of 140a–e in CH_3CN and were characterized as singlets by their reactions with MeOH and Cl^-.[131,133] The ion 141a was not directly detected, but the other ions were observable as transients with lifetimes ranging from 950 ns (141c) to greater than $100\,\mu s$ (141d). These ions react with Cl^- with rate constants of ca. $1–3 \times 10^{10}\,M^{-1}\,s^{-1}$ that are at or near the diffusion-controlled limit.[133] Rate constants for reaction with MeOH are structure dependent and range from $3.7 \times 10^5\,M^{-1}\,s^{-1}$ for 141b to $6.8 \times 10^7\,M^{-1}\,s^{-1}$ for 141c. The unsubstituted ion 141a is subject to an efficient 1,2-rearrangement that leads to an iminium ion, and ultimately to aniline (Scheme 58). Although 141a was not detectable, the rate constant for this rearrangement was estimated to be ca. $10^8\,s^{-1}$ based

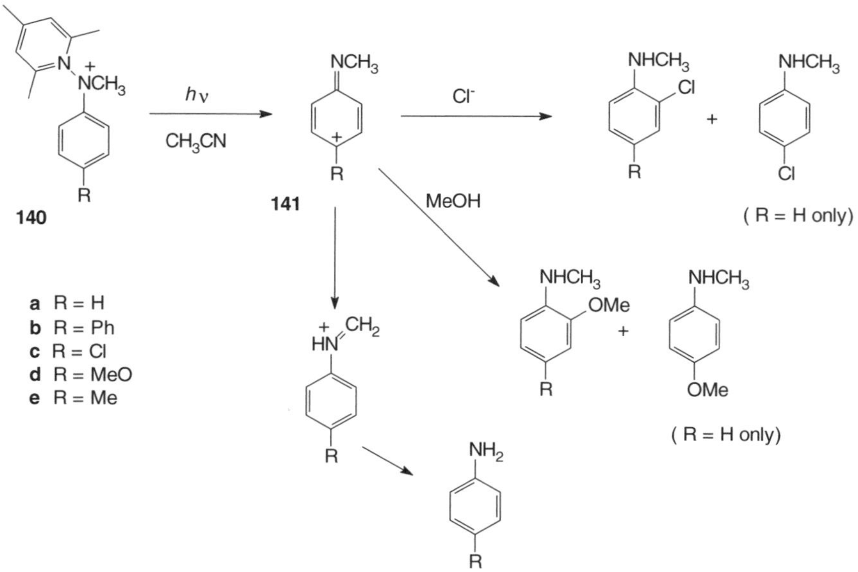

a R = H
b R = Ph
c R = Cl
d R = MeO
e R = Me

Scheme 58

on the ratio of aniline and N-methyl-*para*-anisidine generated in the presence of MeOH, and an estimated rate constant of $10^8 \, M^{-1} \, s^{-1}$ for the reaction of **141a** with MeOH.[131] Other members of this series apparently undergo this rearrangement, but detailed product analyses were not reported.[133]

It was possible to obtain IR spectra of **116** and **141b–e** by employing time-resolved IR spectroscopy following LFP of the precursors.[132,133] For **116** the C—N stretching band at $1392 \, cm^{-1}$ was located by observing the shift induced by ^{15}N substitution. The corresponding band in Ph_2NH is located at $1320 \, cm^{-1}$, indicating that the C—N bonds of **116** have some double bond character.[132] The C—N stretching bands for **141b–e** were too weak to be observed, but aromatic C—C stretches were observed and their frequencies were compared with those calculated for both the singlet and triplet ions using density functional theory (BPW91/cc-pVDZ).[133] Five observed bands in the four cations were found to correspond to those calculated for the singlet ions, with an average deviation of $6 \, cm^{-1}$. The bands calculated for the triplet ions deviated from the observed bands by an average of $21 \, cm^{-1}$. The results suggest that the ions have structures very similar to those calculated for the singlet ions by DFT. Bond lengths and charge distributions determined in the DFT calculations are consistent with the interpretation that these ions can largely be thought of as 4-imino-2,5-cyclohexadienyl cations (Structures **II** and **III** of Scheme 38).[133]

Shortly after Anderson and Falvey reported the first observation of a short-lived nitrenium ion in CH_3CN by UV spectroscopy, Novak and McClelland and co-workers demonstrated that the nitrenium ions **75h** and **75o** could be observed in aqueous solution after LFP of the pivalic acid ester **76h′**, the sulfuric acid ester **76o**, and its N-chloro analogue N-chloro-4-phenylacetanilide.[78] The transients with λ_{max} of *ca.* 450 nm were identified as singlet nitrenium ions, based on the kinetics of their decomposition in the presence of N_3^-, the equivalence of k_{az}/k_s determined by the azide clock method and by direct observation, the lack of sensitivity of the transients to O_2, product studies that showed similar products from solvolytic and photolytic decomposition of N-chloro-4-phenylacetanilide, and identical transient uv spectra for **75o** derived either from **76o** or its N-chloro analogue.[78] A comparison of azide/solvent selectivity data obtained by azide clock and direct observation of **75h** and **75o** is presented in Table 1.

Subsequently, McClelland and co-workers demonstrated that **75g** and **75n** could be observed as transients during photolysis of the corresponding azides **142g** and **142n** (Scheme 59).[79] The transients were identified as singlet ions based largely on the equivalence of k_{az}/k_s measured in photolysis and solvolysis experiments. The nitrenium ions were apparently derived from protonation of the singlet nitrenes **143g** and **143n**.[79] A detailed analysis of product yields and decomposition rates of **75n** as a function of $[OH^-]$, combined with the observed rate constant for appearance of **75n** after a 25 ps pulse $(6.0 \times 10^9 \, s^{-1})$, led to values of k_w^P of $5 \times 10^9 \, s^{-1}$ and k_{OH}^d of

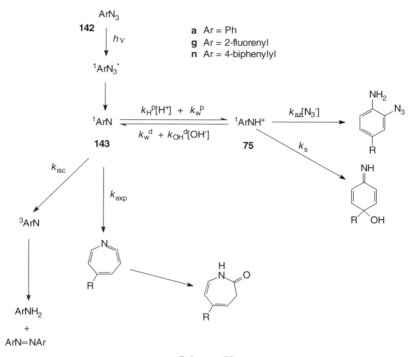

Scheme 59

$3.1 \times 10^8 \, \text{M}^{-1} \, \text{s}^{-1}$.[134] Combined with the experimental pK_w of 14.8 in the solvent employed in this study (20% CH_3CN/H_2O), and the requirement that $k_{OH}^d/k_w^P = K_a/K_w$, these rate constants lead to a calculated pK_a of **75n** of 16.0.[134] Although the parent N-arylnitrenium ion **75a** cannot be directly detected in LFP studies, the pH dependence of yields of nitrene and nitrenium-ion-derived products led to the conclusion that the pK_a of **75a** $\geqslant 12.4$.[134]

Scheme 59 indicates that protonation of singlet nitrenes in aqueous solution is a viable route to nitrenium ions as long as $(k_H^P[H^+] + k_w^P) \geqslant (k_{isc} + k_{exp})$ and $(k_H^P[H^+] + k_w^P) \geqslant (k_w^d + k_{OH}^d[OH^-])$. The latter requirement is met under acidic to neutral conditions for many nitrenium ions, because the pK_a of **75** $\geqslant 12$ as long as R is not more electron withdrawing than H. The former requirement is met by **143g** and **143n** under all pH conditions. For **143a**, k_{exp}, the rate constant for nitrene ring expansion, is in the range $2–4 \times 10^{10} \, \text{s}^{-1}$ (ca. 20- to 40-fold greater than for **143g** or **143n**) and $k_H^P/k_{exp} \approx 1 \, \text{M}^{-1}$, so significant yields of products derived from **75a** are obtained only at pH $\leqslant 1$.[134]

The protonation of photochemically generated singlet nitrenes in aqueous solution has recently been used to study a wide range of nitrenium ions.[83,85,86] Data on the rate constants for reaction of **75g**, **75n**, and many other nitrenium ions generated by this technique with solvent H_2O and N_3^-, are included in Table 1. Platz and co-workers have also shown that this technique can work in CH_3CN containing H_2SO_4 on photochemically generated singlet nitrenes such as C_6F_5N that have significantly reduced k_{exp}.[135]

Nitrenium ions can be protonated on N to generate dications (Scheme 60). A few stable examples of such dications are known.[25,26,119] Some indirect evidence for the involvement of transient dications in nitrenium ion reactions had been presented,[24,36] but no evidence requiring the intermediacy of such species was presented until quite recently. In 1996 McClelland and co-workers showed that k_{obs} for the reaction of **75g** and **75n** with solvent became pH dependent, increasing in acidic solution according to equation (4) where all the terms are defined in Scheme 60.[134]

$$k_{obs} = (k_s K_a' + k_s'[H^+])/(K_a' + [H^+]) \tag{4}$$

In 20 vol% CH_3CN-H_2O at 20°C, $\mu = 1.0$, the pK_a of the conjugate acid of **75g**, **144g**, is 0.6, k_s is $1.3 \times 10^4\,s^{-1}$ and k_s' is $1.9 \times 10^6\,s^{-1}$.[134] For **75n** and **144n** the corresponding values are 0.1, $1.1 \times 10^6\,s^{-1}$ and $6.0 \times 10^7\,s^{-1}$.[134] In this same pH range, the N-acetylated nitrenium ion **75o** shows no acceleration of its reaction with the solvent. In fact, there is a small (20%) rate decrease that was attributed to a salt effect of replacing Na^+ with H_3O^+ in the pH range from *ca.* 0–2. It was argued that the basicities of **75g** and **75n** and the relatively small differences in k_s and k_s' for both cations and their conjugate acids are further evidence that nitrenium ions should be thought of primarily in terms of their carbenium ion resonance contributors.[134]

McClelland and co-workers have examined the acid–base chemistry of a series of N-substituted benzidine nitrenium ions **75nn–rr**.[136,137] The N-acetylated ions **75nn** and **75oo** were generated by irradiation of the azides **142nn** and **142oo** (Scheme 61).[136] Both ions exhibit a λ_{max} at *ca.* 560 nm. The 4'-N-methylacetylamino ion **75nn** is effectively quenched by N_3^- ($k_{az} = 8 \times 10^9\,M^{-1}\,s^{-1}$) and reacts with solvent with $k_s = 3.8 \times 10^4\,s^{-1}$ to generate the expected product **78nn**, which is hydrolyzed under the reaction conditions to produce **80nn**.[136] The reactivity of **75nn** with H_2O lies between that of **75p** and **75q** as would be expected based on the previous observations of 4'-substituted-4-biphenylylnitrenium ion reactivity.[85] The 4'-acetylamino

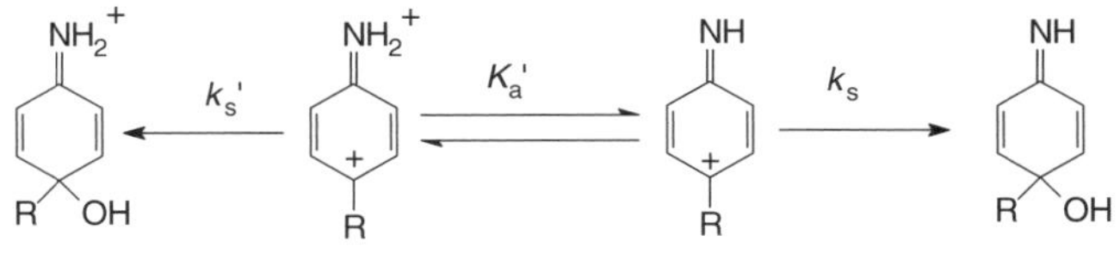

Scheme 60

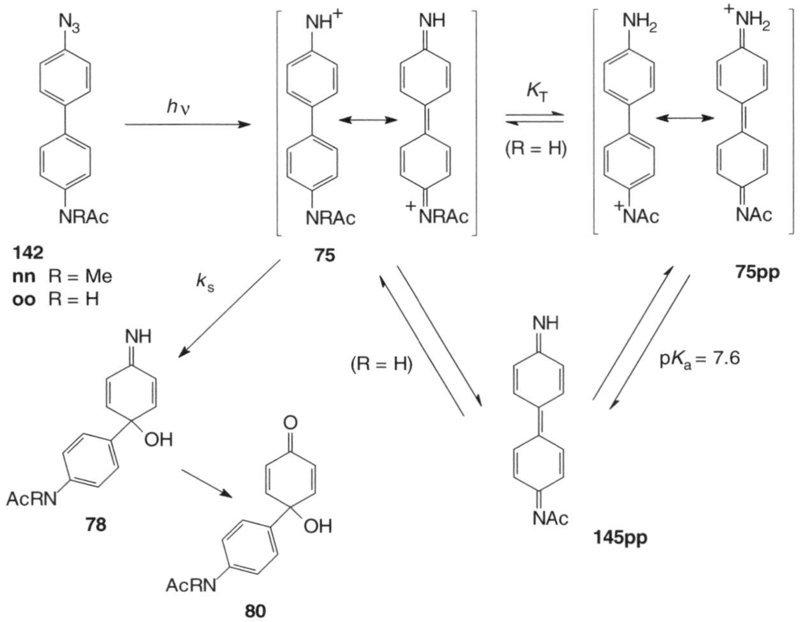

Scheme 61

ion **75oo** has a uv spectrum very similar to that of **75nn**, but it reacts quite differently. In acid solution **75oo** decays into a transient with $\lambda_{max} = 430$ nm, while in base solution **75oo** generates a different transient with $\lambda_{max} = 410$ nm. These transients are in a pH-dependent equilibrium with a measured pK_a of 7.6.[136] These intermediates have considerably greater lifetimes than **75nn** or **75oo** in H_2O, decaying predominately (*ca.* 70% yield) into **78oo** and subsequently **80oo**.[136] The long-lived intermediates were identified as the tautomeric nitrenium ion **75pp** and its conjugate base **145pp**. The hydrolysis product **80oo** must be formed from the more reactive tautomer **75oo**. The equilibrium constant K_T was estimated as 2×10^4, based on the assumptions that k_s for **75oo** is equivalent to that of **75nn** and that 70% of the hydrolysis product comes from **75oo**.[136] The stability difference of the tautomers **75oo** and **75pp** was attributed to the greater basicity of NH_2 compared to NHAc, which allows it to conjugate more strongly with the positive charge of the cation (Scheme 61).[136]

The photolysis of the azides **142qq** and **142rr** (Scheme 62) allowed McClelland and co-workers to investigate the equilibrium that governed protonation of the nitrenium ions **75qq** and **75rr** to generate the corresponding dications **144qq** and **144rr** and the deprotonation of **75qq** to generate the bis-imine **145qq**.[137] The dications were also obtained by oxidation of the corresponding amines under acidic conditions and both procedures resulted

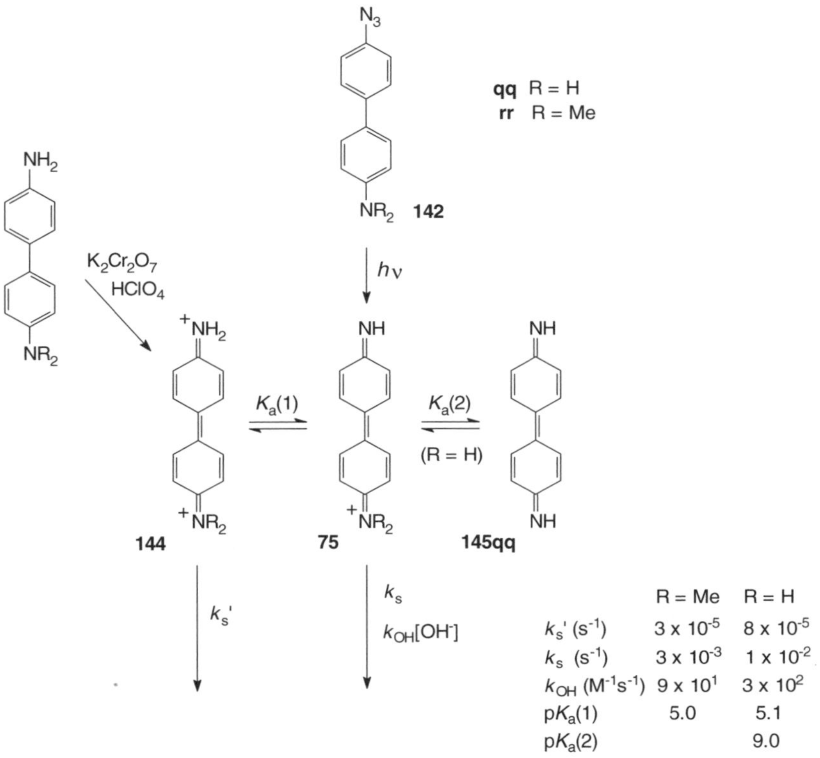

Scheme 62

in identical spectra at all pH. The pK_as shown in Scheme 62 were determined by spectrophotometric titration and by kinetic methods. The rate constants provided in Scheme 62 show that these are remarkably long-lived species in aqueous solution. The cations **75qq** and **75rr** are both at least two orders of magnitude more stable than predicted based on the previous Yukana–Tsuno correlations published for other 4′-substituted-4-biphenylylnitrenium ions.[85] This stabilization is not unique to the nitrenium ion structure because similar stabilizing effects are observed for the 4-dimethylamino substituent in trityl cations.[74]

One unusual aspect of these benzidine species is that the dications are less reactive toward solvent than are the monocations.[137] This was not observed for the 2-fluorenyl and 4-biphenylyl nitrenium ions **75g** and **75n** and their conjugate acids **144g** and **144n**.[134] The reason for this is not clear, but may be related to the fact that the two positive charges in **144qq** and **144rr** can be localized onto the two nitrogens on opposite ends of the structures.[137]

The bis-imine **145qq** is not noticeably reactive under these conditions. The k_{OH} rate term shown in Scheme 62 could be interpreted as solvent reacting with the neutral bis-imine, but **75rr** shows a term of similar magnitude that cannot be due to a bis-imine.[137]

HETEROARYLNITRENIUM IONS

Research into heteroarylnitrenium ions has been spurred by their apparent involvement in the carcinogenicity of heterocyclic arylamines and the antibiotic effects of 2-nitroimidazoles against anaerobic bacteria and protozoa, and by theoretical considerations.[138]

Several biological properties of the 2-nitroimidazoles appear to be associated with reductive metabolism.[138a] One potential reductive metabolite of a 2-nitroimidazole is the corresponding 2-hydroxylaminoimidazole (**146**, Scheme 63). McClelland and co-workers have extensively examined the hydrolysis reactions of **146**.[77,139–140] Rate vs. pH profiles and the observation

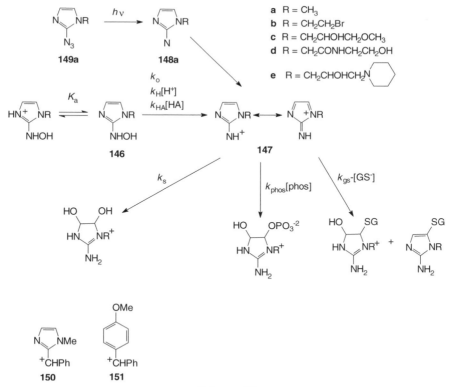

Scheme 63

of H$^+$ and general acid-catalyzed and spontaneous decomposition of **146** are consistent with the hydrolysis mechanism of Scheme 63.[77,139] An intermediate that can be trapped by the aqueous solvent,[139] phosphate,[140] or glutathione[77,139] was identified as the 1-alkyl-2-imidazolylnitrenium ion **147**. The rate constant ratio k_{gs^-}/k_s was estimated as $5 \times 10^5 \, M^{-1}$ for the 1-methyl ion **147a** from the variation of product yield data with [GS$^-$].[77] Since k_{gs^-} cannot exceed the diffusion limit of *ca.* $5 \times 10^9 \, M^{-1} \, s^{-1}$, this placed an upper limit on k_s of $10^4 \, s^{-1}$.[77] Subsequently Gadosy and McClelland directly observed **147a** produced by protonation of the corresponding nitrene **148a**, which was generated by LFP of the azide **149a**.[141] The rate constants k_s and k_{gs^-} were determined to be $9.4 \, s^{-1}$ and $3 \times 10^7 \, M^{-1} \, s^{-1}$, respectively.[141] The nitrenium ion **147a** has a lifetime of over 100 ms at neutral pH in the absence of buffers or other nucleophiles.[141] This ion is *ca.* 10^4-fold longer-lived than the carbenium ion **150**.[141] This is another example of an aryl group that stabilizes a nitrenium ion center far more than it does a carbenium ion center. The σ^+ value assigned to the 1-methyl-2-imidazolyl group on the basis of solvolysis rate constants for S$_N$1 reactions involving carbenium ions is -0.82, only slightly more negative than σ^+ for 4-methoxyphenyl.[142] The

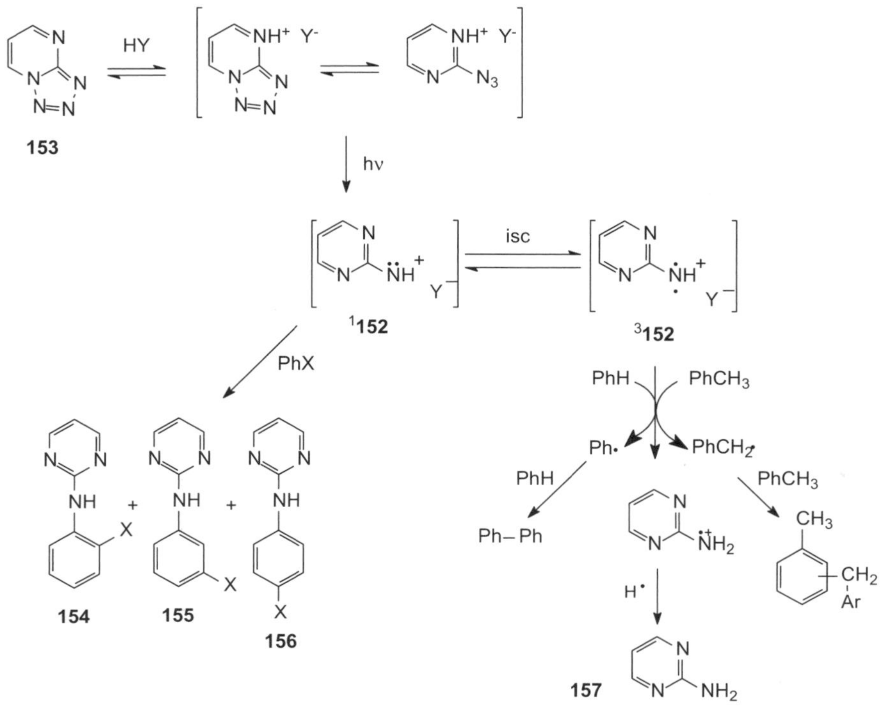

Scheme 64

rate constants for reaction of **150** and its 4-methoxyphenyl analogue **151** with aqueous solvent are within a factor of six of each other, but k_s for **147a** is five orders of magnitude smaller than k_s for **75cc**.[86,141]

Not all heteroarylnitrenium ions are stabilized species. Takeuchi and Watanabe apparently generated the 2-pyrimidylnitrenium ion **152** by photolysis of **153** in aromatic solvents containing TFA (Scheme 64).[143] A series of products of electrophilic aromatic substitution on the aromatic solvents (**154–156**) and the reduction product 2-aminopyrimidine, **157**, were observed. Partial rate factors for formation of the *meta*- and *para*-substituted products **155** and **156** correlated with σ^+, but the sensitivity of the reaction to substituents in the aromatic solvent was small ($\rho^+ = -2.7$). A similar experiment performed with phenyl azide, in which **75a** is the apparent intermediate, led to $\rho^+ = -4.5$.[36] The yield of **157** could be increased by adding 10 vol% CH_2Cl_2 or CH_2Br_2 to the solvent mixture.[143] The reduction product was also accompanied by apparent radical coupling products of the aromatic solvent (Scheme 64). It was concluded that the singlet–triplet gap in **152** was sufficiently small that ^{3}**152** was accessible and that the rate of intersystem crossing could be affected by heavy-atom-containing solvents. It was argued that the effect of the pyrimidyl nitrogens was to localize the positive charge on the exocyclic N, destabilizing the singlet ion relative to the triplet.[143] This appears to be consistent with the apparently low selectivity of ^{1}**152**, its predominant reaction with aromatics at N, and the substantial yield of the apparently triplet-derived **157**.

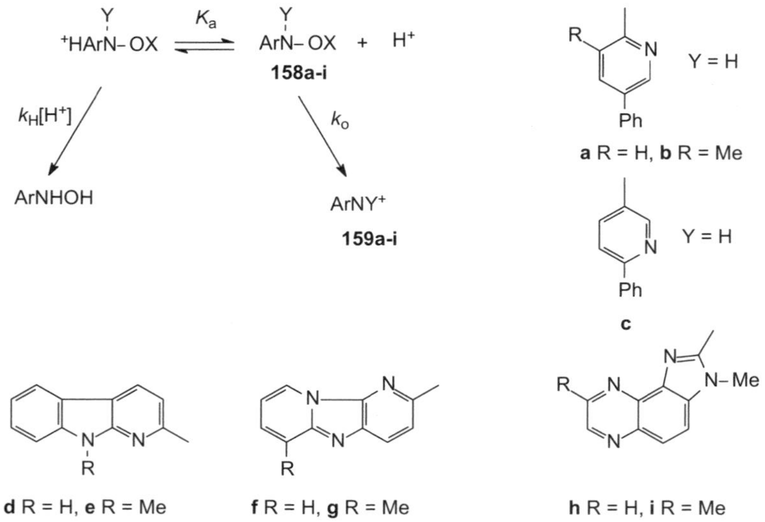

Scheme 65

Novak and co-workers have examined the hydrolysis reactions of a series of esters, **158a–i**, of hydroxylamines or hydroxamic acids that are derived from carcinogenic and mutagenic heterocyclic arylamines.[144–147] Hydrolysis rate constants could be fitted to equation (5). The rate law is consistent with the kinetic mechanism provided in Scheme 65.

$$k_{obs} = k_H[H^+]^2/(K_a + [H^+]) + k_o K_a/K_a + [H^+]) \qquad (5)$$

The first term of the rate law requires acid-catalyzed decomposition of the conjugated acid of the ester. This term predominates only under strongly acidic conditions. It has not been investigated in detail, but the major product of the acid catalyzed reaction is the corresponding hydroxylamine. The second term predominates under neutral to mildly acidic conditions. This term is consistent with uncatalyzed heterolysis of the N—O bond of the neutral ester to generate a heteroarylnitrenium ion.[144] The rate law is more complicated than that for reactive esters of carbocyclic hydroxylamines or hydroxamic acids that show pH-independent decomposition over a wide pH range.[58,76,87] The kinetic behavior of the heterocyclic esters is caused by protonation of a pyridyl or imidazolyl N under mildly acidic conditions. The protonated substrates are not subject to spontaneous uncatalyzed decomposition, so k_{obs} decreases under acidic conditions until acid-catalyzed

Table 4 Rate constant ratios k_{az}/k_s, $k_{d\text{-}G}/k_s$, and k_{phos}/k_s for heteroarylnitrenium ions with comparisons with some carbocyclic ions.

Ion	k_{az}/k_s (M^{-1})	$k_{d\text{-}G}/k_s$ (M^{-1})	k_{phos}/k_s (M^{-1})
159a	10^a		
159b	300^a	83^b	
159c	79^a		
159d	$3.5 \times 10^{4\,c}$	$8.2 \times 10^{3\,c}$	
159e	$4.5 \times 10^{4\,c}$	$8.8 \times 10^{3\,c}$	
159f	$2.3 \times 10^{6\,d}$	$3.1 \times 10^{4\,d}$	$5.2 \times 10^{2\,d}$
159g	$5.1 \times 10^{6\,d}$	$5.0 \times 10^{4\,d}$	$5.3 \times 10^{2\,d}$
159h	$5.2 \times 10^{4\,e}$	$9.1 \times 10^{2\,e}$	$4.4 \times 10^{2\,e}$
159i	$1.2 \times 10^{5\,e}$	$8.4 \times 10^{2\,e}$	$5.2 \times 10^{2\,e}$
75g	$1.2 \times 10^{5\,f}$	$2.9 \times 10^{4\,f}$	
75n	$2.9 \times 10^{3\,f}$	$1.1 \times 10^{3\,f}$	

[a]Ref. 144: 5 vol% CH$_3$CN-H$_2$O, $\mu = 0.5$ (NaClO$_4$), 20°C.
[b]Unpublished data: 5 vol% CH$_3$CN-H$_2$O, $\mu = 0.5$ (NaClO$_4$), 20°C.
[c]Ref. 145: 20 vol% CH$_3$CN-H$_2$O, $\mu = 0.5$ (NaClO$_4$), 20°C.
[d]Ref. 146: 5 vol% CH$_3$CN-H$_2$O, $\mu = 0.5$ (NaClO$_4$), 20°C.
[e]Ref. 147: 5 vol% CH$_3$CN-H$_2$O, $\mu = 0.5$ (NaClO$_4$), 20°C.
[f]Refs. 76, 79, 107, 109: 5 or 20 vol% CH$_3$CN-H$_2$O, $\mu = 0.5$ (NaClO$_4$), 20°C.

decomposition of the protonated substrate becomes important. The kinetic and spectrophotometric pK_as are in good agreement and range from $ca.$ 0.6 to 4.2 for the examples shown in Scheme 65.[144–147]

The apparent nitrenium ions **159a–i** were characterized by their reactions with N_3^-, d-G and the aqueous solvent. The ratios k_{az}/k_s and k_{d-G}/k_s derived from competition kinetics are provided in Table 4, with some comparisons with previously examined carbocyclic nitrenium ions. The more selective ions **159f–159i** exhibit considerable reactivity with HPO_4^{2-}, and k_{phos}/k_s data are provided for those ions also. Based on analogies to carbocyclic nitrenium ions, k_{az} should be at or near the diffusion limit for all ions with $k_{az}/k_s < 5 \times 10^5 \, M^{-1}$, so k_{az}/k_s can be used to evaluate the kinetic stability of these ions within those limits. Comparisons of k_{az}/k_s for **159a**, **159c**, and **75n** show that a 3-pyridyl-N and 2-pyridyl-N kinetically destabilize the cation by $ca.$ 35-fold and 300-fold, respectively, as would be expected, based on differences in the electronegativities of N and C and the resulting differences in their abilities to stabilize a positive charge. The effect of a heterocyclic N can be quite opposite in situations in which the lone pair on the N can participate in resonance stabilization. This is true in each of the cations **159d–i**, and it leads to considerable stabilization in each case. For **159f** and **159g**, k_{az}/k_s is

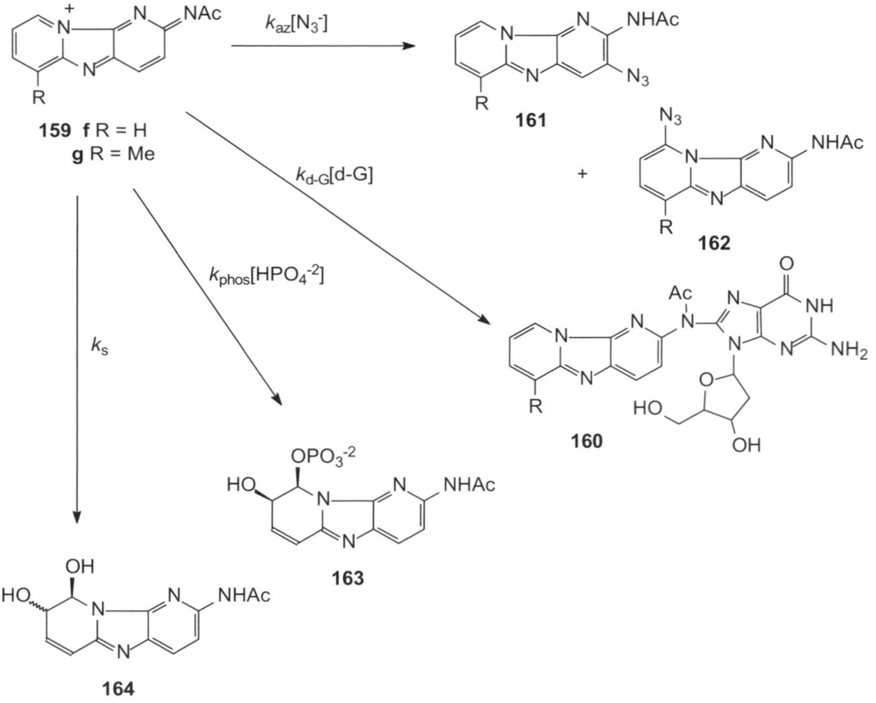

Scheme 66

somewhat beyond the range where k_{az} can be confidently predicted to be near the diffusion limit. These ions have k_{az}/k_s similar to that of **75p**. That ion has k_{az} within a factor of 2 of the apparent diffusion limit.[85]

Reaction products for **159f** and **159g** are summarized in Scheme 66.[146] The d-G adduct **160** has the characteristic structure previously observed for the reaction of carbocyclic nitrenium ions such as **75g** and **75n** with d-G. Similar C-8 adducts have been isolated from the reactions of **159b**, **159d**, **159h**, and **159i**.[144–147] These are also the major DNA adducts obtained from *in vivo* or *in vitro* experiments involving the parent amines.[138b] The N_3^--adducts **161** and **162** are similar to those observed in studies of carbocyclic esters.[75–87] The phosphate and solvent-derived products **163** and **164** are analogous to those previously reported by McClelland and co-workers for the 1-methyl-2-imidazolylnitrenium ion **147a**.[139,140]

Some of the heterocyclic ions are subject to acid–base reactions that occur within the readily accessible pH range. For example, the apparent k_{nuc}/k_s for trapping of **159d** by N_3^-, Br^-, and d-G is pH dependent, decreasing from pH 3 to 8 and conforming to a titration curve with an apparent pK_a, pK_a^{app}, of 5.0.[145] These results are consistent with deprotonation of 9-NH to yield a neutral species **159d′**, which is trapped with relatively less efficiency by non-solvent nucleophiles than **159d** (Scheme 67).[145] The apparent pK_a obtained from the trapping data is $pK_a + \log(k_s^+/k_s^o)$.[145] Since it is likely that $k_s^+ > k_s^o$, it is likely that $pK_a^{app} > pK_a$. In support of this interpretation it was found that the 9-NMe cation **159e**, which cannot be deprotonated at 9-N, does not exhibit pH-dependent trapping in this pH range.[145] McClelland has discovered similar pH-dependent trapping behavior in the cation **159j** obtained from LFP of the corresponding azide.[148] Data from his study allowed the pK_a of **159d** to be estimated as 3.0.[145]

Figure 5 provides a comparison of $\log(k_{d\text{-}G}/k_s)$ vs. $\log(k_{az}/k_s)$ for a series of carbocyclic and heterocyclic ions for which both ratios are available. Several conclusions can be drawn from this comparison.

(1) The patterns of selectivity exhibited by the heterocyclic and carbocyclic ions are similar.
(2) Data points for most ions fall on a line of unit slope that would be expected if both k_{az} and $k_{d\text{-}G}$ were diffusion limited. The intercept of this line indicates that $k_{az} \approx 4.6\ k_{d\text{-}G}$ for these ions. A similar conclusion was reached from examining directly measured k_{az} and $k_{d\text{-}G}$ for several of these ions (see Tables 1 and 3).

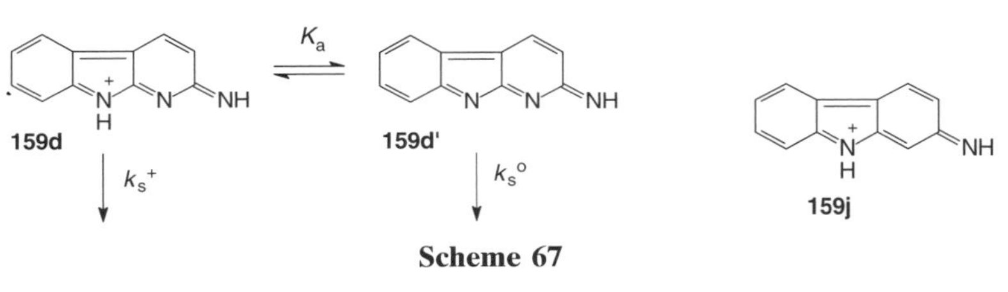

Scheme 67

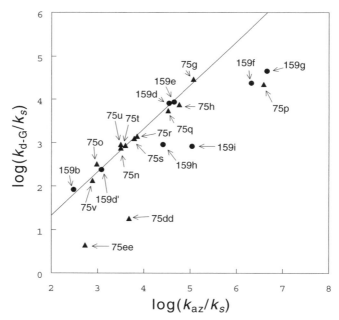

Fig. 5 Log (k_{d-G}/k_s) vs. log (k_{az}/k_s) for carbocyclic (▲) and heterocyclic (●) nitrenium ions. Individual ions are labeled.

(3) The points that fall off the line do so in the same direction: k_{d-G}/k_s is one to two orders of magnitude smaller than expected for these ions, based on the correlation established by the other ions.

For three of the seven ions in Fig. 5 that fall off the correlation, k_{az} has been directly measured and is within a factor of two of the expected diffusion limit, so it appears that these ions fall off the correlation line because k_{d-G} is at least an order of magnitude below the diffusion limit. Figure 5 shows that this tendency to fall off the line is not related to the magnitude of k_s for these ions. These ions have k_s ranging from *ca.* $10^3 \, s^{-1}$ to $10^7 \, s^{-1}$.

McClelland suggested that this unexpectedly low selectivity toward d-G by certain ions might be related to the tendency of substituents in these ions to localize the positive charge on a heteroatom other than the nitrenium N.[86] It was suggested that this would reduce the electrophilic reactivity at the nitrenium N necessary for formation of C-8 adducts with d-G.[86] All seven of the ions that fall off the correlation line have a dominant resonance structure in which the positive charge is localized onto a heteroatom (O or N) with all heavy atoms maintaining an octet of electrons, but so do several of the ions that fall on the line (**159d** and **159e**). This phenomenon is not fully understood.

CALCULATIONS

Calculations of the properties of nitrenium ions continue to be performed by semi-empirical and *ab initio* methods, in an effort to provide information concerning:

(1) Singlet–triplet gaps.
(2) Structure and stability of the ions and the effects of substituent groups on that stability.
(3) Correlation of calculated properties with known reactivity data or with mutagenicity/carcinogenicity of the parent amines.

Calculations of singlet–triplet gaps in arylnitrenium ions are difficult to evaluate because of the lack of experimental data with which to calibrate the calculations. The experimental singlet–triplet gap of +30.1 kcal/mol for NH_2^+ can be reproduced at sufficiently high levels of theory,[1–3] but arylnitrenium ions are a considerably more complicated species. The DFT methods, used in recent calculations by Cramer and co-workers, appear to have been validated by the excellent agreement recently obtained for the experimental (-66 ± 3 kcal/mol) and theoretical (-64.7 kcal/mol) gap for the highly stabilized ion **165** (the negative sign means that the singlet state is more stable).[149] These DFT calculations were performed at the BPW91/cc-pVDZ level also used for recent calculations on arylnitrenium ions.[150–152]

These calculations indicate that the singlet–triplet gap in **75a** is -18.8 kcal/mol in the gas phase.[151] Corrections for transfer to aqueous solution provide a gap of -20.6 kcal/mol.[151] Replacement of NH by NMe and NAc reduced the gap to -14.1 kcal/mol and -6.8 kcal/mol, respectively in the gas phase.[150,152] These effects were explained by steric destabilization of the NMe singlet state and lack of conjugation of the acyl group with the aromatic π-system of the NAc singlet state, caused by the near perpendicularity of the acyl and aryl groups in the singlet state.[152] Although N-acyl- and N-alkyl-N-arylnitrenium ions have reduced singlet–triplet gaps compared to the unsubstituted ion, these species do appear to be singlet ground states.

According to calculations, introduction of sufficient steric bulk, as in **166**, can cause the triplet to become the ground state by forcing large C—N—C bond angles that favor the triplet.[153] Introduction of nitrogen atoms into the aromatic ring, particularly at the *ortho-* and *para*-positions, destabilizes the singlet state to a greater extent than the triplet.[152] A single nitrogen substitution appears to be insufficient to cause the triplet to be the ground state, but the 2-pyridyl ion **152** (Scheme 64) is calculated to be a ground state triplet by 7.0 kcal/mol in the gas phase and by 5.5 kcal/mol in aqueous solution.[152] This calculation is in general agreement with conclusions reached by Takeuchi based on experimental results described above.[143]

DFT calculations also indicate that electron-donating substituents at the *para*-position stabilize the singlet state, while electron-withdrawing substituents destabilize the singlet state.[151] The effects do not appear to be sufficient to cause the triplet to be the ground state for any of the substituents examined (substituent; gas-phase singlet–triplet gap (kcal/mol): CHO; −12.2, CO_2H; −16.2, CO_2CH_3; −16.5, $COCH_3$; −13.5, CF_3; −17.9, CN; −17.5, NO_2; −16.8, H; −18.8).[151] Falvey and Srivastava obtained experimental data for the 4-NO_2 substituted ion **131h** (Scheme 55) that suggests this ion has a triplet ground state.[126] This ion also has a 2-$COCH_3$ substituent and an N-*tert*-Bu substituent, both of which should destabilize the singlet state.

Calculations of the structures of nitrenium ions at various levels of theory have provided a consistent picture of nitrenium ion structure in both the singlet and triplet electronic states.[89,133,149–158] These results are exemplified by DFT calculation at the BVWN5/cc-pVTZ/BVWN5/cc-pVDZ level of theory on **75a** in both its singlet and triplet states.[154] Singlet **75a** has strongly alternating C—C bond lengths in the aromatic ring, a short C—N bond of 1.311Å, an N—H bond in the plane of the ring and a C—N—H bond angle of 105.9°.[154] Rotation about the C—N bond through a perpendicular structure does not occur. The transition state for inversion through nitrogen is linear (C—N—H bond angle = 180°) and lies 26.0 kcal/mol above the global minimum for the singlet ion.[154] The calculated structure is consistent with the view that this ion can be thought of as a 4-imino-2, 5-cyclohexadienyl cation. The global minimum for the triplet has the N—H bond perpendicular to the plane of the ring, but the planar structure is a transition state only 1.8 kcal/mol above the perpendicular structure.[154] The C—N bond length is longer than the singlet (1.33Å), and the C—N—H bond angle is larger (129.9°). The ease of rotation about the C—N bond in the triplet shows that double-bond character is not present. The preference for the perpendicular structure is small enough that certain electron-withdrawing substituents can apparently reverse that preference.[151]

At all levels of theory, the N-acetyl group of N-acetyl-N-arylnitrenium ions is rotated out of the plane of the aromatic ring, although to different extents.[89,152,155,156] The N-acetyl group destabilizes the ion by *ca.* 20 kcal/mol relative to an N-methyl substituent in comparison with the neutral amide and amine precursors.[155] This destabilization was attributed by Ford and Herman to loss of resonance in the amide precursor on going to the nitrenium ion, not to inductive destabilization of the ion by the acyl group.[155]

Recently Ford and co-workers performed calculations of the structures and relative stabilities of a series of 20 polycyclic nitrenium ions at the HF/6-31G(d) level.[158] Except for symmetrical cases, all ions existed as distinct syn and anti isomers defined by the configuration of the N—H bond with respect to the unsymmetrical aryl group. The energies of configurational isomers differed by between 0.2 and 3.7 kcal/mol. Inversion barriers through a linear transition state were fairly constant in the range from

25–28 kcal/mol.[158] These barriers are of similar magnitude to the value calculated for **75a** by DFT methods.[154] It was pointed out that barriers of this magnitude meant that essentially no interconversion of isomers would occur during the μs to ns lifetimes of most nitrenium ions.[158] The polycyclic aryl groups were found to stabilize the ions relative to the phenyl group by 14–40 kcal/mol, depending on the ring system and on the site of substitution.[158] Charges calculated on N tend to be significantly negative (−0.35 to −0.50), in large part because of strong polarization of the N—H bond.[157,158] If the charge of the NH group is considered, overall charges range from +0.16 to −0.08.[158] To the extent that these charge calculations are meaningful, they are consistent with the picture derived from calculated bond lengths and most experimental data.[158]

There have been several attempts to correlate observed chemical, biological, or spectral properties of nitrenium ions with calculated properties.[71,81,89,133,159–161] The correlations of azide–solvent selectivities with the calculated relative driving force for cation hydration[81,89] and observed and calculated IR bands for **141b–e**[133] have been discussed above. Ford and coworkers have had success in correlating quantitative bacterial mutagenicity data for a range of carbocyclic and heterocyclic amines, with the relative stabilities of the nitrenium ions calculated at the semi-empirical AM1 level from the isodesmic reaction of Scheme 68.[159,160] The correlations are quite remarkable when one considers all the variables that contribute to the relative mutagenicities of these amines, including rates of metabolism, transport properties, DNA adduct repair rates, and differential genetic effects of the adducts.

Ford and Herman have been able to correlate the calculated AM1 stabilities of nitrenium ions vs. those of the corresponding arylmethyl carbocations, as defined by the isodesmic reactions of Scheme 69, through a simple relationship shown in equation (6)

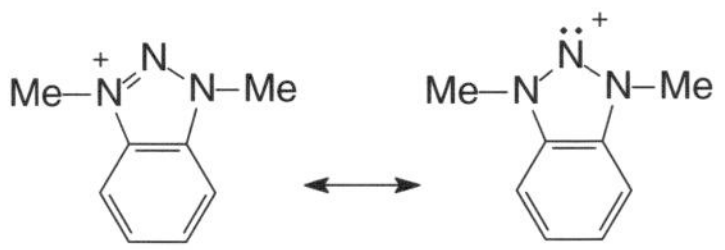

165 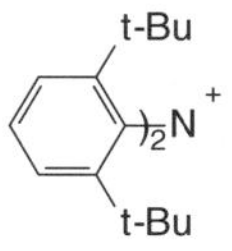   **166**

$$ArNH_2 \; + \; PhNH^+ \longrightarrow ArNH^+ \; + \; PhNH_2$$

Scheme 68

$$ArH \; + \; PhNH^+ \longrightarrow ArNH^+ \; + \; PhH$$

$$ArH \; + \; PhCH_2^+ \longrightarrow ArCH_2^+ \; + \; PhH$$

Scheme 69

$$\Delta H(\text{ArNH}^+) = 0.911\Delta H(\text{ArCH}_2^+) + 64.712\Delta q_{\text{CH}_2} - 0.771 \qquad (6)$$

where Δq_{CH_2} is the difference in charge at the CH_2 group for ArCH_2^+ and PhCH_2^+.[157] The second term of the equation indicates that nitrenium ions are differentially stabilized relative to arylmethyl carbocations when the aryl group is more electron donating than Ph. This conclusion is similar to those made by others concerning stabilization of nitrenium ions by aryl groups from both experimental data and calculations.[81,83,85,89]

Attempts to rationalize the regioselectivity of attack of nucleophiles on the aryl rings of nitrenium ions in terms of calculated properties of the ions (LUMO coefficients, localization energies, etc.) have been moderately successful.[71,89,114,152,161] An adequate explanation of electrophilic reactivity of nitrenium ions at N with certain nucleophiles such as glutathione, C-8 of d-G, and other carbon nucleophiles has not yet appeared.[89,114,152]

4 The future

Our understanding of the chemistry of N-arylnitrenium ions is significantly more advanced than it was a decade ago. Nevertheless, this field of research is still considerably less developed than that of carbenium ions, carbenes, or nitrenes. For example, although singlet nitrenium ions behave as one might expect that their 4-imino-2,5-cyclohexadienyl resonance contributors would in their reactions with H_2O, N_3^-, or Cl^-, their reactions with carbon, nitrogen, and sulfur nucleophiles, particularly d-G, are not so easily rationalized. Except for d-G, these reactions with soft nucleophiles have not been examined systematically and the regiochemistry exhibited by these nucleophiles is incompletely understood.

Other facets of nitrenium ion chemistry that require additional investigation in the near future include:

(1) Experimental determination of singlet–triplet gaps. This has not been reported for any N-arylnitrenium ions, and no unambiguous examples of ions with triplet ground states have been reported.

(2) Reactions of nitrenium ions with lifetimes in aqueous solution $\leqslant 1$ ns. It is clear from the work presented to date that these species react predominately by ion-pair or preassociation mechanisms, but the detailed processes are far from clear. The possible transition to a true bimolecular substitution mechanism (S_N2) has also not been systematically investigated.

(3) Reactions of highly stabilized nitrenium ions. Just as little is known of the chemistry of very short-lived nitrenium ions, very little has been reported on the chemistry of ions with lifetimes $\geqslant 1$ ms. Recently, results have been reported for some benzidine nitrenium ions that fall

into this reactivity range, but systematic studies have not been performed. For example, it is not understood how azide/solvent selectivities vary in this range of stability.

(4) Chemistry of heteroarylnitrenium ions. Research in this area has been spurred by the apparent importance of heterocyclic amines produced during the cooking of protein-containing foods as a ubiquitous class of human carcinogens. This chemistry has been under investigation for only a short period of time.

(5) Reactions of nitrenium ions with DNA. Most of what is known about their reactions with DNA bases is derived from studies with monomeric bases. Some work with DNA oligomers has been reported, but little is known of the effects of DNA tertiary structure on these reactions.

Many of these areas are currently under investigation by one or more of the research groups that have made contributions to the field in recent years. New developments in these areas are likely to be reported in the near future.

References

1. Bender, C.F., Meadows, J.H. and Schaefer, H.F. (1977). *Faraday Discuss. Chem. Soc.* **62**, 58. Peyerimhoff, S.D. and Buenker, R.J. (1979). *Chem. Phys.* **42**, 167. Pope, S.A., Hillier, I.H. and Guest, M.F. (1984). *Faraday Symp. Chem. Soc.* **19**, 109. Pople, J.A. and Schleyer, P.v.R. (1986). *Chem. Phys. Lett.* **129**, 279. Pople, J.A. and Curtiss, L.A. (1987). *J. Phys. Chem.* **91**, 155. vanHuis, T.J., Leininger, M.L., Sherrill, C.D. and Schaefer, H.F. (1998). *Collect. Czech. Chem. C.* **63**, 1107. Cramer, C.J., Dulles, F.J., Storer, J.W. and Worthington, S.E. (1994). *Chem. Phys. Lett.* **218**, 387
2. Ford, G.P. and Herman, P.S. (1989). *J. Am. Chem. Soc.,* **111**, 3987. Falvey, D.E. and Cramer, C.J. (1992). *Tetrahedron Lett.* **33**, 1705
3. Gibson, S.T., Greene, P.J. and Berkowitz, J. (1985). *J. Chem. Phys.* **83**, 4319.
4. (a) Srivastava, S., Kercher, M. and Falvey, D.E. (1999). *J. Org. Chem.* **64**, 5853. (b) Takeuchi, H. (1987). *J. Chem. Soc., Chem. Commun.* 961. (c) Takeuchi, H., Hayakawa, S. and Murai, H. (1988). *J. Chem. Soc., Chem. Commun.* 1287. (d) Takeuchi, H., Higuchi, D. and Adachi, T. (1991). *J. Chem. Soc., Perkin Trans. 1,* 1525. (e) Takeuchi, H., Hayakawa, S., Tanahashi, T., Kobayashi, A., Adachi, T. and Higuchi, D. (1991). *J. Chem. Soc., Perkin Trans. 2,* 847
5. Gassman, P.G. and Cryberg, R.L. (1968). *J. Am. Chem. Soc.* **90**, 1355. (1969). **91**, 2047. (1969). **91**, 5176. Gassman, P.G. and Hartman, G.D. (1973). *J. Am. Chem. Soc.* **95**, 449. Gassman, P.G. and Dygos, J.H. (1970). *Tetrahedron Lett.* **11**, 4745. Gassman, P.G., Uneyama, K. and Hahnfeld, J.L. (1977). *J. Am. Chem. Soc.* **99**, 647
6. Edwards, O.E., Vocelle, D. and ApSimon, J.W. (1972). *Can. J. Chem.* **50**, 1167. Edwards, O.E., Bernath, G., Dixon, J., Paton, J.M. and Vocelle, D. (1974). *Can. J. Chem.* **52**, 2123. Furtoss, R., Tadayoni, T. and Waegall, B. (1977). *Nouv. J. Chem.* **1**, 167. Hoffman, R.V., Kumar, A. and Buntain, G.A. (1985). *J. Am. Chem. Soc.* **107**, 4731
7. Schell, F.M. and Ganguly, R.N. (1980). *J. Org. Chem.* **45**, 4069
8. Miller, J.A. (1970). *Cancer Res.* **30**, 559. Lotlikar, P.D., Scribner, J.D., Miller, J.A. and Miller, E.D. (1966). *Life Sci.* **5**, 1263

9. Abramovitch, R.A. and Davis, B.A. (1964). *Chem. Rev.* **64**, 149
10. Shine, H.J. (1967). *Aromatic Rearrangements*, pp. 182–190. Elsevier, New York
11. Abramovitch, R.A. and Jeyarman, R. (1984). In *Azides and Nitrenes Reactivity and Utility*, Scriven, E.F.V. (ed.), pp. 297–357. Academic Press, New York
12. Bamberger, E. (1894). *Chem. Ber.* **27**, 1347. (1894). **27**, 1548
13. Bamberger, E. and Lagutt, J. (1898). *Chem. Ber.* **31**, 1500
14. Bamberger, E. (1901). *Chem. Ber.* **34**, 61
15. Bamberger, E. (1921). *Liebigs Ann.* **424**, 297. (1925). **441**, 297
16. Bamberger, E. (1895). *Chem. Ber.* **28**, 245
17. Bamberger, E. and Brady, F. (1900). *Chem. Ber.* **33**, 3642. Bamberger, E. (1907). *Chem. Ber.* **40**, 1906. (1907). **40**, 1918
18. Bamberger, E. (1900). *Chem. Ber.* **33**, 3600
19. Smith, P.A.S. (1984). In *Azides and Nitrenes Reactivity and Utility*, Scriven, E.F.V. (ed.), pp. 95–204. Academic Press, New York
20. Heller, H.E., Hughes, E.D. and Ingold, C.R. (1951). *Nature* **168**, 909
21. Kukhtenko, I.I. (1971). *Russ. J. Org. Chem. (Engl. Transl.)* **7**, 324. Oae, S. and Kitao, T. (1961). *Yuki Gosei Kagaku Kyokai Shi* **19**, 880
22. Sone, T., Tokuda, Y., Sakai, T., Shinkai, S. and Manabe, O. (1981). *J. Chem. Soc., Perkin Trans.* **2**, 298
23. Kohnstam, G., Petch, W.A. and Williams, D.L.H. (1984). *J. Chem. Soc., Perkin Trans,* **2**, 423
24. Okamoto, T., Shudo, K. and Ohta, T. (1975). *J. Am. Chem. Soc.* **97**, 7184. Shudo, K., Ohta, T., Endo, Y. and Okamoto, T. (1977). *Tetrahedron Lett.* **18**, 105. Shudo, K., Ohta, T. and Okamoto, T. (1981). *J. Am. Chem. Soc.* **103**, 645
25. Olah, G.A. and Donovan, D.J. (1978). *J. Org. Chem.* **43**, 1743
26. Svanholm, U. and Parker, J.D. (1974). *J. Am. Chem. Soc.* **96**, 1234. Serve, D. (1975). *J. Am. Chem. Soc.* **97**, 432
27. Gassman, P.G., Campbell, G. and Frederick, R. (1968). *J. Am. Chem. Soc.* **90**, 7377
28. Gassman, P.G. and Campbell, G.A. (1970). *J. Chem. Soc., Chem. Commun.* 427
29. Gassman, P.G. and Campbell, G.A. (1971). *J. Am. Chem. Soc.* **93**, 2567
30. Gassman, P.G., Campbell, G.A. and Frederick, R.C. (1972). *J. Am. Chem. Soc.* **94**, 3884
31. Gassman, P.G. and Campbell, G.A. (1972). *J. Am. Chem. Soc.* **94**, 3891
32. Griess, P. (1886). *Chem. Ber.* **19**, 313. Friedlander, P. and Zeitlin, M. (1894). *Chem. Ber.* **27**, 192
33. Bamberger, E. (1921). *Liebigs Ann.* **424**, 233
34. Smith, P.A.S. and Brown, B.B. (1951). *J. Am. Chem. Soc.* **73**, 2438
35. Takeuchi, H. and Koyama, K. (1981). *J. Chem. Soc., Chem. Commun.* 202. Takeuchi, H. and Koyama, K. (1982). *J. Chem. Soc., Perkin Trans. 1*, 1269
36. Takeuchi, H., Takano, K. and Koyama, K. (1982). *J. Chem. Soc., Chem. Commun.* 1254. Takeuchi, H. and Takano, K. (1983). *J. Chem. Soc., Chem. Commun.* 447. Takeuchi, H. and Takano, K. (1986). *J. Chem. Soc., Perkin Trans. 1*, 611
37. Takeuchi, H. and Ihara, R. (1983). *J. Chem. Soc., Chem. Commun.* 175. Takeuchi, H., Koyama, K., Mitani, M., Ihara, R., Uno, T., Okazaki, Y., Kai, Y. and Kasai, N. (1985). *J. Chem. Soc., Perkin Trans 1*, 677
38. Hyatt, J.A. and Swenton, J. S. (1972). *J. Org. Chem.* **37**, 3216. Abramovitch, R.A., Cooper, M., Iyer, S., Jeyaraman, R. and Rodriquez, J.A.R. (1982). *J. Org. Chem.* **47**, 4820. Wassamundt, F.W. and Babic, G.T. (1982). *J. Org. Chem.* **47**, 3585. Takeuchi, H., Maeda, M., Mitani, M. and Koyama, K. (1985). *J. Chem. Soc., Chem. Commun.* 287. (1987). *J. Chem. Soc., Perkin Trans. 1*, 57

39. Sternson, L.A. and Chandrasakar, R. (1984). *J. Org. Chem.* **49**, 4295
40. Giovannini, E., Rosales, J. and deSouza, B. (1971). *Helv. Chim. Acta* **54**, 2111
41. Giovannini, E. and deSouza, B.F.S.E. (1979). *Helv. Chim. Acta* **62**, 185
42. Doppler, T., Schmidt, H. and Hansen, H.-J. (1979). *Helv. Chim. Acta* **62**, 271
43. Doppler, T., Schmidt, H. and Hansen, H.-J. (1979). *Helv. Chim. Acta* **62**, 304
44. Berwick, M.A. (1971). *J. Am. Chem. Soc.* **93**, 5780
45. Haley, N.F. (1977). *J. Org. Chem.* **42**, 3929
46. Kriek, E. (1974). *Biochem. Biophys. Acta* **335**, 177. Miller, E.C. (1978). *Cancer Res.* **38**, 1479. Miller, E.C. and Miller, J.A. (1981). *Cancer* **47**, 2327. Miller, J.A. and Miller, E.C. (1983). *Environ. Health Perspect.* **49**, 3. Garner, R.C., Martin, C.N. and Clayson, D.B. (1984). In *Chemical Carcinogens*, 2nd edn, Washington, DC, vol. 1, pp. 175–276. Beland, F.A. and Kadlubar, F.F. (1985). *Environ. Health Perspect.* **62**, 19. Kadlubar, F.F. and Beland, F.A. (1985). In *Polycyclic Hydrocarbons and Carcinogenesis*, ACS Symposium Series 283, pp. 341–370. American Chemical Society, Washington, DC
47. Kriek, E., Miller, J.A., Juhl, U. and Miller, E.C. (1967). *Biochem.* **6**, 177. Kriek, E. (1971). *Chem.-Biol. Interact.* **3**, 19. Scribner, J.D. and Naimy, N.K. (1975). *Cancer Res.* **35**, 1416. Nelson, J.H., Grunberger, D., Cantor, C.R. and Weinstein, I.B. (1971). *J. Mol. Biol.* **62**, 331. Meerman, J.H.N., Beland, F.A. and Mulder, G.J. (1981). *Carcinogenesis* **2**, 413. Beland, F.A., Dooley, K.L. and Jackson, C.D. (1982). *Cancer Res.* **42**, 1348. Evans, F.E., Miller, D.W. and Levine, R.A. (1984). *J. Am. Chem. Soc.* **106**, 396
48. Kriek, E. (1972). *Cancer Res.* **32**, 2042. Westra, J.G., Kriek, E. and Hittenhausen, H. (1976). *Chem.-Biol. Interact.* **15**, 149. Sage, E., Fuchs, R.P.P. and Leng, M. (1979). *Biochem.* **18**, 1328. Kriek, E. and Hengeveld, G.M. (1978). *Chem.-Biol. Interact.* **21**, 179. Franz, R. and Neumann, H.-G. (1988). *Chem.-Biol. Interact.* **67**, 105. Scribner, J.D., Smith, D.L. and McCloskey, J.A. (1978). *J. Org. Chem.* **43**, 2085. Gaugler, B.J.M., Neumann, H.-G., Scribner, N.K. and Scribner, J.D. (1979). *Chem. Biol. Interact.* **27**, 335
49. Lawley, P.D. (1976). In *Chemical Carcinogens*, ACS Monograph No. 173, Searle, C.E. (ed.), pp. 83–244. American Chemical Society, Washington, DC. Magee, P.N., Montesano, R. and Preussman, R. (1976). Ibid. p. 491
50. Zady, M.F. and Wong, J.L. (1977). *J. Am. Chem. Soc.* **99**, 5096
51. Scribner, J.D., Miller, J.A. and Miller, E.C. (1970). *Cancer Res.* **30**, 1570
52. Scribner, J.D. and Naimy, N.K. (1973). *Cancer Res.* **33**, 1159. Scribner, J.D. and Naimy, N.K. (1975). *Experentia* **31**, 470
53. Scribner, J.D. (1976). *J. Org. Chem.* **41**, 3820
54. Scott, C.M., Underwood, G.R. and Kirsch, R.B. (1984). *Tetrahedron Lett.* **25**, 499. Nicolaou, C. and Underwood, G.R. (1989). *Tetrahedron Lett.* **30**, 1479
55. Underwood, G.R. and Davidson, C.M. (1985). *J. Chem. Soc., Chem. Commun.* 555. Underwood, G.R. and Kirsch, R. (1985). *Tetrahedron Lett.* **26**, 147. Underwood, G.R. and Kirsch, R.B. (1985). *J. Chem. Soc., Chem. Commun.* 136
56. Underwood, G.R. and Callahan, R.J. (1987). *Tetrahedron Lett.* **28**, 5427
57. Gassman, P.G. and Granrud, J.E. (1984). *J. Am. Chem. Soc.* **106**, 1498
58. Novak, M., Pelecanou, M., Roy, A.K., Andronico, A.F., Plourde, F.M., Olefirowicz, J.M. and Curtin, T.J. (1984). *J. Am. Chem. Soc.* **106**, 5623
59. Novak, M. and Roy, A.K. (1985). *J. Org. Chem.* **50**, 571
60. Novak, M. and Roy, A.K. (1985). *J. Org. Chem.* **50**, 4884
61. Pelecanou, M. and Novak, M. (1985). *J. Am. Chem. Soc.* **107**, 4499
62. Novak, M., Pelecanou, M. and Pollack, L. (1986). *J. Am. Chem. Soc.* **108**, 112
63. Novak, M., Pelecanou, M. and Zemis, J.N. (1986). *J. Med. Chem.* **29**, 1424

64. Scribner, J.D., Scribner, N.K., Smith, D.L., Jenkins, E. and McCloskey, J.A. (1982). *J. Org. Chem.* **47**, 3143
65. Kreuger, J.H., Blanchet, P.F., Lee, A.P. and Sudbury, B.A. (1973). *Inorg. Chem.* **12**, 2714
66. Gassman, P.G. and Granrud, J.E. (1984). *J. Am. Chem. Soc.* **106**, 2448
67. Novak, M., Rovin, L.H., Pelecanou, M., Mulero, J.J. and Lagerman, R.K. (1987). *J. Org. Chem.* **52**, 2002
68. Novak, M. and Lagerman, R.K. (1988). *J. Org. Chem.* **53**, 4762
69. Lagerman, R.K. and Novak, M. (1989). *Tetrahedron Lett.* **30**, 1923
70. (a) Gutschke, D. and Heesing, A. (1973). *Chem. Ber.* **106**, 2379. (b) Gessner, U., Heesing, A., Keller, L. and Homann, W.K. (1982). *Chem. Ber.* **115**, 2865
71. Ford, G.P. and Scribner, J.D. (1981). *J. Am. Chem. Soc.* **103**, 4281
72. Ford, G.P. and Scribner, J.D. (1983). *J. Org. Chem.* **48**, 2226
73. Richard, J.P. and Jencks, W.P. (1982). *J. Am. Chem. Soc.* **104**, 4689. (1982). **104**, 4691. (1984). **106**, 1383. Richard, J.P., Rothenberg, M.E. and Jencks, W.P. (1984). *J. Am. Chem. Soc.* **106**, 1361. Kemp, D.S. and Casey, M.L. (1973). *J. Am. Chem. Soc.* **95**, 6670. Rappaport, Z. (1979). *Tetrahedron Lett.* 2559. Richard, J.P., Amyes, T.L. and Vontor, T. (1991). *J. Am. Chem. Soc.* **113**, 5871
74. McClelland, R.A., Kanagasabapathy, V.M., Banait, N.S. and Steenken, S. (1989). *J. Am. Chem. Soc.* **111**, 3966. (1991). **113**, 1009
75. Fishbein, J.C. and McClelland, R.A. (1987). *J. Am. Chem. Soc.* **109**, 2824
76. Novak, M., Kahley, M.J., Eiger, E., Helmick, J.S. and Peters, H.E. (1993). *J. Am. Chem. Soc.* **115**, 9453
77. Bolton, J.L. and McClelland, R.A. (1989). *J. Am. Chem. Soc.* **111**, 8172
78. Davidse, P.A., Kahley, M.J., McClelland, R.A. and Novak, M. (1994). *J. Am. Chem. Soc.* **116**, 4513
79. McClelland, R.A., Davidse, P.A. and Hadzialic, G. (1995). *J. Am. Chem. Soc.* **117**, 4173
80. Fishbein, J.C. and McClelland, R.A. (1996). *Can. J. Chem.* **74**, 1321
81. Novak, M., Kahley, M.J., Lin, J., Kennedy, S.A. and Swanegan, L.A. (1994). *J. Am. Chem. Soc.* **116**, 11626
82. Novak, M., VandeWater, A.J., Brown, A.J., Sanzenbacher, S.A., Hunt, L.A., Kolb, B.A. and Brooks, M.E. (1999). *J. Org. Chem.* **64**, 6023
83. Bose, R., Ahmad, A.R., Dicks, A.P., Novak, M., Kayser, K.J. and McClelland, R.A. (1999). *J. Chem. Soc., Perkin Trans. 2*, 1591
84. Novak, M., Kayser, K.J. and Brooks, M.E. (1998). *J. Org. Chem.* **63**, 5489
85. Ren, D. and McClelland, R.A. (1998). *Can. J. Chem.* **76**, 78
86. Sukhai, P. and McClelland, R.A. (1996). *J. Chem. Soc., Perkin Trans. 2*, 1529. Ramlall, P. and McClelland, R.A. (1999). *J. Chem. Soc., Perkin Trans. 2*, 225
87. Novak, M., Kahley, M.J., Lin, J., Kennedy, S.A. and James, T.G. (1995). *J. Org. Chem.* **60**, 8294
88. Brown, H.C., Kelley, D.P. and Periasamy, M. (1980). *Proc. Natl. Acad. Sci. U.S.A.* **77**, 6956
89. Novak, M. and Lin, J. (1999). *J. Org. Chem.* **64**, 6032
90. Yukawa, Y., Tsuno, Y. and Sawada, M. (1966). *Bull. Chem. Soc. Jpn.* **39**, 2274
91. (a) Eigen, M. (1964). *Angew. Chem., Int. Ed. Engl.* **3**, 1. (b) Hand, E.S. and Jencks, W.P. (1975). *J. Am. Chem. Soc.* **97**, 6221
92. Richard, J.P. and Jencks, W.P. (1984). *J. Am. Chem. Soc.* **106**, 1373. Jencks, W.P. (1981). *Chem. Soc. Rev.* **10**, 345
93. Fishbein, J.C. and McClelland, R.A. (1995). *J. Chem. Soc., Perkin Trans. 2*, 663
94. Fishbein, J.C. and McClelland, R.A. (1995). *J. Chem. Soc., Perkin Trans. 2*, 653

95. McClelland, R.A., Ren, D., Ghobrial, D. and Gadosy, T.A. (1997). *J. Chem. Soc., Perkin Trans 2*, 451
96. Novak, M., Helmick, J.S., Oberlies, N., Rangappa, K.S., Clark, W.M. and Swenton, J.S. (1993). *J. Org. Chem.* **58**, 867
97. Panda, M., Novak, M. and Magonski, J. (1989). *J. Am. Chem. Soc.* **111**, 4524
98. Biggs, T.N. and Swenton, J.S. (1993). *J. Am. Chem. Soc.* **115**, 10416
99. Ulbrich, R., Famulok, M., Bosold, F. and Boche, G. (1990). *Tetrahedron Lett.* **31**, 1689
100. Novak, M., Martin, K.A. and Heinrich, J.L. (1989). *J. Org. Chem.* **54**, 5430. Helmick, J.S., Martin, K.A., Heinrich, J.L. and Novak, M. (1991). *J. Am. Chem. Soc.* **113**, 3459
101. Novak, M. and Rangappa, K.S. (1992). *J. Org. Chem.* **57**, 1285. Novak, M., Rangappa, K.S. and Manitsas, R.K. (1993). *J. Org. Chem.* **58**, 7813
102. Nagai, T., Shingaki, T. and Yamada, H. (1977). *Bull. Chem. Soc. Jpn.* **50**, 248
103. Takeuchi, H., Taniguchi, T. and Ueda, T. (2000). *J. Chem. Soc., Perkin Trans. 2*, 295
104. Famulok, M. and Boche, G. (1989). *Angew. Chem. Int. Ed. Engl.* **28**, 468. Famulok, M., Bosold, F. and Boche, G. (1989). *Angew. Chem. Int. Ed. Engl.* **28**, 337. Meier, C. and Boche, G. (1990). *Tetrahedron Lett.* **31**, 1693. Bosold, F. and Boche, G. (1990). *Angew. Chem. Int. Ed. Engl.* **29**, 63
105. Defranq, E., Leterme, A., Pelloux, N., Lhomme, M.-F. and Lhomme, J. (1991). *Tetrahedron* **47**, 5725. Defranq, E., Pelloux, N., Leterme, A., Lhomme, M.-F. and Lhomme, J. (1991). *J. Org. Chem.* **56**, 4817. Pelloux, N., Fouilloux, L., Lhomme, M.F., Coulombeau, C. and Lhomme, J. (1995). *New J. Chem.* **19**, 221
106. Novak, M. and Kennedy, S.A. (1995). *J. Am. Chem. Soc.* **117**, 574
107. Kennedy, S.A., Novak, M. and Kolb, B.A. (1997). *J. Am. Chem. Soc.* **119**, 7654
108. McClelland, R.A., Kahley, M.J. and Davidse, P.A. (1996). *J. Phys. Org. Chem.* **9**, 355
109. McClelland, R.A., Gadosy, T.A. and Ren, D. (1998). *Can. J. Chem.* **76**, 1327
110. McClelland, R.A., Ahmad, A., Dicks, A.P. and Licence, V.E. (1999). *J. Am. Chem. Soc.* **121**, 3303
111. Novak, M. and Kennedy, S.A. Unpublished data
112. Humphreys, W.G., Kadlubar, F.F. and Guengerich, F.P. (1992). *Proc. Natl. Acad. Sci. U.S.A.* **89**, 8278
113. Novak, M. and Kennedy, S.A. (1998). *J. Phys. Org. Chem.* **11**, 71
114. Moran, R.J., Cramer, C.J. and Falvey, D.E. (1997). *J. Org. Chem.* **62**, 2742
115. Takeuchi, H., Hirayama, S., Mitani, M. and Koyama, K. (1988). *J. Chem. Soc., Perkin Trans. 1*, 521
116. Gassman, P.G., Grutzmacher, G. and Smith, R.H. (1972). *Tetrahedron Lett.* **13**, 497
117. Takeuchi, H., Taniguchi, T., Masuzawa, M. and Isoda, K. (1998). *J. Chem. Soc., Perkin Trans. 2*, 1743
118. Novak, M. and Lin, J. (1996). *J. Am. Chem. Soc.* **118**, 1302
119. Rieker, A. and Speiser, B. (1990). *Tetrahedron Lett.* **31**, 5013
120. Anderson, G.B. and Falvey, D.E. (1993). *J. Am. Chem. Soc.* **115**, 9870
121. Robbins, R.J., Yang, L.L.-N., Anderson, G.B. and Falvey, D.E. (1995). *J. Am. Chem. Soc.* **117**, 6544
122. Robbins, R.J., Laman, D.M. and Falvey, D.E. (1996). *J. Am. Chem. Soc.* **118**, 8127
123. Bartl, J., Steenken, S., Mayr, H. and McClelland, R.A. (1990). *J. Am. Chem. Soc.* **112**, 6918
124. Anderson, G.B., Yang, L.L.-N. and Falvey, D.E. (1993). *J. Am. Chem. Soc.* **115**, 7254

125. Robbins, R.J. and Falvey, D.E. (1994). *Tetrahedron Lett.* **35**, 4943
126. Srivastava, S. and Falvey, D.E. (1995). *J. Am. Chem. Soc.* **117**, 10186
127. Falvey, D.E. (1999). *J. Phys. Org. Chem.* **12**, 589
128. Abramovitch, R.A., Evertz, K., Huttner, G., Gibson, H.H., Jr. and Weems, H.G. (1998). *J. Chem. Soc., Chem. Commun.* 325. Abramovitch, R.A. and Shi, Q. (1994). *Heterocycles* **37**, 1463
129. Takeuchi, H. and Koyama, K. (1988). *J. Chem. Soc., Perkin Trans. 1*, 2277
130. (a) Moran, R.J. and Falvey, D.E. (1996). *J. Am. Chem. Soc.* **118**, 8965. (b) McIlroy, S., Moran, R.J. and Falvey, D.E. (2000). *J. Phys. Chem. A.* **104**, 11154
131. Chiapperino, D. and Falvey, D.E. (1997). *J. Phys. Org. Chem.* **10**, 917
132. Srivastava, S., Toscano, J.P., Moran, R.J. and Falvey, D.E. (1997). *J. Am. Chem. Soc.* **119**, 11552
133. Srivastava, S., Ruane, P.H., Toscano, J.P., Sullivan, M.B., Cramer, C.J., Chiapperino, D., Reed, E.C. and Falvey, D.E. (2000). *J. Am. Chem. Soc.* **122**, 8271
134. McClelland, R.A., Kahley, M.J., Davidse, P.A. and Hadzialic, G. (1996). *J. Am. Chem. Soc.* **118**, 4794
135. Michalak, J., Zhai, H.B. and Platz, M.S. (1996). *J. Phys. Chem.* **100**, 14028
136. Dicks, A.P., Ahmad, A.R., D'Sa, R. and McClelland, R.A. (1999). *J. Chem. Soc., Perkin Trans. 2*, 1
137. McClelland, R.A., Ren, D., D'Sa, R. and Ahmed, A.R. (2000). *Can. J. Chem.* **78**, 1178
138. (a) Rauth, A.M. (1984). *Int. J. Radiat. Oncol. Biol. Phys.* **10**, 1293. (b) Eisenbrand, G. and Tang, W. (1993). *Toxicology* **84**, 1. (c) Bolton, J.L. and McClelland, R.A. (1988). *J. Mol. Struct. (Theochem.)* **165**, 379
139. McClelland, R.A. and Panicucci, R. (1985). *J. Am. Chem. Soc.* **107**, 1762
140. McClelland, R.A., Panicucci, R. and Rauth, A.M. (1987). *J. Am. Chem. Soc.* **109**, 4308
141. Gadosy, T.A. and McClelland, R.A. (1999). *J. Am. Chem. Soc.* **121**, 1459
142. Noyce, D.S. and Stowe, G.T. (1973). *J. Org. Chem.* **38**, 3762
143. Takeuchi, H. and Watanabe, K. (1998). *J. Phys. Org. Chem.* **11**, 478
144. Novak, M., Xu, L. and Wolf, R.A. (1998). *J. Am. Chem. Soc.* **120**, 1643
145. Novak, M. and Kazerani, S. (2000). *J. Am. Chem. Soc.* **122**, 3606
146. Novak, M., Toth, K. and Hott, L. (2001). to be submitted to *J. Org. Chem.*
147. Novak, M., Rajagopal, S. and Brooks, M. (2001). work in progress
148. McClelland, R.A. Personal Communication
149. McIlroy, S., Cramer, C.J. and Falvey, D.E. (2000). *Org. Lett.* **2**, 2451
150. Cramer, C.J., Truhlar, D.G. and Falvey, D.E. (1997). *J. Am. Chem. Soc.* **119**, 12338
151. Sullivan, M.B., Brown, K., Cramer, C.J. and Truhlar, D.G. (1998). *J. Am. Chem. Soc.* **120**, 11778
152. Sullivan, M.B. and Cramer, C.J. (2000). *J. Am. Chem. Soc.* **122**, 5588
153. Cramer, C.J. and Falvey, D.E. (1997). *Tetrahedron Lett.* **38**, 1515
154. Cramer, C.J., Dulles, F.J. and Falvey, D.E. (1994). *J. Am. Chem. Soc.* **116**, 9787
155. Ford, G.P. and Herman, P.S. (1990). *J. Mol. Struct. (Theochem.)* **204**, 121
156. Ford, G.P. and Herman, P.S. (1991). *J. Chem. Soc. Perkin Trans. 2*, 607
157. Ford, G.P. and Herman, P.S. (1991). *J. Mol. Struct. (Theochem.)* **236**, 269
158. Ford, G.P., Herman, P.S. and Thompson, J.W. (1999). *J. Computational Chem.* **20**, 231
159. Ford, G.P. and Herman, P.S. (1992). *Chem.-Biol. Interactions* **81**, 1
160. Ford, G.P. and Griffin, G.R. (1992). *Chem.-Biol. Interactions* **81**, 19
161. Ford, G.P. and Thompson, J.W. (1999). *Chem. Res. Toxicol.* **12**, 53

Kinetics and Spectroscopy of Substituted Phenylnitrenes

NINA P. GRITSAN† and MATTHEW S. PLATZ‡

†Institute of Chemical Kinetics and Combustion, Novosibirsk, Russia
‡The Ohio State University, Department of Chemistry, Columbus, Ohio

1 Introduction

Phenylazide (**PA**) was first synthesized by Greiss.[1] Thermal decomposition of phenylazide was first studied by Wolf.[2] In the presence of aniline, thermolysis of **PA** leads to extrusion of molecular nitrogen, a reactive intermediate C_6H_5N and eventual formation of azepine **1**, a reaction elucidated by Huisgen *et al.*[3]

Doering and Odum[4] showed that photolysis of **PA** leads to the evolution of molecular nitrogen, the formation of a diethylamine trappable intermediate, and ultimately azepine **2**.

ADVANCES IN PHYSICAL ORGANIC CHEMISTRY
VOLUME 36   ISBN 0-12-033536-0

For almost a hundred years, chemists have argued over the identity(ies) of the C_6H_5N specie(s). Candidate structures for "C_6H_5N" have been singlet (^{1}**PN**) and triplet (^{3}**PN**) phenylnitrene, benzazirine **(BZ)** and cyclic ketenimine **(K)**, a menagerie of species described by Schrock and Schuster[5] as "wonderfully complex".

These questions are not just of academic interest as aryl azides have important application as photoresists in lithography,[6] in the formation of electrically conducting polymers,[7] organic synthesis,[8] photoaffinity labeling,[9] and in the covalent modification of polymer surfaces.[10]

Chemical analysis of reaction mixtures provides evidence for each of these intermediates under specific conditions. Singlet *ortho*-biphenylnitrene is trapped intramolecularly to form carbazole.[8(a)]

Triplet phenyl and triplet *ortho*-biphenylnitrene and other triplet arylnitrenes dimerize to form azo compounds **(AZO)**.[11]

AZO

Benzazirine **BZ** is intercepted by ethanethiol to form *ortho*-substituted anilines.[12]

Ketenimine (**K**) can be trapped with amines to form azepines **1** and **2**.[4,12]

The traditional organic chemistry of aryl azides and the intermediates derived from them has been reviewed many times[8(b),14–21] and so will receive only limited attention in this essay. Unfortunately, the major product obtained upon decomposition of phenyl azide (and many if not most of its derivatives) in solution is polymeric tar.[7] Thus, progress in classical nitrene chemistry was much slower than with carbenes, which form robust, easily characterized, adducts with most organic functional groups, even alkanes.[22]

Before moving on to the contribution of spectroscopic methods, we will note two experiments. First, high dilution of phenyl azide suppresses polymer formation and encourages the formation of azo compound,[5,23,24] implying that a singlet intermediate such as benzazirine and/or ketenimine can serve as a reservoir for triplet arylnitrenes which subsequently dimerize.

Secondly, Leyva *et al.*[25] found that the solution phase photochemistry of phenylazide (**PA**) was temperature dependent. Photolysis of **PA** in the presence of diethylamine at ambient temperature yields azepine **2**, first prepared by Doering and Odum.[4] Lowering the temperature suppresses the yield of **2** and encourages the formation of azo compound. Thus, high temperatures favor reactions of singlet state intermediates, whilst low temperatures favor reactions associated with triplet phenylnitrene.

Wasserman and co-workers[26] obtained the EPR spectrum of triplet phenylnitrene, immobilized in a frozen solid. Compared with optical spectroscopy, this would later prove to be an unambiguous result. EPR spectroscopy also demonstrated that ^{3}**PN** is lower in energy than singlet phenylnitrene.

Reiser and co-workers published an important series of papers beginning in 1965.[27–30] They were the first to observe the low-temperature UV–Vis spectrum of triplet phenylnitrene.[28] Later studies in low-temperature glassy matrices by Leyva *et al.*[25] would reveal an additional long-wavelength band in the spectrum of ^{3}**PN** and that the spectrum of ^{3}**PN**, originally reported by Reiser *et al.*,[28] was contaminated by the presence of ketenimine **K**. The difficulty is that ^{3}**PN** is extremely light sensitive and, upon excitation at 77 K, rapidly isomerizes to the isomeric ketenimine.[25]

Porter and Ward[31] reported what they believed to be the gas-phase absorption spectrum of triplet phenylnitrene. Ozawa and co-workers[32] obtained a much higher resolution spectrum of the same species, attributed again to ^{3}**PN**. However, in a subsequent study, Cullin et al.[33] demonstrated that the carrier of the gas-phase spectrum was the cyanocyclopentadienyl radical **3**.

3

To the best of our knowledge, triplet phenylnitrene has never been detected in the gas phase.

Confusion over the matrix and gas-phase optical spectroscopy of ^{3}**PN** spilled over to the liquid phase. Initial flash photolysis experiments involving phenyl azide gave conflicting results, with different authors favoring the presence of triplet phenylnitrene,[34,35] benzazirine **BZ**,[13] or cyclic ketenimine **K**[5] as the carrier of the transient spectra.

The currently accepted spectroscopic assignments were obtained by a combination of multiple techniques. Leyva et al.[25] applied matrix absorption and emission spectroscopy along with flash photolysis techniques. Chapman and LeRoux[36] obtained the matrix IR spectrum of cyclic ketenimine **K** and Hayes and Sheridan[37] obtained the matrix IR and UV–Vis spectrum of triplet phenylnitrene and cyclic ketenimine **K**. Schuster and co-workers[38,39] applied time resolved IR and UV–Vis spectroscopy and demonstrated the formation of cyclic ketenimine **K** in solution, the species that absorbs strongly at 340 nm.

By 1992 Schuster and Platz[18] could write Scheme 1, which economically explained much of the photochemistry of phenyl azide. UV photolysis of **PA** produces singlet phenylnitrene and molecular nitrogen. In the gas phase, ^{1}**PN** is born with excess vibrational energy and isomerizes over a barrier of >30 kcal/mol to form cyanocyclopentadiene, the global minimum on the C_6H_5N surface.[40,41] This species is also vibrationally excited and sheds a hydrogen atom to form radical **3** (Scheme 1), the species detected in gas-phase absorption and emission measurements.[33]

In the liquid phase, singlet phenylnitrene is rapidly relaxed by collision with solvent and cannot surmount the barrier to form cyanocyclopentadiene at ambient temperature. Under these conditions ^{1}**PN** isomerizes over a small barrier to form cyclic ketenimine **K**. Later, computational work of Karney and Borden[42] would show this to be a two-step process involving benzazirine **BZ**, the species trapped by ethanethiol (Scheme 2). In the liquid phase, ^{1}**PN** prefers rearrangement to intersystem crossing (ISC) to the lower-energy triplet state at ambient temperature. Intersystem crossing is not an activated process and its rate is not expected to vary with temperature. The rate of

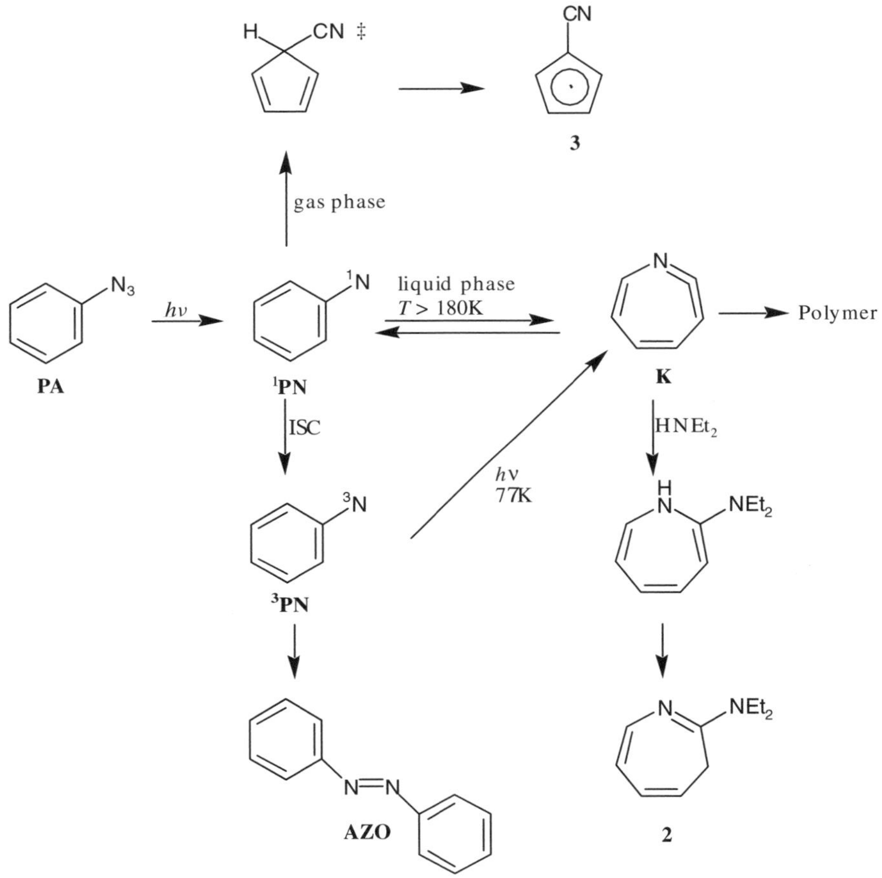

Scheme 1

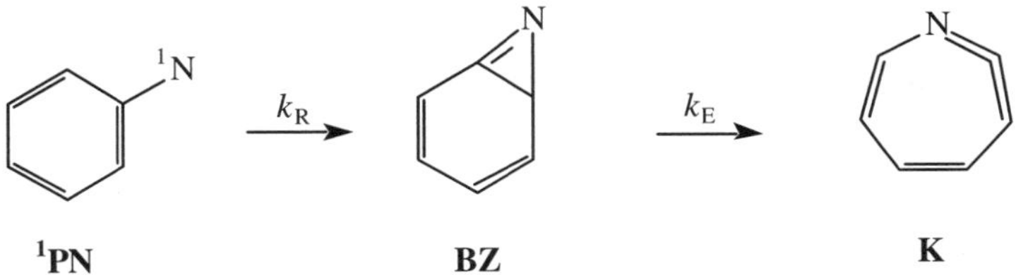

Scheme 2

cyclization slows upon cooling, however. The isokinetic temperature is ≈ 180 K, obtained with two precursors **PA** and sulfoximine **4**.[25,43] Below 180K, spin relaxation (ISC) to triplet **PN** predominates.

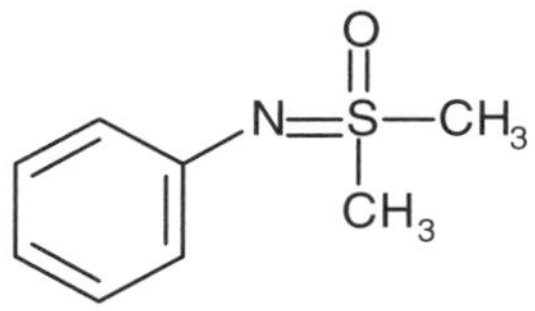

4

The key intermediate of Scheme 1 is singlet phenylnitrene; the only intermediate which in 1992 had not been detected directly or chemically intercepted in the parent system. In 1997 our group[44] and the Wirz group,[45] simultaneously reported that laser flash photolysis of phenyl azide or phenyl isocyanate **5** produces a previously undetected transient with $\lambda_{max} = 350$ nm and a lifetime of ≈ 1 ns at ambient temperature.

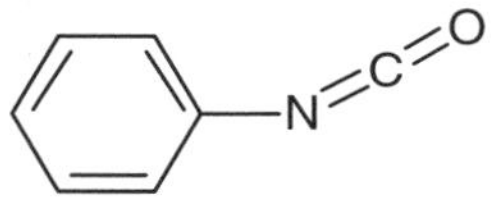

5

The transient decays at the same rate as cyclic ketenimine **K** is formed,[44] implying that the newly detected transient is singlet phenylnitrene. The assignment was secured with the aid of computational chemistry[46] and by studying the temperature dependence of the kinetics.[44,46] In 1986[25] we guessed that the ISC rate constant of singlet phenylnitrene would resemble the same rate constants as those of aryl carbenes, which were known at that time to be 10^{9-10} s^{-1}. We also assumed then that the pre-exponential factor to nitrene rearrangement was 10^{12-14} s^{-1}. The latter assumption was eventually validated, the former was not. It was later shown[46] that k_{ISC} of phenylnitrene singlet is 3.2×10^6 s^{-1}, thus our estimate of the barrier to rearrangement of ^{1}**PN** in 1986 was much too low.

2   Matrix spectroscopy of triplet phenylnitrene and theory

In 1992 the Schaefer group[47] and the Borden group[48] independently predicted that the singlet–triplet splitting of phenylnitrene is 18 kcal/mol. This prediction was confirmed by negative ion photoelectron spectroscopy by Ellison and co-workers[49] in the same year. Thus, intersystem crossing of singlet to triplet phenylnitrene is irreversible, as opposed to aryl carbenes which typically have small (2–5 kcal/mol) singlet–triplet energy separations.[50–54] The calculations also revealed that, whereas singlet phenylcarbene (^{1}PC) has a closed-shell singlet configuration, singlet and triplet phenylnitrene both have open-shell electronic structures.[47,48]

^{1}PC ^{1,3}PN

Calculations[47,48] predict that the ground state of phenylnitrene has a triplet multiplicity ($^3A_2$) in accordance with the earlier EPR experiment of Wasserman and co-workers.[26] Figure 1 represents the electronic absorption spectrum of ^{3}PN in an EPA matrix at 77 K. There is a strong sharp band at 308 nm, a broad structured band at 370 nm and a broad unstructured feature which tails out to 500 nm.[25,28]

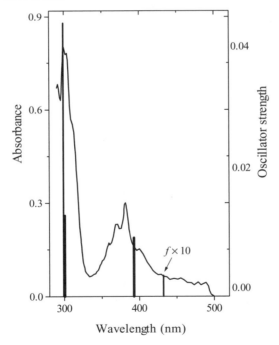

Wavelength (nm)

Fig. 1 The absorption spectrum of triplet phenylnitrene in EPA glass at 77 K. The computed positions and oscillator strengths (f, right-hand axis) of the absorption bands are depicted as solid vertical lines. For very small oscillator strength, the value multiplied by 10 is presented ($f \times 10$).

The π system of ^{3}**PN** is closely related to that of the benzyl and anilino radicals. Thus, it is no surprise that the triplet absorption spectrum of ^{3}**PN** is very similar to the experimental spectra of the benzyl ($C_6H_5CH_2^\bullet$) and anilino ($C_6H_5NH^\bullet$) radicals. Benzyl radical has a medium intensity feature at 316 nm and a very weak band at 452 nm.[55] The anilino radical has a medium intensity band at 308 nm and a weak transition at 400 nm.[56–59]

Kim et al.[47] performed configuration interaction calculations of ^{3}**PN** ground and excited states with all single and double excitations, but they failed to reproduce the electronic absorption spectrum of triplet phenylnitrene quantitatively. The spectrum of ^{3}**PN** recently calculated[46] using the CASPT2 level of theory is in very good agreement with experiment (Fig. 1). The improved correspondence is a result of the combination of an improved reference description and an adequate treatment of the dynamical electron correlation in the CASPT2 procedure.

CASPT2 calculations predict that the vertical excitation energy to the first excited state (1^3B_1) will be at 432 nm ($f = 3.4 \times 10^{-4}$). This excited state consists principally of two electronic configurations ($\pi(1a_2) \rightarrow \pi$ ($3b_1$) and π ($3b_1$) $\rightarrow \pi_1^*$ ($2a_2$), where π ($3b_1$) is a singly occupied π orbital). The second excited state (T_2) is the 2^3A_2 state and has a vertical excitation energy of 393 nm (9.4×10^{-3}) which is associated with π ($2b_1$) $\rightarrow \pi$ ($3b_1$) and π ($3b_1$) $\rightarrow \pi_2^*$ ($4b_1$) transitions.

^{3}**PN** has a very strong absorption band at 308 nm. The CASPT2 calculations predict that transitions to the 2^3B_1 (at 301 nm, $f = 0.013$) and 3^3B_1 (at 299 nm, $f = 0.044$) states contribute to this absorption. The electronic configurations for the 3^3B_1 state are the same as for the 1^3B_1 state. The main configuration involved in the $1^3A_2 \rightarrow 2^3B_1$ transition consists of excitation of an electron from the lone pair orbital (n_z) on nitrogen, to the singly occupied nitrogen 2p orbital that lies in the molecular plane (p_y). The transitions of triplet phenylnitrene around 300 nm are very similar to those observed for the triplet ground states of the parent NH (336 nm),[60] methylnitrene (315 nm),[61] 1-norbornylnitrene (298 nm)[62] and perfluoromethylnitrene (354 nm).[63]

3 Transient spectroscopy of singlet phenylnitrene and theory

The electronic absorption spectrum of ^{1}**PN** was first detected only in 1997.[44] Laser flash photolysis (266 nm, 35 ps) of **PA** in pentane at 233 K produces a transient absorption spectrum with two sharp bands with maxima at 335 and 352 nm (Fig. 2). Spectrum 1 was measured, point by point, 2 ns after the laser pulse. In later work,[46] the spectrum of ^{1}**PN** was reinvestigated and an additional very weak, long-wavelength absorption band at 540 nm was observed (Spectrum 2). The transient spectrum of Fig. 2 was assigned to singlet phenylnitrene[44,46] in its lowest open-shell electronic configuration ($^1A_2$).

The assignment of the transient absorption spectrum of Fig. 2 to ^{1}**PN** is supported by the similarity of its spectrum to that of the longer-lived per-fluorinated singlet arylnitrenes.[64] The decay of this transient absorption is accompanied by the formation of cyclic ketenimine **K**. Furthermore, the electronic absorption spectrum of ^{1}**PN** in the $^1A_2$ state calculated at the CASPT2 level is in good agreement with the transient spectrum (Fig. 2).

Calculations of ^{1}**PN** are more challenging than that of ^{3}**PN** because it is, of course, an excited state of phenylnitrene. The first two electronically excited singlet states of ^{1}**PN** are both of A_1 symmetry and are calculated to be at 1610 and 765 nm. Neither of these transitions have been detected, since both of these states have zero oscillator strength due to symmetry considerations, and they lie outside the wavelength range accessible to our spectrometer.[46]

The CASPT2 calculations predict a transition to a 1^1B_1 excited state at 581 nm with a very small oscillator strength (1.6×10^{-4}). This transition could be assigned to a very weak band with a maximum around 540 nm (Fig. 2). As in the case of long-wavelength transition in ^{3}**PN** it consists of the same electronic configurations ($\pi(1a_2) \rightarrow \pi$ ($3b_1$) and π ($3b_1$) $\rightarrow \pi_1^*$ ($2a_2$)).

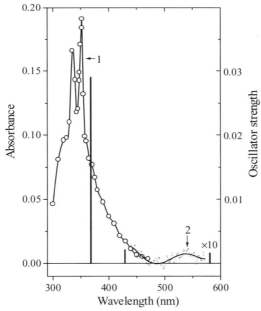

Fig. 2 Transient spectrum of singlet phenylnitrene produced upon LFP of phenyl azide. Spectrum 1 was recorded 2 ns after the laser pulse (266 nm, 35 ps) at 233 K. Long-wavelength band (2) was recorded with an optical multichannel analyzer at 150 K (with 100 ns window immediately after the laser pulse, 249 nm, 12 ns). The computed positions and oscillator strengths (f, right-hand axis) of the absorption bands are depicted as solid vertical lines. For very small oscillator strength, the value multiplied by 10 is presented ($f \times 10$).

As in ^{3}**PN**, the next excited state in the singlet manifold is the 2^1A_2 state. This transition has a small oscillator strength (2.1×10^{-3}) and a 429 nm excitation energy. In the experimental spectrum (Fig. 2), this band seems to be a shoulder on the tail of a strong band at 350 nm.

In the ^{1}**PN** absorption spectrum, the only intense absorption band is localized around 350 nm, which is a pronounced shift from the 308 nm band in ^{3}**PN**. This band has a long tail out to 450 nm and displays some fine structure that may be associated with the vibrations of the phenyl ring in ^{1}**PN** (Fig. 2). The strongest absorption band in ^{1}**PN**, predicted by the CASPT2 method, is the transition to the 2^1B_1 excited state, which has a 368 nm excitation energy. The main configuration involved in this transition is similar to that of 2^3B_1 state and consists of an electron from the lone pair orbital on nitrogen (n_z) promoted to the singly occupied nitrogen 2p orbital that lies in the molecular plane (p_y).

The electronic absorption spectra of ^{1}**PN** and ^{3}**PN** are very similar (Figs 1 and 2), but all of the calculated and experimental bands of ^{1}**PN** exhibit a red-shift compared to those of ^{3}**PN**. This is very reasonable because both these species have very similar open-shell electronic configurations ($^3A_2$ and $^1A_2$).

4 Dynamics of singlet phenylnitrene

The decay of ^{1}**PN** in pentane was monitored at 350 nm over a temperature range of 150–270 K, which allows direct measurement of k_{ISC} and accurate barriers to cyclization.[46] The disappearance of singlet phenylnitrene at 298 K was faster than the time resolution of the spectrometer and the lifetime (τ) of ^{1}**PN** was estimated to be ~1 ns under these conditions (*vide infra*). The lifetime of ^{1}**PN** was measured in CH_2Cl_2 at ambient temperature to be about 0.6 ns.[45]

The formation of the products (cyclic ketenimine **K** and/or triplet nitrene ^{3}**PN**) was monitored at 380 nm.[44] The decay of singlet phenylnitrene and the growth of the products are exponential and can be analyzed to yield an observed rate constant k_{OBS}. An Arrhenius treatment of the k_{OBS} data (open circles), is presented in Fig. 3. The magnitude of k_{OBS} decreases with decreasing temperature until about 170 K, whereupon it reaches a value of about $3.2 \times 10^6 \, s^{-1}$. Below this temperature, k_{OBS} remains constant.[46] The breakpoint in the Arrhenius plot is around 180–200 K, and is in exactly the same temperature range where the solution-phase chemistry changes from the trapping of ketenimine **K** with diethylamine, to the dimerization of ^{3}**PN**.[25] Thus, the low-temperature data of Fig. 3 was associated with k_{ISC}, the rate constant for intersystem crossing of ^{1}**PN** to ^{3}**PN**, and the high-temperature data with k_R, the rate constant for rearrangement of ^{1}**PN** (Scheme 1).

The temperature-independent rate constant observed at low temperature $(3.2 \times 10^6 \, s^{-1})$ was identified as the rate constant of ISC to the triplet ground

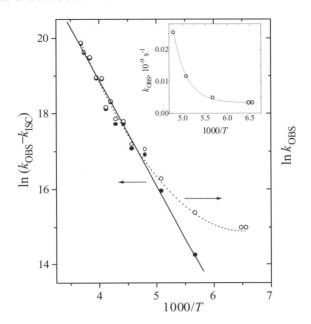

Fig. 3 Arrhenius treatment of the k_{OBS} data (open circles) and k_R data (filled circles) for singlet phenylnitrene deduced upon assuming that k_{ISC} is independent of temperature. Insert: temperature dependence of k_{OBS} data.

state (k_{ISC}). The rate constant k_{OBS} is equal to $k_R + k_{ISC}$, where k_R is the absolute rate constant for rearrangement (see Scheme 1). As $k_{OBS} = k_R + k_{ISC}$, it was possible to deduce values of k_R as a function of temperature and to obtain its associated Arrhenius parameters. Indeed, an Arrhenius plot[46] of $k_R = k_{OBS} - k_{ISC}$ was linear (Fig. 3, solid circles) with an activation energy for rearrangement of $E_a = 5.6 \pm 0.3$ kcal/mol and pre-exponential factor $A = 10^{13.1\pm0.3}$ s^{-1}.

Recent *ab initio* calculations[42] at CASSCF/CASPT2 levels of theory reveal that ^{1}**PN** ($^1A_2$) undergoes ring expansion to ketenimine **K** via the intermediacy of azabicyclo[4.1.0] heptatriene **BZ** (Scheme 2). The calculations also find that the barrier to the ring opening of **BZ** to **K** is only about half as large as the barrier to the cyclization of ^{1}**PN**. Indeed **BZ** can be intercepted by ethanethiol to form an *ortho*-substituted aniline,[12] but **BZ** has not been observed spectroscopically, suggesting that the cyclization step was rate determining (i.e. $k_R \ll k_E$).

The calculated barrier[42] for the cyclization of ^{1}**PN** to **BZ** is 6 kcal/mol after taking into consideration that the CASPT2 method overestimates the energy difference between open-shell and closed-shell states by 3 kcal/mol. The predicted 6 kcal/mol barrier is in nearly exact agreement with the experimental value (5.6 + 0.3 kcal/mol).[46]

The value of k_{ISC} is 3 orders of magnitude smaller than those for aryl carbenes.[65] There are at least three reasons why arylcarbenes can undergo ISC much faster than singlet phenylnitrene. The rate of a radiationless transition increases as the energy separation between the two states goes to zero.[66] The calculated gas-phase singlet–triplet splitting of phenylcarbene (PC) is ~4 kcal/mol,[50–53] in phenylnitrene it is 18 kcal/mol.[49] Secondly, carbenes are divalent and have a bending mode with which to couple singlet and triplet surfaces, a vibration that is, of course, lacking in monovalent nitrenes. However, the most important factor is probably the electronic structure of the respective singlet intermediates. Singlet **PC** has a closed-shell electronic structure with one filled and one empty non-bonding orbital.[50–53] In such an "ionic" singlet, spin–orbit coupling (SOC) is a particularly effective mechanism of intersystem crossing.[67] Singlet phenylnitrene, on the other hand, is an open-shell singlet.[47,48] SOC is forbidden in this case and is ineffective in promoting ISC.[67–69] This point will be considered in detail in Section 6.

5 Spectroscopy of substituted phenylnitrenes.

Direct observations of singlet arylnitrenes before 1997 were exceedingly rare. Before the detection of the spectrum of ^{1}**PN**[44,46] and its 2,4,6-tribromo-substituted analogue,[45] only the spectrum of singlet 1-pyrenyl nitrene (^{1}**6**), reported by Sumitani et al.[70] was known. Kobayashi et al.[71] studied p-(dimethylamino)phenyl azide by picosecond LFP. They detected the transient spectrum of triplet nitrene (^{3}**7**) and its precursor with a lifetime of 120 ps. The authors did not specify the nature of this precursor, but in our opinion this specie must have been singlet p-(dimethylamino)phenylnitrene (^{1}**7**).

^{1}**6** ^{1}**7**

Miura and Kobayashi[72] studied the photochemistry of 4,4-biphenyl bisazide. They concluded that photolysis of this diazide leads to extrusion of a single molecule of nitrogen with the formation of a singlet state species, "X", with a lifetime of 19 ns. Miura and Kobayashi did not specify the nature of X. This species absorbs at 380 nm and its spectrum and lifetime are similar to our results with singlet para-biphenylnitrene.[73] Therefore we conclude that X is singlet 4′-azido-4-biphenylnitrene.

As the spectrum and dynamics of parent phenylnitrene were revealed, our group began a comprehensive study of the influence of substituents on the spectroscopy and reactivity of simple substituted phenylnitrenes.[74–78] The spectra of many *para-* and *ortho*-substituted singlet phenylnitrenes as well as *ortho,ortho*-disubstituted singlet phenylnitrenes were recorded (Table 1). The spectra of most singlet arylnitrenes reveal strong absorption bands in the near UV region with maxima in the range of 320–405 nm (Table 1). We were

Table 1 Maxima (in nm) of the most intense absorption bands in electronic absorption spectra of substituted singlet and triplet phenylnitrenes (near UV and visible).

Substituent	Singlet nitrene	Ref.	Triplet nitrene	Ref.
4-F	365	74	*a*	
4-Cl	360	–	*a*	
4-Br	361	–	*a*	
2,4,6-triBr	395	45	326, 340	25
4-I	328	74	*a*	
4-Me	365	–	315	127
4-CF₃	~320	–	*a*	
4-COCH₃	334	–	276, 410	127
4-Ph	345	73	320	–
4-(4′-azidophenyl)	380	72	*a*	
2-Me	350	77	*a*	
2,6-diMe	350	–	297,310	25
2,4,6-triMe	348, 366	–	319	–
2-F	342	78	294, 315	78
2,6-diF	331, 342	–	313	25
2,3,4,5,6-pentaF	330	64	315	–
2-CN	382	76	328	76
2,6-diCN	385, 405	–	341	–

*a*Spectrum was not detected.

able to detect the spectra of all singlet aryl nitrenes studied with the notable exceptions of *para*-nitro- and *para*-cyanophenylnitrenes.

Figure 4 displays representative spectra of singlet *ortho*-fluoro-, *ortho*-cyano- and *ortho,ortho*-dicyanophenylnitrenes as well as that of parent singlet **PN**. Figure 4 shows that the maximum of the *o*-fluoro-substituted ^{1}**PN** is shifted slightly to the blue region and the maxima of cyano-substituted nitrenes undergo a more pronounced shift to the red. It was noted before (Section 3) that the electronic absorption spectra of ^{1}**PN** and ^{3}**PN** are very similar because both these species have very similar open-shell electronic configurations ($^3A_2$ and $^1A_2$).

In the case of ^{1}**PN** the origin of the absorption band at 350 nm is the excitation of an electron from the lone pair orbital on nitrogen (n_z) to the singly occupied nitrogen 2p orbital that lies in the molecular plane (p_y). In the case of ^{3}**PN** two transitions ($T_0 \rightarrow T_3$, $T_0 \rightarrow T_4$) contribute to the absorption band around 300 nm, one of which is the same in nature as in the case of ^{1}**PN**. It is reasonable to assume that the same situation will be found with the substituted phenylnitrenes. Therefore, we can predict that the influence of the substituents on the maxima of the intensive absorption bands of substituted singlet and triplet phenylnitrenes will be similar. Indeed, Fig. 5

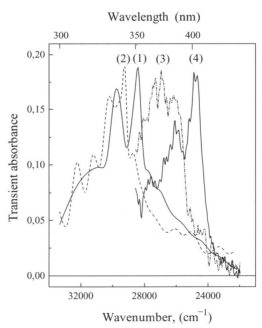

Fig. 4 Electronic absorption spectra of selected singlet arylnitrenes: phenylnitrene (1), 2-fluorophenylnitrene (2) and 2-cyanophenylnitrene (3) in pentane, and 2,6-dicyanophenylnitrene (4) in CH_2Cl_2.

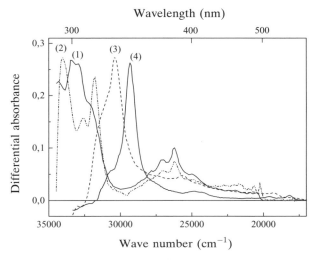

Fig. 5 Electronic absorption spectra of selected triplet arylnitrenes: phenylnitrene (1, EPA), 2-fluorophenylnitrene (2, MCH), 2-cyanophenylnitrene (3, MCH) and 2,6-dicyanophenylnitrene (4, MCH) at 77 K.

shows that the maxima of triplet *ortho*- and *ortho*,*ortho*-dicyanophenyl-nitrenes are indeed shifted to the red just as with the singlet phenylnitrenes (Fig. 4).

In the case of the triplet *ortho*-fluorophenylnitrene it is most probable that the two excited states (T_3 and T_4) are separated ($\sim$2200 cm^{-1}, Fig. 5) in energy. One of the transitions is shifted to the blue as with the singlet nitrene (Fig. 4). A similar separation of T_3 and T_4 states was observed experimentally[25] and verified computationally[79] for triplet perfluorophenylnitrene.

Analysis of the data of Table 1 verifies the same finding that the shift of the near-UV absorption band of singlet arylnitrenes correlates with the shift of the intense near-UV absorption band of triplet nitrenes. Furthermore, the *ortho*-substituents influence the absorption spectra of singlet and triplet phenylnitrenes more significantly than do *para*-substituents.

6 Dynamics of substituted singlet phenylnitrenes

SUBSTITUENT EFFECTS ON INTERSYSTEM CROSSING

Values of k_{OBS} of substituted singlet phenylnitrenes were measured by following the decay of singlet nitrene absorption at the wavelength of their maxima as a function of temperature.[74–78] In all cases the magnitude of k_{OBS} decreases as the temperature decreases until a limiting value is reached

(Figs 6 and 7) similar to the trend observed with parent singlet phenylnitrene (Fig. 3). The temperature-independent rate constant observed at low temperature was associated with k_{ISC}. In the case of 4-bromo-, 4-iodophenyl-nitrene (Fig. 6) and 2,2-dimethylphenylnitrene (Fig. 7) the values of k_{OBS} are independent of temperature over a very large temperature range ($\sim$120–200 K). This proves that indeed the rate constants of ISC in arylnitrenes are temperature independent in solution over typical temperature ranges.

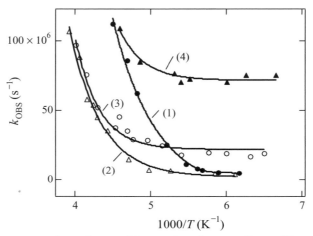

Fig. 6 Temperature dependence of k_{OBS} values for *para*-fluoro (1), *para*-chloro (2), *para*-bromo (3), and *para*-iodo (4) singlet phenylnitrene in pentane.

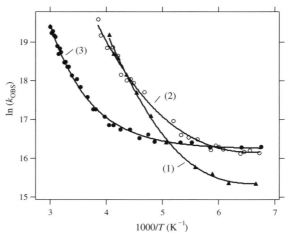

Fig. 7 Arrhenius treatment of k_{OBS} values for *para*-methyl (1), *ortho*-methyl (2) singlet phenylnitrene in pentane and singlet *ortho,ortho*-dimethylphenyl nitrene in hexane (3).

Para-substituted derivatives of phenylnitrene

Values of k_{ISC} for singlet *para*-substituted phenylnitrenes measured by Gritsan et al.[74] are given in Table 2. Table 2 also contains the k_{ISC} value of singlet *para*-dimethylaminophenylnitrene obtained by Kobayashi et al.[71] and a lower limit for k_{ISC} for *para*-nitrophenylnitrene based on the data of Liang and Schuster.[23]

The rate constant of ISC for *para*-bromo singlet phenylnitrene is about seven times larger than that of parent ¹**PN** and the *para*-fluoro and *para*-chloro analogues. This is easily attributable to a small heavy-atom effect. The heavy-atom effect of iodine is larger than that of bromine, as expected, and increases the rate of ISC by more than a factor of 20, relative to parent ¹**PN**.

Very large acceleration in k_{ISC} is observed with *para*-methoxy and dimethylamino substituents (Table 2). This is consistent with the solution-phase photochemistry of *para*-methoxy and *para*-dimethylaminophenyl azides.[39]

Calculations predict that the lowest state of ¹**PN** has an open-shell electronic configuration.[47,48] The Salem–Rowland Rule[67] for ISC promoted by spin–orbit coupling (SOC) predicts that singlet to triplet relaxation will have its maximum rate when the singlet state is closed-shell. This is the case with diaryl carbenes where the absolute rate constants of ISC are in the order of $10^{9-10}\,s^{-1}$.[65] Michl[68] has recently pointed out the importance of donor–acceptor interactions in promoting ISC, which explains the lifetimes of certain localized singlet biradicals.[69]

The CH_3, CF_3, acetyl, fluoro and chloro substituents are not sufficiently strong π donors or acceptors to significantly influence the size of k_{ISC} (Table 2).

Table 2 Kinetic parameters of *para*-substituted singlet aryl nitrenes ($X-C_6H_4-N$) in pentane.

Para-X	τ_{295K} (ns)	k_{ISC} ($\times 10^6\,s^{-1}$)	E_a (kcal/mol)	Log A (s^{-1})	Ref.
H	~ 1	3.2 ± 0.3	5.6 ± 0.3	13.1 ± 0.3	46
CH_3	~ 1	5.0 ± 0.4	5.8 ± 0.4	13.5 ± 0.2	74
CF_3	1.5	4.6 ± 0.8	5.6 ± 0.5	12.9 ± 0.5	–
$C(O)CH_3$	5.0	8 ± 3	5.3 ± 0.3	12.5 ± 0.3	–
F	~ 0.3	3.5 ± 1.4	5.3 ± 0.3	13.2 ± 0.3	–
Cl	~ 1	3.9 ± 1.5	6.1 ± 0.3	13.3 ± 0.3	–
Br	~ 3	17 ± 4	4.0 ± 0.2	11.4 ± 0.2	–
I	*a*	72 ± 10	*a*	*a*	–
OCH_3	< 1	> 500	*a*	*a*	–
CN	8 ± 4	6 ± 2	7.2 ± 0.8	13.5 ± 0.6	76
Ph	15 ± 2	12 ± 1	6.8 ± 0.3	12.7 ± 0.3	Our unpublished results
$N(CH_3)_2^b$	0.12	8300 ± 200	*a*	*a*	71
NO_2^c	< 20	> 50	*a*	*a*	23

*a*Not measured, *b*in toluene, *c*in benzene

The strong π-donating *para*-methoxy and *para*-dimethylamino groups have a huge influence on k_{ISC}, however. We propose that there could be some charge separation in singlet *para*-methoxy and dimethylaminophenylnitrene. The increased ionic character in these open-shell singlet biradicals can increase spin–orbit coupling and rate constant of intersystem crossing.

The electron-withdrawing substituents (CF_3, $COCH_3$, CN and NO_2) have a smaller, but measurable influence on k_{ISC}. It is interesting to note that both donating and withdrawing substituents accelerate the ISC.

Ortho- *and* meta-*substituted derivatives of phenylnitrene*

Intersystem crossing rate constants of *ortho*- and *meta*-substituted singlet phenyl nitrenes are presented in Table 3. Mono- and di-*ortho*-fluorine substituents have no influence on ISC rate constants. No effect with *meta*, *meta*-difluoro substitution is observed either. Pentafluoro substitution has no efffect on k_{ISC} in pentane although a modest acceleration is observed in the more polar solvent methylene chloride.

An increase of triplet nitrene absorption relative to azepine absorption was observed upon LFP of perfluorophenyl azide[80] in methanol. This effect was not observed in acetonitrile, which has a similar dielectric constant, or in

Table 3 Intersystem crossing rate constants of *ortho*- and *meta*-substituted phenyl-nitrenes.

Substituent	Solvent	$k_{ISC}(\times 10^6\,\mathrm{s}^{-1})$	Ref.
2-methyl	Pentane	10 ± 1	77
2,6-dimethyl	Pentane	15 ± 3	–
2,6-dimethyl	$CF_2ClCFCl_2$	30 ± 8	–
2,4,6-trimethyl	Pentane	20 ± 1	–
–	$CF_2ClCFCl_2$	29 ± 3	–
2-fluoro	Pentane	3.3 ± 0.5	78
3,5-difluoro	Pentane	3.1 ± 1.5	–
2,6-difluoro	Hexane	2.4 ± 0.3	–
2,6-difluoro	CCl_4	2.7 ± 0.3	–
2,3,4,5,6-pentafluoro	Pentane	3.3 ± 1.5	64
	CH_2Cl_2	10.5 ± 0.5	
2-cyano	Pentane	2.8 ± 0.3	76
2,6-dicyano	CH_2Cl_2	4.5 ± 0.5	–
–	Pentane	6.2 ± 0.8	–
–	THF	5.9 ± 1.5	–
2-pyrimidyl	CH_2Cl_2	800 ± 200	75

tetrahydrofuran, a solvent which contains an oxygen atom but cannot donate hydrogen bonds. It was proposed that the ISC rate constant of singlet perfluorophenylnitrene is dramatically increased in methanol, which explains much of the solution-phase organic chemistry of this nitrene in this solvent. Additional experiments are needed to fully understand this effect.

An *ortho* cyano group has little influence on k_{ISC}, but two *ortho* cyano groups slightly accelerate intersystem crossing. Singlet arylnitrenes with electron-withdrawing groups in the *para* position have little influence on the rate constant of ISC.

An *ortho* methyl group accelerates intersystem crossing relative to singlet *para*-tolylphenylnitrene. Two *ortho* methyl groups are more effective than one at accelerating intersystem crossing. Singlet 2,4,6-trimethylphenylnitrene undergoes intersystem crossing about as readily as 2,6-dimethylphenylnitrene. These results are consistent with the general trend that electron-donating groups (methyl, methoxy, dimethylamino) accelerate intersystem crossing. We speculate that such groups increase the zwitterionic character of the singlet nitrene relative to the parent system, which facilitates a spin–orbit coupling mechanism of intersystem crossing.

CYCLIZATION TO AZIRINES

Cyclic ketenimine **K** is the major, trappable, reactive intermediate in solution when phenyl azide (at moderate concentrations) is decomposed photolytically at 298 K. The rate of decay of singlet phenylnitrene is equal to the rate of formation of the cyclic ketenimine. Nevertheless, the calculations of Karney and Borden[42] reveal that this is a two-step process (Scheme 2). The first step, cyclization to benzazirine **BZ** is rate determining, followed by fast electrocyclic ring opening to cyclic ketenimine **K**. The predicted potential energy surface is shown in Fig. 8.

In the absence of nucleophiles the cyclic ketenimine polymerizes. At high dilution it can slowly revert to benzazirine **BZ**, and to the singlet nitrene. Eventually the singlet nitrene relaxes to the lower-energy triplet nitrene (at high dilution), which subsequently dimerizes.[5,39]

A study by Younger and Bell[81] nicely demonstrated the interconversion of a disubstituted benzazirine and singlet nitrene.

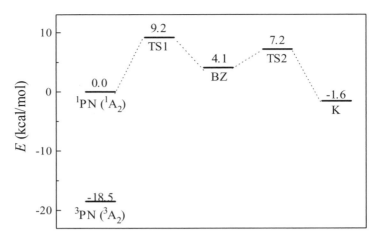

Reaction coordinate

Fig. 8 CASPT2N/6-311G(2d,p) relative energies of species involved in the ring expansion of phenylnitrene (PN). Energies are for CASSCF/6-31G* geometries and include ZPE corrections.[42]

There is rather little direct experimental evidence for the intermediacy of **BZ**. Cyclic ketenimine **K** has been detected by matrix IR spectroscopy,[36,37] benzazirine **BZ** has not. However, fluorinated[82] and naphthalenic[83] derivatives of **BZ** have been generated as persistent species in cryogenic matrices and characterized. Parent benzazirine **BZ** has been intercepted with ethanethiol,[12] and certain derivatives of **BZ** have been trapped with amines.[84–87]

Once the spectroscopy and dynamics of parent singlet phenylnitrene were understood, we began a systematic study of the effect of substitution on the kinetics of singlet phenylnitrenes. For most of the aryl azides of interest[74–78] the rate constants of singlet nitrene decay and product formation (triplet nitrene and/or ketenimine) are the same (Fig. 9). With these nitrenes, cyclization to substituted benzazirines is the rate-limiting step of the process of nitrene isomerization to ketenimine in a manner similar to the parent phenylnitrene. The only exception, o-fluorophenylnitrene, will be examined in detail in the last section of this review.

As shown in the previous section (Figs 6 and 7), the magnitude of k_{OBS} decreases as the temperature decreases until a limiting value is reached. The pattern is similar to that observed with parent singlet phenylnitrene (Fig. 3). As before, the temperature-independent observed rate constants are associated with k_{ISC}. Plots of ln $(k_{OBS} - k_{ISC})$ were linear (Figs 10, 11) and these plots were used to deduce the Arrhenius parameters to cyclization of the substituted singlet arylnitrenes (Tables 2, 4 and 6).

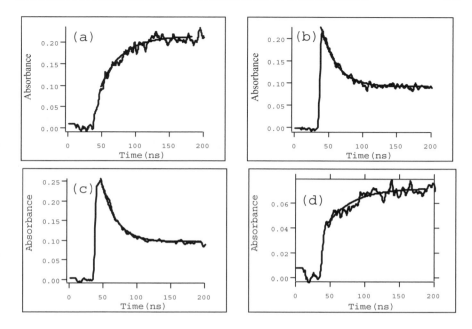

Fig. 9 Changes in transient absorption at selective wavelengths after LFP of 2,4,6-trimethylphenyl azide in Freone-113 at 253 K: (a) 320 nm, (b) 345 nm, (c) 366 nm and (d) 400 nm.

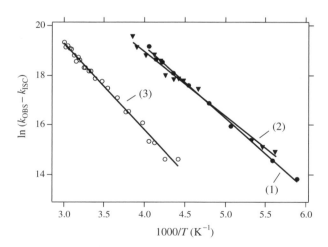

Fig. 10 Arrhenius treatment of $k_R(= k_{OBS} - k_{ISC})$ data for singlet *para*-methyl **8b** (curve 1) and *ortho*-methyl **8a** (curve 2) phenylnitrene in pentane and for singlet *ortho,ortho*-dimethylphenylnitrene in hexane (curve 3).

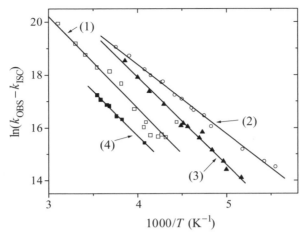

Fig. 11 Arthenius treatment of $k_R(= k_{OBS} - k_{ISC})$ data for *para*-cyanophenylnitrene **8e** (1) and *o*-cyanophenylnitrene **8c** (2) in pentane, for 2,6-dicyanophenylnitrene **8f** (3) in CH_2Cl_2 and for *para*-biphenylnitrene in pentane (4).

Table 4 Summary of kinetic results for singlet methyl-substituted phenylnitrenes obtained by Gritsan *et al.*[78]

Substituent	$\tau(295)$ (ns)	$\log A$ (s^{-1})	E_a (kcal/mol)	Solvent
4-methyl	$\sim 1^a$	13.2 ± 0.2	5.8 ± 0.4	C_5H_{12}
2-methyl	$\sim 1^a$	12.8 ± 0.3	5.3 ± 0.4	C_5H_{12}
2,6-dimethyl	12 ± 1	13.0 ± 0.3	7.0 ± 0.3	C_6H_{14}
2,6-dimethyl	13 ± 1	12.9 ± 0.3	7.5 ± 0.5	$CF_2ClCFCl_2$
2,4,6-trimethyl	8 ± 1	13.4 ± 0.4	7.3 ± 0.4	$CF_2ClCFCl_2$

^{a}Lifetime estimated by extrapolation of the data to 295 K.

Influence of para substituents: the electronic effect

Activation parameters of cyclization of *para*-substituted singlet phenyl-nitrenes are presented in Table 2. It is readily seen from the table that polar substituents such as *para*-CH$_3$, CF$_3$, halogen and acetyl have little influence on k_R. This is not very surprising, given that theory predicts emphatically that singlet phenylnitrene has an open-shell electronic structure.[47,48] Therefore, cyclization of singlet **PN** only requires that the nitrogen bends out of the molecular plane, so that the singly occupied σ non-bonding molecular orbital (NBMO) can interact with the singly occupied π NBMO.[42] Azirine formation is simply the cyclization of a quinoidal

Table 5 Product ratio of *3H*-azepines[a] formed upon photolysis of *ortho*-cyanophenyl azide at ambient temperature in the presence of 0.1 M diethylamine.[76]

		13c (%)	14c (%)
0.025 M	Pentane	37	63
0.05 M	Pentane	48	52
0.05 M	CH_2Cl_2	67	33
0.05 M	THF	64	36

[a] A species with the same fragmentation pattern as **14c** was also detected by GC-MS, but attempts to isolate this compound failed. It is attributed to the *1H*-azepine analogue of **14c** which is formed initially and isomerizes to **14c**. The data in the table is the sum of the *1H*- and *3H*-azepine yields. *1H*-azepines related to **13c** were not observed by GC-MS.

Table 6 Summary of kinetic results for singlet cyano-substituted phenylnitrenes.[76]

Substituent	$\tau(295)$ (ns)	$\log A$ (s^{-1})	E_a (kcal/mol)	Solvent
o-cyano, **8c**	$\sim 2^a$	12.8 ± 0.3	5.5 ± 0.3	C_5H_{12}
p-cyano, **8e**	8 ± 4	13.5 ± 0.6	7.2 ± 0.8	C_5H_{12}
2,6-dicyano, **8f**	$\sim 2.5^a$	13.3 ± 0.2	6.4 ± 0.3	CH_2Cl_2
2,6-dicyano, **8f**	$\sim 2.3^a$	13.5 ± 0.2	6.5 ± 0.4	C_5H_{12}
2,6-dicyano, **8f**	$\sim 2.3^a$	13.1 ± 1.0	6.0 ± 1.1	THF

[a] Lifetime estimated by extrapolation of the data to 295 K.

1,3-biradical, which originally has two electrons with, anti-parallel spins in two orthogonal orbitals. Thus, polar effects are not anticipated.

We could not study the effect of the strong π-donor *para*-methoxy and dimethylamino substituents, or the iodine substituent on this reaction, because of rapid intersystem crossing at all temperatures.[74]

Two *para* substituents, phenyl and cyano, depress k_R and retard the rate of cyclization significantly (Table 2). *Para*-phenyl and *para*-cyano are both radical stabilizing substituents. These substituents concentrate spin density on the carbon atom *para* to the nitrene nitrogen and reduce spin density *ortho* to the nitrene nitrogen. The reduced spin density at carbons *ortho* to the nitrogen lowers the rate at which the 1,3-biradical cyclizes. The effect with 4-cyano and 4-biphenyl singlet phenylnitrene is quite dramatic. The lifetimes of these singlet nitrenes at ambient temperature are 8 and 15 ns, respectively and the activation barriers to cyclization are 7.2 and 6.8 kcal/mol, respectively.[73,76]

The influence of ortho substituents: steric and electronic effects

Ortho substituents can influence the rate of cyclization to azirines by both steric and electronic (spin localization) effects. Sundberg et al.[88] demonstrated that the steric effect is dominant with simple alkyl substituents.

A single ortho- (8a) or para- (8b) methyl substituent has no influence on the rate of cyclization of the singlet tolylnitrene to the azirine[77] (Fig. 10, Table 4, Scheme 3). Spin localization effects are not observed as with cyano and phenyl substitution. Cyclization of 2,6-dimethylphenyl or 2,4,6-trimethylphenylnitrenes necessarily proceeds towards a carbon bearing a substituent. The steric effect raises the barrier to cyclization by 1.5–2.0 kcal/mol, in excellent agreement with the predictions of Karney and Borden.[89] The steric effect extends the lifetime of 2,6-dimethylphenylnitrene at ambient temperature to 13 ns in freon-113 and of 2,4,6-trimethylphenylnitrene to 8 ns, in the same solvent.

A cyano group is a smaller substitutent than methyl, thus cyclization towards and away from a cyano-substituted carbon should be more evenly balanced. Consistent with this hypothesis, Smalley and co-workers[90] deduced that singlet ortho-cyanophenylnitrene 8c undergoes rearrangement to afford not only 9c, the product formed by cyclization away from the cyano substituent, but also 10c, the product formed by cyclization toward the cyano group (Scheme 3) upon isolation of 13c and 14c. Similar results have been found in the ring expansion of singlet ortho-acetylphenylnitrene.[91]

In our hands,[76] photolysis of ortho-cyanophenyl azide in the presence of diethylamine gives 3H-azepine trapping products, 13c and 14c (Scheme 3). Variation of the solvent led to subtle variation in the product distribution. The solvent effect on the relative rates of cyclization towards and away from the cyano group is small, but finite. The compositions of the mixtures formed under different reaction conditions are shown in Table 5.

Laser flash photolysis studies were performed on 2-cyano (8c), 4-cyano (8e) and 2,6-dicyanophenyl (8f) azide.[76] The results are given in Table 6. In pentane the barrier to cyclization of ortho-cyanophenylnitrene is the same, within experimental error, to that of parent phenylnitrene. The barrier to cyclization of 2,6-dicyanophenylnitrene (8f) is about 1 kcal/mol larger than that of parent phenylnitrene (^{1}PN). Variation of solvent has only a small effect on the kinetics.

Product studies (Table 5) demonstrate that 2-cyanophenylnitrene (8c) prefers to cyclize towards the cyano group in pentane solvent. Thus, the spin localization effect and steric effect essentially cancel and there is no

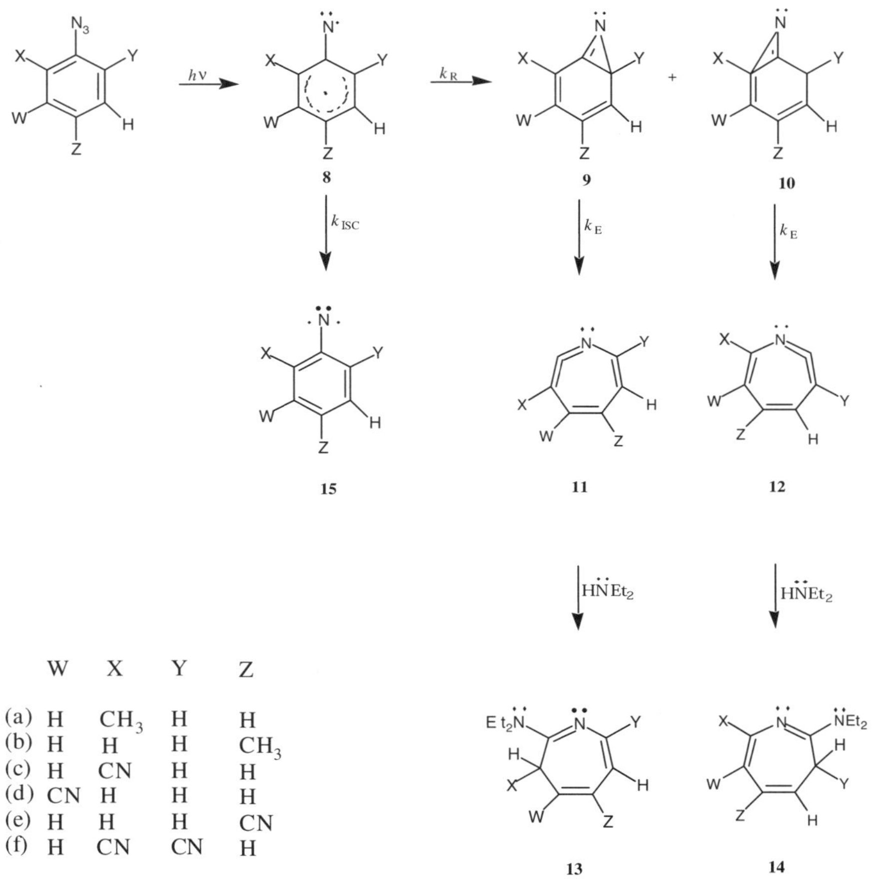

	W	X	Y	Z
(a)	H	CH_3	H	H
(b)	H	H	H	CH_3
(c)	H	CN	H	H
(d)	CN	H	H	H
(e)	H	H	H	CN
(f)	H	CN	CN	H

Scheme 3

net influence on the reaction barrier. It is somewhat surprising then, that the barrier to cyclization of 2,6-dicyanophenylnitrene **8f** increases, but the increase is smaller than that found for 2,6-dimethylphenylnitrene.[77]

Theoretical analysis of the influence of cyano substitution

The qualitative predictions and experimental findings in the case of cyano substituents have been analyzed computationally by performing (8/8)CASSCF and CASPT2/6-31G* *ab initio* calculations.[76] Table 7 summarizes the results for the cyclization reactions of *ortho*-, *meta*-, *para*-, and

2,6-dicyanophenylnitrene (**8c–f**). The zero-point corrected energies of the two possible products, **9** and **10**, are given, relative to the reactants. Also shown are the relative energies of the transition structures, **TS (8→9)** and **TS (8→10)**, leading to each of the products. For comparison, the CASSCF and CASPT2 relative energies for the cyclization reactions of unsubstituted phenylnitrene[42] are given as well.

CASSCF and CASPT2 calculations both overestimate the stability of the open-shell electronic structure of singlet nitrenes **8c–f** by about 3 kcal/mol[76] as in the case of parent ^{1}**PN**.[42] The ring opening is also computed to require passage over a 2–3 kcal/mol lower energy barrier than reversion of the intermediates to the reactants.[76] Therefore, cyclization is the rate-determining step in the ring expansion reactions of nitrenes **8c–f** to derivatives of **11** and **12** (Scheme 3).

Of particular interest are the results in Table 7 for cyclization of singlet *ortho*-cyanophenylnitrene (**8c**). The barrier to cyclization of **8c** away from the cyano substituent to give **9c** is calculated to be about the same as that for cyclization of ^{1}**PN**, and the barrier to cyclization of **8c** toward the cyano substituent to give **10c** is predicted to be either about the same as (CASSCF) or slightly lower than (CASPT2) the barrier to cyclization of **8c** away from the cyano group. This prediction is very different from the computational[89] and experimental results[77] for cyclization of *ortho*-methyl-phenylnitrene where cyclization away from the *ortho* substituent is strongly preferred over cyclization toward the substituent.

Table 7 (8/8)CASSCF and CASPT2/6-31G* energies (kcal/mol),[a] relative to the reactants, for the transition structures and products in the cyclization reactions of singlet phenylnitrene and of the *ortho-*, *meta-*, *para-*, and 2,6-dicyano derivatives.[76]

Substituent	Cyclization Mode[b]	Azirine	CASSCF		CASPT2	
			TS	Product	TS	Product
H	–	**BZ**	8.9	4.7	8.6	1.6
2-cyano, **8c**	Away from	**9c**	8.3	4.5	8.6	2.2
	Toward	**10c**	8.4	2.6	7.5	0.3
3-cyano, **8d**	Away from	**9d**	8.6	4.4	8.2	1.2
	Toward	**10d**	8.1	2.9	7.6	−0.7
4-cyano, **8e**	–	**9e = 10e**	9.4	5.0	9.8	3.3
2,6-dicyano, **8f**	–	**9f = 10f**	8.2	3.1	8.0	1.5

[a] Including zero-point energy (ZPE) corrections, which range from −0.3 to 0.1 kcal/mol for transition structures and from 0.9 to 1.4 kcal/mol for products.
[b] Mode of cyclization, toward or away from the substituted carbon.

This difference between **8c** and singlet *ortho*-methylphenylnitrene **8a** can reasonably be attributed to the greater ability of cyano, compared with methyl, to localize the electron in the π NBMO at the *ortho* carbon to which the substituent is attached. Since cyclization at the substituted carbon in **8c** is predicted to be slightly faster than cyclization at the unsubstituted carbon, it seems likely that cyclization of singlet 2,6-dicyanophenylnitrene (**8f**) would also be computed to be slightly faster than that of unsubstituted phenylnitrene (^{1}**PN**). However, with cyano groups at both *ortho* carbons, as in **8f**, the unpaired π spin density at each of these carbons should be smaller than at the single, cyano-substituted, *ortho* carbon in **8c**. Therefore, the barrier to cyclization might be expected to be somewhat higher for **8f** than for **8c**.

Unlike the case in either **8c** or **8f**, in the cyclization of *meta*-cyanophenylnitrene (**8d**) the cyano group resides on a carbon at which the π NBMO in the reactant has a node, and it seems unlikely that radical stabilization will influence whether **8d** cyclizes to **9d** or **10d** and the barrier heights connecting **8d** to **9d** and **10d** are quite comparable (Table 7).

Table 7 shows that the CASPT2 barrier for cyclization of *para*-cyanophenylnitrene (**8e**) is more than 1 kcal/mol higher than that for cyclization of the *ortho* (**8c**) or *meta* (**8d**) isomers. This is in quantitative agreement with the experimental data (Table 6).

7 Reactivity of fluoro-substituted singlet phenylnitrenes

Abramovitch and co-workers[92,93] and Banks and co-workers[92,93] discovered that, unlike most arylnitrenes, polyfluorinated arylnitrenes have bountiful bimolecular chemistry. Perfluorophenylnitrene reacts with diethylamine to form a hydrazine, with tetramethylethylene to form an aziridine and forms robust adducts with benzene and even cyclohexane (Scheme 4). Polyfluorinated arylnitrenes are useful reagents in synthetic organic chemistry,[80] in photoaffinity labeling,[99–106] and for the covalent modification of polymer surfaces.[10] To understand the fluorine effect we studied the kinetics of fluoro-substituted phenylnitrenes (Scheme 5, **16a–16e**) and interpreted the data with the aid of modern molecular orbital theory.[78]

Laser flash photolysis of a series of fluorinated aryl azides produces the transient spectra of the corresponding singlet nitrenes. With the exception of singlet 2-fluorophenylnitrene (**16a**), the rate of decay of the singlet nitrene was equal to the rate of formation of the reaction products, e.g. didehydroazepines (**18**) and triplet nitrenes (**20**) (Fig. 12). The typical temperature dependence of k_{OBS} was found. The data was interpreted in the usual manner to give k_{ISC} and the Arrhenius parameters to azirine formation (Fig. 13). The data are summarized in Table 8.

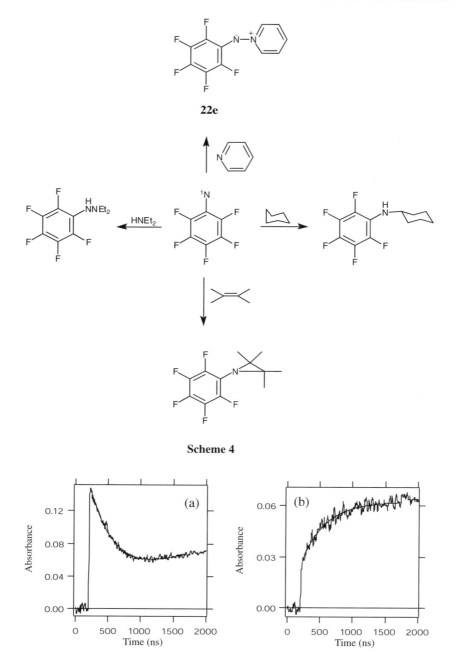

Scheme 4

Fig. 12 The disappearance of singlet *o,o*-difluorophenylnitrene **16d** (a, 340 nm) and the formation of ketenimine **18d** and triplet nitrene **20d** (b, 380 nm) following LFP (249 nm) of 2,6-difluorophenyl azide **15d** in pentane at 295 K.

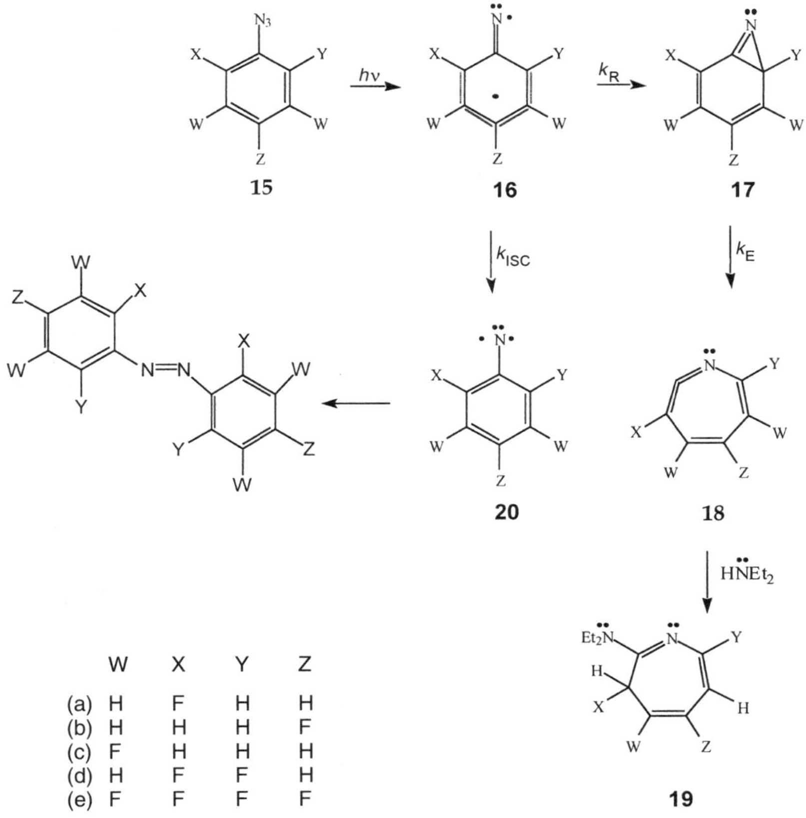

	W	X	Y	Z
(a)	H	F	H	H
(b)	H	H	H	F
(c)	F	H	H	H
(d)	H	F	F	H
(e)	F	F	F	F

Scheme 5

INFLUENCE OF FLUORINE SUBSTITUENTS ON THE CYCLIZATION REACTION: EXPERIMENT AND THEORY

Singlet 2,6-difluorophenylnitrene (**16d**) and singlet perfluorophenylnitrene (**16e**) react with hydrocarbon solvents by insertion into C—H bonds.[107–110] In the case of nitrenes **16d** and **16e** in hydrocarbon solvent, k_{OBS} is actually

$$k_{OBS} = k_{ISC} + k_R + k_{SH}[SH],$$

where the latter term reflects the contribution of the reaction of the singlet nitrene with solvent. In these cases, the slope of a plot of $\log(k_{OBS} - k_{ISC})$ versus $1/T$ is not simply related to the barrier to cyclization. Thus, values of E_a in hydrocarbon solvents are smaller than those measured in the less reactive solvents CH_2Cl_2, CCl_4 and $CF_2ClCFCl_2$ (Table 8). Based on product studies[107,108] we are confident that the activation energy barriers determined

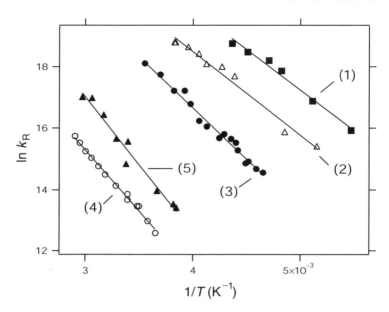

Fig. 13 Arrhenius treatment of $k_R(= k_{OBS} - k_{ISC})$ for singlet *para*-fluoro- **16b** (1), *meta,meta*-difluorophenylnitrene **16c** (2) in pentane and *ortho,ortho*-difluorophenylnitrene **16d** (4) in CCl_4 and k_R for singlet 2-fluorophenylnitrene **16a** (3) calculated as described in the text. (5) Arrhenius treatment of the rate constant of ring opening reaction (k_E) for benzazirine **17a**.

Table 8 Kinetic parameters of fluoro-substituted singlet phenylnitrenes.

Substituent		τ_{298} (ns)	$\log A$ (s^{-1})	E_a (kcal/mol)	Solvent	Ref.
H	^{1}**PN**	~ 1	13.1 ± 0.3	5.6 ± 0.3	C_5H_{12}	46
2-fluoro-	**16a**	8 ± 1	13.0 ± 0.3	6.7 ± 0.3	C_5H_{12}	78
		10 ± 2	–	–	CH_2Cl_2	78
		10 ± 2	–	–	$CF_2ClCFCl_2$	78
4-fluoro-	**16b**	~ 0.3	13.2 ± 0.3	5.3 ± 0.3	C_5H_{12}	78
3,5-difluoro-	**16c**	~ 3	12.8 ± 0.3	5.5 ± 0.3	C_5H_{12}	78
2,6-difluoro-	**16d**	240 ± 20	11.5 ± 0.5	7.3 ± 0.7	C_6H_{14}	78
		260 ± 20	12.0 ± 1.2	8.0 ± 1.5	CCl_4	78
2,3,4,5,6-pentafluoro-	**16e**	56 ± 4	12.8 ± 0.6	7.8 ± 0.6	C_5H_{12}	78
		32 ± 3	13.8 ± 0.3	8.8 ± 0.4	CH_2Cl_2	64
Perfluoro-4-biphenyl	**16f**	260 ± 10	13.2 ± 0.2	9.4 ± 0.4	CH_2Cl_2	64
		220 ± 10	12.5 ± 0.4	8.9 ± 0.3	CH_3CN	123
4-CONHC$_3$H$_8$-2,3,5,6-tetrafluoro	**16g**	210 ± 20	12.0 ± 0.2	7.5 ± 0.3	CH_3CN	123

in the latter solvents can be associated with the cyclization of the singlet nitrene.

Placement of fluorine substituents at both *ortho* positions (**16d**) raises the barrier to cyclization by about 3 kcal/mol, relative to the unsubstituted system (Table 8). One can worry of course that compensating experimental errors in the activation energies and pre-exponential terms may obscure or falsely amplify trends in the barrier heights. For this reason it is useful to compare singlet aryl nitrene lifetimes at 298 K, which are controlled by cyclization. The lifetimes of singlet phenylnitrene (^{1}PN) and 4-fluoro-phenylnitrene (**16b**) are about 1 ns or less at 298 K. The lifetime of 3,5-difluorophenylnitrene (**16c**) is about 3 ns at 298 K but that of 2,6-difluoro-phenylnitrene (**16d**) is 260 ns, in CCl$_4$. As a *para*-fluoro group fails to exert an electronic influence on the cyclization process, it is tempting to attribute the effect of two *ortho*-fluorine substituents on the singlet nitrene lifetime to a simple steric effect.

This interpretation is consistent with the calculations of Karney and Borden,[89] who found that cyclization *away* from an *ortho*-methyl or an *ortho*-fluorine group is favored by 2–3 kcal/mol relative to cyclization *toward* the substituent (Table 9, Fig. 14).

Table 9 (8/8)CASSCF/6-31G*, CASPT2/6-31G* and CASPT2/cc-PVDZ relative energies (kcal/mol) for species involved in the first step of the ring expansion of fluoro-substituted phenylnitrenes (Scheme 5).[89]

Substituent	Species	Mode	CAS/6	PT2/6	PT2/cc
2-F, **16a**	Nitrene[a]		0	0	0
			(−383.41308)	(−384.41203)	(−384.48036)
	TS1	Away	9.5	9.5	9.9
	Azirine1	**17a**	6.1	3.6	4.8
	TS2	Toward	13.6	12.3	13.0
	Azirine2	**17a′**	0.7	−2.4	−0.3
2,6-diF, **16d**	Nitrene[a]		0	0	0
			(−482.25755)	(−483.42762)	(−483.51483)
	TS		13.9	13.0	13.4
	Azirine	**17d**	2.1	−0.5	1.0
3,5-diF, **16c**	Nitrene[a]		0	0	0
			(−482.26440)	(−483.43277)	(−483.52034)
	TS		8.5	7.9	8.6
	Azirine	**17c**	3.2	−0.7	1.1
4-F, **16b**	Nitrene[a]		0	0	0
			(−383.41578)	(−384.41595)	(−384.48417)
	TS		7.9	8.5	9.1
	Azirine	**17b**	3.3	1.6	3.3

[a] Absolute energy of singlet arylnitrenes in parenthesis.

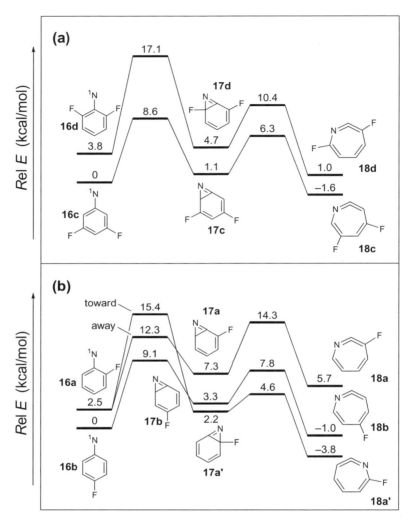

Fig. 14 Relative energies (in kcal/mol) of species involved in the ring expansions of singlet fluoro-substituted phenylnitrenes calculated at the CASPT2/cc-pVDZ// CASSCF(8,8)/6-31G* level. (a) Difluorinated phenylnitrenes. (b) Monofluorinated phenylnitrenes.

The work of Leyva and Sagredo[111] demonstrated, in fact, that cyclization of the singlet nitrene **16a** proceeds away from the fluorine substituent. The steric argument predicts that a single *ortho*-fluorine substituent will have little influence on the rate of conversion of **16a** to **17a**, since cyclization occurs at the unsubstituted *ortho* carbon. However, the barrier to this process is larger (outside of experimental error) than that of the parent system (Table 8). In

17a′   16a   17a

fact, the lifetime of singlet 2-fluorophenylnitrene (16a) at 298 K is 8–10 times longer than that of the parent (^{1}PN) and 20–30 times longer than that of 4-fluorophenylnitrene (16b). Therefore a single *ortho*-fluorine atom exerts a small but significant bystander effect on remote cyclization that is not simply steric in origin. This result is in good quantitative agreement with the computational data of Karney and Borden,[89] who predicted that the barrier to cyclization of 16a *away* from the fluorine substituent is about 1 kcal/mol higher than that for parent system ^{1}PN (Table 9).

In order to understand this substituent effect, the atomic charges for the different centers were computed[78] using the CASSCF(8,8)/6-31G* wave functions and the natural population analysis (NPA) method of Reed, Weinstock and Weinhold.[112] It was found that fluorine substitution makes the adjacent carbon very positively charged (+0.48 e). In the transformation of 2-fluorophenylnitrene (16a) to TS1a (away from F) or TS2a (towards F), there is an increase in positive character at the (ipso) carbon bearing the nitrogen. The increased activation barrier to cyclization for 2-fluorophenyl-nitrene (16a) relative to ^{1}PN or 4-fluorophenylnitrene (16b) is due to a large +...+ interaction between the ortho and ipso carbons in TS1a.

For insertion towards F in TS2a there is an even greater amount of posi-tive-positive charge repulsion between the ortho and ipso carbons than in TS1a, and this effect is responsible, in part, for a higher activation barrier for insertion towards F than away from F. Therefore, the origin of the pronounced influence of ortho,ortho-difluorosubstitution on the lifetime of singlet arylnitrene and the increased activation energy of its cyclization is due to a combination of the steric effect and the extraordinary electronegativity of fluorine atom. In this case the electronic and steric effects reinforce each other. This is opposite to the case of ortho,ortho-dicyanophenylnitrene where the electronic and steric effects oppose each other.

INTERCONVERSION OF SINGLET NITRENE AND AZIRINE IN THE CASE OF
ORTHO-FLUOROPHENYL AZIDE: EXPERIMENT AND THEORY

Unique kinetic results were obtained upon LFP of ortho-fluorophenyl azide 15a.[78] Figure 15 displays the typical kinetics of the decay of singlet 2-fluoro-phenylnitrene (16a) and the formation of products (ketenimine 18a and triplet nitrene **20a**) at different temperatures. Note that for all other substituted singlet phenylnitrenes described in this review the rates of nitrene decay were equal to the rates of product formation. At low temperatures where triplet nitrenes are formed in higher yields, slow growths in absorption were observed on microsecond timescales (Fig. 15g) due to triplet nitrene dimerization to form azobenzenes, which absorb in the UV region. Slowly increasing absorption at low temperatures were observed for all other aryl azides.

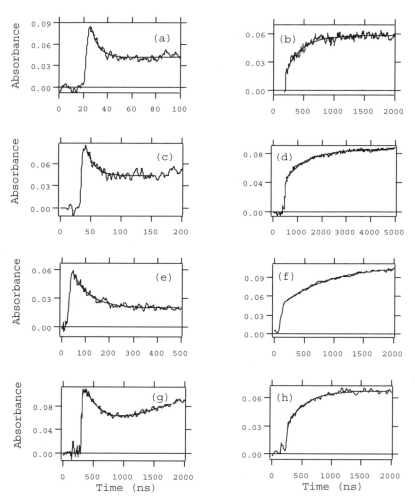

Fig. 15 Changes in transient absorption produced by LFP (266 nm) of 2-fluorophenyl azide **15a** at 342 nm, (a, c, e, g) and 380 nm, (b, d, f, h) at selected temperatures: 295 K (a, b), 273 K (c, d), 233 K (e, f) and 160 K (g, h).

When the characteristic time constants of decay of nitrene **16a** and growth of triplet nitrene **20a** and azepine **18a** are significantly different ($\geqslant$ a factor of 10) the kinetics of decay (a, c, e) and growth (b, d, f) could be fitted to simple mono exponential functions. The kinetics were analyzed to yield observed rate constants of decay (k_{dec}) and growth (k_{gr}).

Figure 16 presents the temperature dependence of k_{dec} and k_{gr}. Figures 15 and 16 reveal that the decay of singlet nitrene **16a** is much faster than the formation of products (**18a** and **20a**) at temperatures above 230 K. Between 147 and 180 K, however, k_{gr} is equal to k_{dec} and both rate constants are temperature independent and close to the value of k_{ISC} for parent ^{1}**PN**. In this temperature range (147–180 K), singlet nitrene **16a** cleanly relaxes to the lower-energy triplet nitrene **20a**.

Above 180 K, **16a** decays by both intersystem crossing (k_{ISC}) and cyclization (k_R), with the latter process gaining relative to the former as

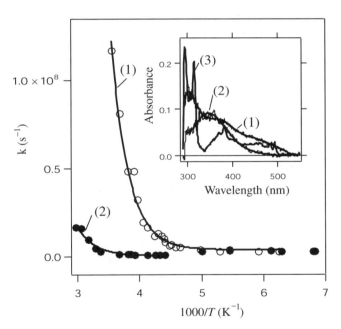

Fig. 16 The temperature dependencies of the rate constant of decay of singlet 2-fluorophenylnitrene **15a** (1) and the apparent rate constant of formation of triplet 2-fluorophenylnitrene (**20a**) and ketenimine (**18a**) (2). Solid lines (1) and (2): results of non-linear global fit of the data to analytical solutions. Insert: transient absorption spectra produced by LFP at 295 K (1) of 2-fluorophenyl azide **15a** in pentane, detected 500 ns after the laser pulse; (2) 4-fluorophenyl azide **15b** detected 50 ns after the laser pulse; and (3) persistent spectrum detected after 20 s of photolysis of 2-fluorophenyl azide **15a** in methylcyclohexane at 77 K.

the temperature increases. The data of Fig. 16 were explained by positing that singlet nitrene **16a** and azirine **17a** interconvert under the experimental conditions[78] (Scheme 6).

This hypothesis was supported by analysis of the transient spectrum obtained upon LFP of 2-fluorophenyl azide, which reveals the presence of triplet nitrene **20a** despite the small ratio of k_{ISC}/k_{OBS}. This is clearly evident in Fig. 16 (Insert: Spectrum 1), which presents the spectrum of the products formed from the decay of singlet nitrene **16a** at room temperature. This spectrum is the sum of the spectrum of triplet nitrene **20a** (narrow band at 303 nm and weak absorption below 450 nm) and ketenimine **18a** (broad band at 350 nm). This complicated spectrum can be compared with the simpler spectrum of ketenimine **18b** (Spectrum 2) and the spectrum of triplet nitrene **20a** observed as a persistent species in a low-temperature matrix (Spectrum 3). It is clear that the yield of triplet nitrene **20a** is significant at room temperature. However, if one postulates that azirine **17a** does not interconvert with singlet nitrene **16a** (Scheme 6, $k_E \gg k_{-R}$), then the yield of triplet nitrene at room temperature should be very small and should be equal to $k_{ISC}/k_{OBS} \sim 0.03$, where k_{OBS} is the observed rate constant for the disappearance of singlet nitrene **16a**. The small ratio of k_{ISC}/k_{OBS} and the appearance of triplet nitrene in the transient spectrum and the large chemical

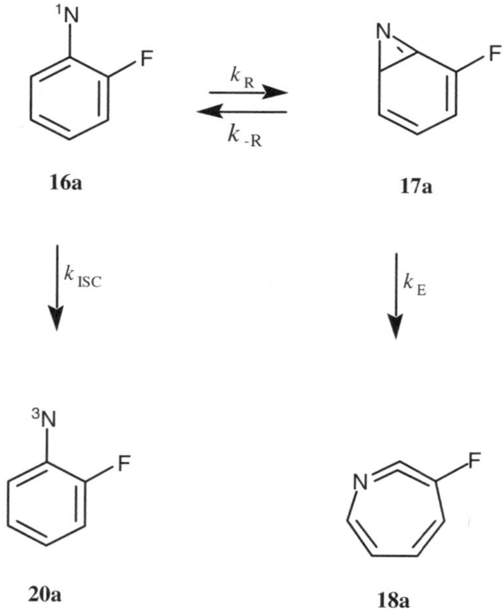

Scheme 6

yield of triplet-derived azo product can be reconciled if benzazirine **17a** serves as a reservoir for singlet 2-fluorophenylnitrene **16a** (at temperatures higher than 180 K), which eventually relaxes to triplet nitrene **20a**.

Kinetic data for singlet *ortho*-fluoronitrene **16a** were analyzed[78] following Scheme 6. The equilibrium constant K_R ($K_R = k_{-R}/k_R$) was estimated to be about 0.5 and ΔG to be very small $\sim$350 cal/mol. Thus, **16a** and **17a** are very close in energy. The rate constant of the ring opening reaction k_E was measured and the Arrhenius parameters were found to be $A = 10^{13.5\pm0.4}\,\mathrm{M}^{-1}\,\mathrm{s}^{-1}$ and $E_a = 9000 \pm 500$ cal/mol.

The large yield (76%) of azo compound **21a** (and triplet nitrene) produced upon photolysis of **16a** is consistent with the conclusion that azirine **17a**, ketenimine **18a** and singlet nitrene **16a** interconvert, leading to an enhanced yield of triplet nitrene.

Quantum chemical calculations

To support the proposed explanation of the unique kinetics observed for **16a**, a series of *ab initio* and density functional theory (DFT) calculations on the second step of the ring expansion (electrocyclic ring opening of azirines **17a–17e** to form the corresponding cyclic ketenimines **18a–18e**) were performed.[78] The CASPT2/cc-pVDZ//CASSCF(8,8)/6-31G* and B3LYP/6-31G* energies are given in Table 10. The CASPT2 results are also depicted graphically in Fig. 14, in a way that permits energetic comparisons of isomeric species.

As shown in Fig. 14, in all cases except the "away" ring expansion of 2-fluorophenylnitrene (**16a**), the transition state for the second step of the ring expansion (**17** → **18**) is computed to be lower in energy than that for the first step (**16** → **17**) at the CASPT2 level of theory. This is consistent with the experimental finding that, for nitrenes **16b–d**, the nitrene decays at the same rate at which the corresponding ketenimine is formed, whereas for nitrene **16a**, nitrene decay is faster than ketenimine growth. In addition, of the five electrocyclic ring openings described here, the opening of **16a** to form **17a** is predicted to be the least exothermic ($\Delta E = -1.6$ kcal/mol). The exothermicity of this step for the other systems ranges from $\Delta E = -2.7$ kcal/mol to $\Delta E = -6.0$ kcal/mol.

The CASPT2 results are supported qualitatively by B3LYP/6-31G* calculations (Table 10). The DFT calculations predict that benzazirine **17a** has the second-highest barrier (after **17e**) to rearrangement to a ketenimine (**18a**). It also has the lowest barrier to reversion to the corresponding singlet nitrene (**16a**). Thus, **17a** reverts to the corresponding singlet nitrene (**16a**) more readily than does the parent system **BZ**. The DFT calculations also predict that of the four fluoro-substituted arylnitrenes the ring opening **17a** → **18a** is the least exothermic. Thus, both CASPT2 and B3LYP calculations correctly predict that **17a** is the benzazirine most likely to revert to the corresponding singlet nitrene. Significantly, this is the only system in

Table 10 Relative energies (in kcal/mol) and zero-point vibrational energies of azirines **17**, ketenimines **18**, and the transition states (**TS**) connecting them.[a 78]

Method	Azirine		Transition state		Ketenimine	
	E	ZPE	Rel E	ZPE	Rel E	ZPE
	BZ		**TS**		**K**	
CASPT2/cc-pVDZ[b]	−285.41815	60.9	2.5	59.8	−4.5	60.8
B3LYP/6-31G*[c]	−286.27659	57.7	4.7	56.7	−5.1	57.6
	17a		**TSa**		**18a**	
CASPT2/cc-pVDZ[b]	−384.47462	55.7	7.0	54.6	−1.6	55.8
B3LYP/6-31G*[c]	−385.50238	52.8	8.1	51.7	−3.0	52.8
B3LYP/6-311+G(2d,p)[c]	−385.62115		7.0		−5.5	
CCSD(T)/6-31+G*[c]	−384.48202		11.2			
	17a′		**TSa′**		**18a′**	
CASPT2/cc-pVDZ[b]	−384.48308	55.9	2.4	54.8	−6.0	55.7
B3LYP/6-31G*[c]	−385.51174	52.7	4.1	51.8	−6.8	52.8
	17b		**TSb**		**18b**	
CASPT2/cc-pVDZ[b]	−384.48077	55.6	4.5	54.5	−4.3	55.5
B3LYP/6-31G*[c]	−385.50865	52.6	5.7	51.5	−5.5	52.6
	17c		**TSc**		**18c**	
CASPT2/cc-pVDZ[b]	−483.52115	50.5	5.2	49.3	−2.7	50.3
B3LYP/6-31G*[c]	−484.74392	47.7	6.4	46.6	−3.9	47.6
	17d		**TSd**		**18d**	
CASPT2/cc-pVDZ[b]	−483.51566	50.7	5.7	49.6	−3.7	50.6
B3LYP/6-31G*[c]	−484.73747	47.8	6.8	46.8	−5.1	47.9
	17e		**TSe**		**18e**	
B3LYP/6-31G*[c]	−782.41002	32.6	8.5	31.5	−6.0	32.6

[a] Azirine energies are absolute energies, in hartrees. Energies for transition states and ketenimines are relative energies, compared to the azirines, and are corrected for differences in zero-point vibrational energy.

[b] Obtained using CASSCF(8,8)/6-31G* optimized geometry and zero-point vibrational energy.

[c] Obtained using B3LYP/6-31G* optimized geometry and zero-point vibrational energy.

which the rates of formation and disappearance of the benzazirine are predicted to be comparable, and the only case where there is compelling kinetic evidence in favor of an intermediate between the singlet nitrene and its ketenimine isomer in solution.

The experimental data reveal that singlet nitrene **16a** and benzazirine **17a** are very close in energy ($\Delta G \approx 350$ cal/mol). This value is smaller than that predicted by CASPT2 calculations (4.8 kcal/mol, Fig. 14). The CASPT2 method typically underestimates by 3–6 kcal/mol[113] the energies of open-shell species, such as **16a**, relative to closed-shell molecules, such as **17a**. Applying an upward correction of ~3 kcal/mol to the energy of the singlet nitrene as in the case of [1]**PN** brings the computational result into much better agreement with experiment.

Why is the barrier for ring opening of **17a** to **18a** so much higher than the corresponding barriers for **BZ** and **17b–17d**? As shown in Fig. 14, for all cases except **17e** → **18e**, the energy of the transition state for this step roughly parallels the energy of the ketenimine product (**18**). The marked instability of ketenimine **18a**, relative to **18a′** and **18b**, is consistent with the recent computational results predicting that fluorine substitution destabilizes ketenimines.[114] This instability can be attributed to Coulombic repulsion between the two carbons of the ketenimine moiety. Because both of these carbons are attached to more electronegative atoms (one to N, one to F), both bear a partial positive charge and severe electrostatic repulsion results.

18a′   **17a′**   **16a**   **17a**   **18a**

The effect of Coulombic repulsion described for ketenimine **18a** can also be used to rationalize the higher energy of nitrene **16a** relative to **16b**, as well as the higher energy of azirine **17a** compared to **17a′** and **17b**. It is possible that the changes in relative orientation of the C=N and C−F bond dipoles that occur for **16a** → **17a** and **17a** → **18a** are at least partly responsible for the fact that this process is predicted to be substantially more endothermic (in the case of **16a** → **17a**) or less exothermic (in the case of **17a** → **18a**) than the other systems studied.

Curiously, the addition of a second *ortho*-fluorine substituent (i.e. in benzazirine **17d**) raises the barrier to reversion to singlet nitrene **16d**, relative to the mono *ortho*-fluoro system (Fig. 14). This is partly due to steric hindrance by fluorine in the transition state for cyclization, but also to the stabilization of **17d** by the fluorine attached directly to the azirine ring (*vide supra*).[89] The addition of the second fluorine substituent (benzazirine **17d**) decreases the barrier to conversion of azirine **17d** to ketenimine **18d** slightly

(Fig. 14). This is related to the more favorable thermodynamics of conversion in the case of **17d** compared with **17a**, due to the slight stabilization of ketenimine **18d** by the fluorine adjacent to nitrogen. The barrier for **17d** → **18d** is still predicted to be *ca.* 2.5 kcal/mol higher than the barrier for **BZ** → **K** at the same level of theory,[42] which helps to explain why Morawietz and Sander[82] successfully detected benzazirine **17d** in their matrix isolation experiments.

KINETICS OF BIMOLECULAR REACTIONS OF FLUORO-SUBSTITUTED PHENYLNITRENES

It was mentioned previously that, unlike most arylnitrenes, polyfluorinated arylnitrenes have bountiful bimolecular chemistry. Banks and Sparkes[94] found that pyrolysis of 4-azido-2,3,5,6-tetrafluoropyridine in cyclohexane produced the product of formal CH insertion in 45% yield. Tetrafluoropyridylnitrene was also captured by alkenes, dimethyl sulfoxide and even benzene.[94] Pyrolysis of perfluorophenyl azide (**15e**) yields a product of formal insertion with a CH-bond of benzene and the formation of adducts with dimethyl sulfoxide.[95,96] Abramovitch *et al.*[92] demonstrated that perfluorophenylnitrene (**16e**) reacted with electron-rich aromatics. Adducts were formed with benzene, toluene, anisole and mesitylene in yields of 2–18%. It was demonstrated that reaction of nitrene **16e** with aromatic substrates proceeds through a heterocyclic intermediate, which can be trapped with tetracyanoethylene.

Photolysis of azide **15e** in cyclohexene, or in cis- and trans-2-butene, produced the corresponding aziridines in 39, 18 and 18% yields respectively.[93]

Formation of the product of formal insertion of nitrene **16e** into the aryl and benzylic CH-bonds of toluene was observed upon photolysis of **15e** in toluene[80,115]

One of the most interesting products obtained from the capture of singlet nitrene **16e** is ylide **22e** produced by photolysis of **15e** in pyridine (Scheme 4). Ylide **22e** has a very intense absorption band with maximum absorption at 390 nm.[107] The pyridine-ylide method was successfully used by our group to probe the dynamics of the fluoro-substituted singlet arylnitrenes.[107,109,116,117]

Poe *et al.*[107] measured the yield of ylide **22e** in the presence of competitive quenchers of singlet nitrene **16e**. Under these conditions, a Stern–Volmer plot of A_{390}^0/A_{390} versus quencher concentration (Q) at constant pyridine concentration was linear (where A_{390}^0 is the yield of ylide **22e** when $[Q] = 0$). The slopes of these plots yield k_Q/k_{PYR} [PYR], where k_{PYR} is the absolute rate constant of the singlet nitrene reaction with pyridine and k_Q is the absolute rate constant of its reaction with concurrent quencher. Similar values of k_Q/k_{PYR} were measured for reactions of four singlet nitrenes (**16d**, **16e**, 2,4,6-triflurophenylnitrene and 4-CO$_2$CH$_3$-2,3,5,6-tetrafluorophenyl-nitrene) with diethylamine, dimethylsulfide, dimethylsulfoxide and tetra-methylethylene. In a subsequent study,[64] the absolute value of k_{PYR} was measured for nitrene **16e**. Using this value, we deduced absolute rate constants of the reactions of nitrene **16e** with other quenchers (Table 11).

Marcinek and Platz[116] used the pyridine-ylide method to measure absolute rate constants of reactions of two *para*-substituted perfluorophenylnitrenes (**16h**, **16j**) with pyridine, amines, isoprene, 2,3-dimethyl-2-butene and other quenchers (Table 11).

16h   **16j**

In 1997 the electronic absorption spectra of phenylnitrene[44] and its perfluorosubstituted analogues[64] were detected. Recently[118] the kinetics of bimolecular reactions of the singlet fluoro-substituted arylnitrenes were studied using direct spectroscopic methods. The absolute rate constants of reaction of singlet perfluoroarylnitrene **16f** and **16g** with amines, pyridine and dimethylsulfoxide are presented in Table 11.

Table 11 The rate constants of bimolecular reactions (k_Q, $M^{-1} s^{-1}$) of singlet *para*-substituted 2,3,5,6-tetrafluorophenylnitrenes with different organic compounds.

4-R	F^a 16e	$CONHCH_3{}^b$ 16h	$CONH(CH_2)_7Ph^b$ 16j	$C_6F_5{}^c$ 16f	$CONHC_3H_8{}^c$ 16g
diethylamine	1.9×10^8	2.5×10^8	–	–	–
piperidine	–	–	–	$(2.0 \pm 0.2) \times 10^8$	$(1.9 \pm 0.2) \times 10^8$
morpholine	–	–	–	$(1.9 \pm 0.2) \times 10^8$	$(1.8 \pm 0.2) \times 10^8$
imidazole	–	–	–	$(4.0 \pm 0.4) \times 10^7$	$(3.9 \pm 0.4) \times 10^7$
indole	–	–	1.5×10^9	–	–
pyridine	5.8×10^7	$(3.1 \pm 0.1) \times 10^7$	$(3.1 \pm 0.1) \times 10^7$	$(1.6 \pm 0.2) \times 10^7$	$(1.7 \pm 0.2) \times 10^7$
dimethyl sulfoxide	1.9×10^8	–	–	$(2.0 \pm 0.2) \times 10^8$	$(2.2 \pm 0.2) \times 10^8$
dimethyl sulfide	4.5×10^8	1.3×10^9	–	–	–
n-butyl disulfide	–	–	7.6×10^8	–	–
2,3-dimethyl-2-butene	–	1.6×10^8	–	–	–
isoprene	–	–	4.5×10^7	–	–
tetramethyl-ethylene	1.3×10^8	–	–	–	–
methanol	1.3×10^7	–	–	–	–
phenol	–	–	6.9×10^7	–	–
H^+ (ref. 123)^d	–	–	–	$(2.4 \pm 0.2) \times 10^8$	$(1.3 \pm 0.1) \times 10^9$

^{a}The rate constants of reactions in CH_2Cl_2 deduced using the data of Poe *et al.*[107] and the absolute rate constant of reaction with pyridine.[64]
^{b}Rate constants measured by Marcinek *et al.*[116] in CH_2Cl_2.
^{c}Rate constants measured by Polshakov *et al.*[118] in CH_3CN.
^{d}Measurement in CH_3CN-H_2O mixture (4:1).

16f   **16g**

It is known[107] that irradiation of perfluorophenyl azide in the presence of diethylamine results in the formation of hydrazine along with some other products. LFP of azides **16f**, **16g** demonstrates[118] that in the presence of amines (piperidine and morpholine) the decay of the arylnitrene absorption (Figure 17, Spectrum 1) is accompanied by formation of the transient absorption with maximum at 320 nm (Figure 17, Spectrum 2). Unlike the adduct of singlet arylnitrene with pyridine (ylide **22e**), this intermediate is unstable and its lifetime is about 2.5 μs. The product of its transformations absorbs slightly in the near-UV region (Figure 17, Spectrum 3), which is typical of hydrazines (**24**).

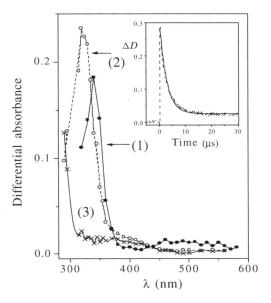

Fig. 17 Transient absorption spectra detected at ambient temperature in acetonitrile 30 ns after LFP of perfluoro-4-biphenyl azide (**16f**) in the absence of morpholine (1) and 200 ns (2) and $10 \, \mu s$ (3) after LFP of **16f** in the presence of 0.1 M morpholine. Insert: decay of the adduct of singlet nitrene **16f** with morpholine in dry acetonitrile.

It is reasonable to assume that the intermediate with intense absorption at 320 nm is ylide **23**.

16   **23**   **24**

Semi-empirical PM3 calculations[118] reveal that ylide **23** is a minimum on the potential energy surface and that both steps are exothermic. The enthalpy of the reaction of ylide formation in CH_3CN was estimated to be $-43 \, kcal/mol$ and the enthalpy of reaction of the second step, 1,2-hydrogen shift, was calculated to be $-12.5 \, kcal/mol$.

It is known[119] that the 1,2-hydrogen shift reaction is catalyzed by base (triethylamine, alcohols, water). Indeed, the decay of the ylidic adducts of nitrenes **16f** and **16g** with morpholine was accelerated in the presence of water (3.3%vol) by factors of 2 and 2.3 respectively, in agreement with the proposed two-step mechanism.

Protonation of singlet arylnitrenes

Recently, McClelland et al.[120,121] demonstrated, using LFP techniques, that singlet arylnitrenes can be trapped by protonation to form nitrenium ions. Water is a sufficiently strong acid to protonate singlet 4-biphenyl- and 2-fluorenylnitrenes and some of their derivatives[121,122] prior to their rearrangement to azirines. Unlike these nitrenes, singlet phenylnitrene could be protonated only in the presence of acids.[121] In 1996 Michalak et al.[117] demonstrated the protonation of a series of polyfluorinated singlet arylnitrenes in acetonitrile solution in the presence of sulfuric acid.

McClelland et al.[120,121] detected transient absorption spectra of a series of arylnitrenium ions and studied the kinetics of their reactions. Using pico-second spectroscopy, this group was able to resolve the growth of the nitrenium ions formed from protonation of singlet 2-fluorenyl nitrene (90 ps) and singlet biphenyl nitrene (160 ps) in 20% acetonitrile–water at ambient temperature.[121] Born et al.[45] were able to measure the rate constant of protonation of the singlet 2,4,6-tribromophenylnitrene (**25**). Using LFP with picosecond time resolution they observed that proton transfer in 1:1 aqueous acetonitrile produced the nitrenium ion **26**.

The rate of formation (k_{OBS}) and the yield of **26** increased upon addition of perchloric acid, $k_{OBS} = k_0 + k_{H^+}[H^+]$. The decay rate of the singlet nitrene increased accordingly, and k_{H^+} was measured to be $3.5 \pm 0.1 \times 10^9\,M^{-1}\,s^{-1}$, a value that is about one order of magnitude lower than the diffusion limit.

25   26

In subsequent work,[123] the protonation of fluoro-substituted singlet arylnitrenes **16f** and **16g** was studied in 1:4 water–acetonitrile mixture on the nanosecond timescale. LFP studies of aryl azides **15f** and **15g** in the presence of HCl demonstrated that the decay of the arylnitrene absorption was accompanied by the formation of transient absorption with maximum at

325 nm (Fig. 18, Spectrum 1). This spectrum is similar to the spectra detected by Michalak et al.[117] upon LFP of a series of polyfluorinated aryl azides in acetonitrile solution in the presence of sulfuric acid. These spectra were assigned to the nitrenium ions,[117,123] but the possible formation of a dication or of complexation of the nitrenium ions with solvent was not excluded. The intermediate detected by Polshakov et al.[123] had a lifetime 160 ns in a water–acetonitrile (1:4) mixture. The absorption spectrum of the product of its transformation is presented in Fig. 18 (Spectrum 2). The lifetime of the intermediate with spectrum 1 (Fig. 18) was significantly longer ($\sim 10\,\mu s$) in dry acetonitrile.

The rate of formation (k_{OBS}) of these intermediates in a water–acetonitrile mixture (1:4) increased upon addition of the acid, $k_{OBS} = k + k_{H^+}[H^+]$ (Fig. 18, insert). The decay rate of the singlet nitrene increased accordingly, and k_{H^+} was measured to be $2.4 \pm 0.2 \times 10^8\,M^{-1}\,s^{-1}$ and $1.3 \pm 0.1 \times 10^9\,M^{-1}\,s^{-1}$ for protonation of singlet nitrenes **16f** and **16g** respectively. These values are about 1–2 orders of magnitude lower than the diffusion limit, similar to the case of protonation of singlet nitrene **25**.

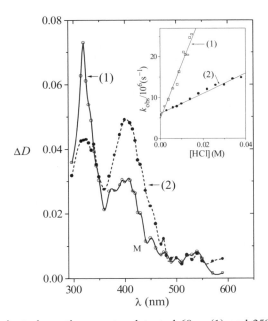

Fig. 18 Transient absorption spectra detected 60 ns (1) and 350 ns (2) after LFP of n-propyl-4-azido-2,3,4,6-tetrafluorobenzamide (**15g**) in water–acetonitrile mixture (1:4) at room temperature in the presence of 0.057 M of HCl. Insert: dependencies of the rate constants of the decay of singlet nitrenes **16g** (1) and **16f** (2) on the concentration of HCl.

8 Conclusions

In our separate, earlier reviews[19,20] both authors wrote that the most important tasks remaining in the field were the direct observation of singlet aryl nitrenes, direct study of the kinetics of singlet nitrene reactions and high-level quantum chemical calculations of the nitrene potential energy surface. The present review illustrates that great progress has been made in these areas over the past few years. Singlet phenylnitrene has been detected directly and its spectrum analyzed with the aid of modern computational methods. The rate constant of intersystem crossing to the lower-energy triplet state has been measured and it is much smaller than the corresponding values observed with aryl carbenes. This is a consequence of the open-shell electronic structure of phenylnitrene. The activation parameters to cyclization of singlet phenylnitrene to benzazirine have been obtained and are in good agreement with modern quantum chemical calculations.

The effect of substituents on the spectra and kinetics of singlet aryl nitrenes has been examined systematically. Groups which act as strong π donors dramatically accelerate intersystem crossing (ISC). Electron-withdrawing groups also slightly accelerate ISC. *Para* substituents such as cyano and phenyl, reduce spin density *ortho* to the nitrene-bearing carbon and reduce the rate of cyclization to the corresponding benzazirine. *Ortho* substituents generally direct cyclization away from the substituted center because of unfavorable steric interactions. *Ortho* fluorine substituents retard cyclization towards and even away from the substituted carbon because of the development of unfavorable Coulombic interactions between the aryl carbons bearing the nitrogen and the fluorine substituent. The kinetics of cyclization of singlet *ortho*-fluorophenylnitrene reveal that cyclization to the corresponding benzazirine is reversible. All of these effects are in accordance with computational chemistry.

In the early 1990s, singlet aryl nitrenes had never been detected and the influence of structure on reactivity was only dimly appreciated. Laser flash photolysis studies in combination with theory has provided insight and has led to a comprehensive theory of substituent effects. We have been proud to be part of this process.

Acknowledgements

The authors are deeply indebted to their graduate and postdoctoral students (Dean Tigelaar, Anna Gudmundsdottir, Monica Cerro Lopez, Meng-Lin Tsao and Dmitrii Polshakov) whose efforts led to this review article. The authors have enjoyed and learned much from their collaborations with the following theoreticians: Professors Weston T. Borden, Christopher M. Hadad, William Karney and Carl Kemnitz. Support of this work by the National Science Foundation and the Russian Foundation for Basic Research is gratefully acknowledged.

References

1. Greiss, P. (1864). *Phil. Trans. R. Soc. London.* **13**, 377
2. Wolf, L. (1912). *Ann.* **394**, 59
3(a). Huisgen, R., Vossius, D. and Appl, M. (1958). *Chem. Ber.* **91**, 1
3(b). Huisgen, R. and Appl, M. (1958). *Chem. Ber.* **91**, 12
4. Doering, W.v.E. and Odum, R.A. (1966). *Tetrahedron.* **22**, 81
5. Schrock, A.K. and Schuster, G.B. (1984). *J. Am. Chem. Soc.* **106**, 5228
6. Breslow, D.S. (1984). In *Azides and Nitrenes. Reactivity and Utility* (ed. E.F.V. Scriven), p. 491. Academic Press, New York
7. Meijer, E.W., Nijhuis, S. and Von Vroonhoven, F.C.B.M. (1988). *J. Am. Chem. Soc.* **110**, 7209
8(a). Smith, P.A.S. and Brown, B.B. (1951). *J. Am. Chem. Soc.* **73**, 2435
8(b). Smith, P.A.S. (1970). In *Nitrenes* (ed. W. Lwowski), p. 99. Wiley-Interscience, New York
9. Bayley, H. (1983). *Photogenerated Reagents in Biochemistry and Molecular Biology.* Elsevier, Amsterdam
10. Cai, S.X., Glenn, D.R. and Keana, J.F.W. (1992). *J. Org. Chem.* **57**, 1299
11. Swenton, J.S., Ikeler, T.J. and Williams, B.H. (1970). *J. Am. Chem. Soc.* **92**, 3103
12. Carroll, S.E., Nay, B., Scriven, E.F.V., Suschitzky, H. and Thomas, D.R. (1977). *Tetrahedron Lett.* 3175
13. DeGraff, B.A., Gillespie, D.W. and Sundberg, R.J. (1974). *J. Am. Chem. Soc.* **96**, 7491
14. Scriven, E.F.V. (1982). In *Reactive Intermediates* (ed. R.A. Abramovitch), vol. 2, p. 1. Plenum, New York
15. Wentrup, C. (1984). *Reactive Molecules.* Wiley-Interscience, New York
16. Platz, M.S. (1984). In *Azides and Nitrenes. Reactivity and Utility* (ed. E.F.V. Scriven), p. 359. Academic Press, New York
17. Platz, M.S. and Maloney, V.M. (1990). In *Kinetics and Spectroscopy of Carbenes and Biradical* (ed. M.S. Platz), p. 239. Plenum, New York
18. Schuster, G.B. and Platz, M.S. (1992). *Adv. Photochem.* **17**, 69
19. Gritsan, N.P. and Pritchina, E.A. (1992). *Russ. Chem. Rev.* **61**, 500
20. Platz, M.S. (1995). *Acc. Chem. Res.* **28**, 487
21. Borden, W.T., Gritsan, N.P., Hadad, C.M., Karney, W.L., Kemnitz, C.R. and Platz, M.S. (2000). *Acc. Chem. Res.* **33**, 765
22. Baron, W.J., DeCamp, M.R., Henric, M.E., Jones, M., Jr., Levin, R.H. and Sohn, M.B. (1973). In *Carbenes* (eds M. Jones, Jr. and R.A. Moss), vol. 1, p.1. John Wiley, New York
23. Liang, T.-Y. and Schuster, G.B. (1987). *J. Am. Chem. Soc.* **109**, 7803
24. Gritsan, N.P. and Pritchina, E.A. (1989). *J. Inf. Rec. Mat.* **17**, 391
25. Leyva, E., Platz, M.S., Persy, G. and Wirz, J. (1986). *J. Am. Chem. Soc.* **108**, 3783
26. Smolinsky, G., Wasserman, E. and Yager, Y.A. (1962). *J. Am. Chem. Soc.* **84**, 3220
27. Reiser, A. and Frazer, V. (1965). *Nature (London)* **208**, 682
28. Reiser, A., Bowes, G. and Horne, R. (1966). *Trans. Faraday. Soc.* **62**, 3162
29. Reiser, A., Terry, G.C. and Willets, F.W. (1966). *Nature (London).* **211**, 410
30. Reiser, A., Wagner, H.M., Marley, R. and Bowes, G. (1967). *Trans. Faraday Soc.* **63**, 2403
31. Porter, G. and Ward, B. (1968). *Proc. R. Soc. London, Ser. A* **303**, 139
32. Ozawa, K., Ishida, T., Fuke, K. and Kaya, K. (1988). *Chem. Phys. Lett.* **150**, 249
33(a). Cullin, D.W., Yu, L., Williamson, J., Platz, M.S. and Miller, T.A. (1990). *J. Phys. Chem.* **94**, 3387

33(b). Cullin, D.W., Soundarajan, N., Platz, M.S. and Miller, T.A. (1990). *J. Phys. Chem.* **94**, 8890

34. Waddell, W.H. and Feilchenfeld, N.B. (1983). *J. Am. Chem. Soc.* **105**, 5499

35. Feilchenfeld, N.B. and Waddell, W.H. (1983). *Chem. Phys. Lett.* **98**, 190

36. Chapman, O.L. and LeRoux, J.-P. (1978). *J. Am. Chem. Soc.* **100**, 282

37. Hayes, J.C. and Sheridan, R.S. (1990). *J. Am. Chem. Soc.* **112**, 5879

38. Shields, C.J., Chrisope, D.R., Schuster, G.B., Dixon, A.J., Popiakoff, M. and Turner, J.J. (1987). *J. Am. Chem. Soc.* **109**, 4723

39. Li, Y.-Z., Kirby, J.P., George, M.W., Poliakoff, M. and Schuster, G.B. (1988). *J. Am. Chem. Soc.* **110**, 8092

40. Wentrup, C. and Crow, W.D. (1970). *Tetrahedron* **26**, 3965,

41. Wentrup, C. and Crow, W.D. (1970). *Tetrahedron* **26**, 4375

42. Karney, W.L. and Borden, W.T. (1997). *J. Am. Chem. Soc.* **119**, 1378

43. Marcinek, A., Leyva, E., Whitt, D. and Platz, M.S. (1993). *J. Amer. Chem. Soc.* **115**, 8609

44. Gritsan, N.P., Yuzawa, T. and Platz, M.S. (1997). *J. Am. Chem. Soc.* **119**, 5059

45. Born, R., Burda, C., Senn, P. and Wirz, J. (1997). *J. Am. Chem. Soc.* **119**, 5061

46. Gritsan, N.P., Zhu, Z., Hadad, C.M. and Platz, M.S. (1999). *J. Am. Chem. Soc.* **121**, 1202

47. Kim, S.-J.I., Hamilton, T.P., Schaefer, H.F., III. (1992). *J. Am. Chem. Soc.* **114**, 5349

48. Hrovat, D., Waali, E.E. and Borden, W.T. (1992). *J. Am. Chem. Soc.* **114**, 8698

49. Travers, M.J., Cowles, D.C., Clifford, E.P. and Ellison, G.B. (1992). *J. Am. Chem. Soc.* **114**, 8699

50. Cramer, C.J. and Dulles, F.J.J. (1994). *J. Am. Chem. Soc.* **116**, 9787

51. Matzinger, S., Bally, T., Patterson, E.V. and McMahon, R.J. (1996). *J. Am. Chem. Soc.* **118**, 1535

52. Schreiner, P., Karney, W., Schleyer, P.v.R., Borden, W.T., Hamilton, T. and Schaeffer, H.F., III (1996). *J. Org. Chem.* **61**, 7030

53. Wong, M.W. and Wentrup, C. (1996). *J. Org. Chem.* **61**, 7022

54. Admasu, A., Gudmundsdottir, A.D. and Platz, M.S. (1997). *J. Phys. Chem. A* **101**, 3832

55. Huggenberger, C. and Fischer, H. (1981). *Helv. Chim. Acta* **64**, 338

56. Porter, G. and Wright, F.J. (1955). *Trans. Faraday Soc.* **51**, 1469

57. Land, E.J. and Porter, G. (1963). *Trans. Faraday Soc.* **59**, 2027

58. Porter, G. and Ward. B. (1964). *J. Chim. Phys.*, 1517

59. Leyva, E., Platz, M.S., Niu, B. and Wirz, J. (1987). *J. Phys. Chem.* **91**, 2293

60. Fairchild, P.W., Smith, G.P., Crosly, D.R. and Jeffries, J.B. (1984). *Chem. Phys. Lett.* **107**, 181

61. Carrick, P.G and Engelking, P.C. (1984). *J. Chem. Phys.* **81**, 1661

62. Radziszewski, J.G., Downing, J.W., Wentrup, C., Kaszynski, P., Jawdosiuk, M., Kovacic, P. and Michl, J. (1985). *J. Am. Chem. Soc.* **107**, 2799

63. Gritsan, N.P., Likhotvorik, I., Zhu, Z. and Platz, M.S. (2001). *J. Phys. Chem.* **105**, 3039

64. Gritsan, N.P., Zhai, H.B., Yuzawa, T., Karweik, D., Brooke, J. and Platz, M.S. (1997) *J. Phys. Chem. A.* **101**, 2833

65(a). Sitzmann, E.V., Langen, J. and Eisenthal, K.B. (1984). *J. Am. Chem. Soc.* **106**, 1868

65(b). Grasse, P.B., Brauer, B.E., Zupancic, J.J., Kaufmann, K.J. and Schuster, G.B. (1983). *J. Am. Chem. Soc.* **105**, 6833

66. Michl, J. and Bonacic-Koutécky, V. (1990). *Electronic Aspects of Organic Photochemistry*. John Wiley, New York

67. Salem, L. and Rowland, C. (1972). *Angew. Chem. Int. Ed. Engl.* **11**, 92
68. Michl, J. (1996). *J. Am. Chem. Soc.* **118**, 3568
69. Kita, F., Nau, W.M., Adam, W. and Wirz, J. (1995). *J. Am. Chem. Soc.* **117**, 8670
70. Sumitani, M., Nagakura, S. and Yoshihara, K. (1976). *Bull. Chem. Soc. Japan* **49**, 2995
71. Kobayashi, T., Ohtani, N., Suzuki, K. and Yamaoka, T. (1985). *J. Phys. Chem.* **89**, 776
72. Miura, A. and Kobayashi, T. (1990). *J. Photochem. Photobiol. A* **53**, 223
73. James, T. (1998). *M.Sc. Thesis.* The Ohio State University
74. Gritsan, N.P., Tigelaar, D. and Platz, M.S. (1999). *J. Phys. Chem. A* **103**, 4465
75. Cerro-Lopez, M., Gritsan, N.P., Zhu, Z. and Platz, M.S. (2000). *J. Phys. Chem. A.* **104**, 9681
76. Gritsan, N.P., Likhotvorik, I., Tsao, M.-L., Çelebi, N., Platz, M.S., Karney, W.L., Kemnitz, C.R. and Borden, W.T. (2001). *J. Am. Chem. Soc.*, **123**, 1425
77. Gritsan, N.P., Gudmundsdóttir, A.D., Tigelaar, D. and Platz, M.S. (1999). *J. Phys. Chem. A.* **103**, 3458
78. Gritsan, N.P., Gudmundsdóttir, A.D., Tigelaar, D., Zhu, Z., Karney, W.L., Hadad C.M. and Platz, M.S. (2001). *J. Am. Chem. Soc.* **123**, 1951
79. Kozankiewicz, B., Deparasinska, I., Zhai, H.B., Zhu, Z. and Hadad, C.M. (1999). *J. Phys. Chem.* **103**, 5003
80. Poe, R., Grayzar, J., Young, M.J.T., Leyva, E., Schnapp, K.A. and Platz, M.S. (1991). *J. Am. Chem. Soc.* **113**, 3209
81. Younger, C.G. and Bell, R.A. (1992). *J. Chem. Soc., Chem. Commun.* 1359
82. Morawietz, J. and Sander, W. (1996). *J. Org. Chem.* **61**, 4351
83. Dunkin, I.R. and Thomson, P.C.P. (1980). *J. Chem. Soc., Chem. Commun.*. 499
84. Carroll, S.E., Nay, B. and Scriven, E.F.V. (1977). *Tetrahedron Lett.* 943
85. Rigaudy, J., Igier, C. and Barcelo, J. (1975). *Tetrahedron* 3845
86. Hilton, S.E., Scriven, I.F.V. and Suschitzky, H. (1974). *J. Chem. Soc., Chem. Commun.* 853
87. Leyva, E. and Platz, M.S. (1987). *Tetrahedron* **28**, 11
88. Sundberg, R.J., Suter, S.R. and Brenner, M. (1972). *J. Am. Chem. Soc.* **94**, 513
89. Karney, W.L. and Borden, W.T. (1997). *J. Am. Chem. Soc.* **119**, 3347
90. Lamara, K., Redhouse, A.D., Smalley, R.K. and Thompson, J.R. (1994). *Tetrahedron* **50**, 5515
91. Berwick, M.A. (1971). *J. Am. Chem. Soc.* **93**, 5780
92. Abramovitch, R.A., Challand, S.R. and Scriven, E.F.V. (1972). *J. Am. Chem. Soc.* **94**, 1374
93. Abramovitch, R.A., Challand, S.R. and Scriven, E.F.V. (1975). *J. Org. Chem.* **40**, 1541
94. Banks, R.E. and Sparkes, G.R. (1972). *J. Chem. Soc. Perkin Trans. 1* 1964
95. Banks, R.E. and Venayak, N.D. (1980). *J. Chem. Soc., Chem. Commun.* 900
96. Banks, R.E. and Prakash, A. (1973). *Tetrahedron Lett.* 99
97. Banks, R.E. and Prakash, A. (1974). *J. Chem. Soc. Perkin Trans. 1* 1365
98. Banks, R.E. and Madany, I.M. (1985). *J. Fluorine Chem.* **30**, 211
99. Crocker, P.J., Imai, N., Rajagopalan, K., Kwiatkowski, S., Dwyer, L.D., Vanaman, T.C. and Watt, D.C. (1990). *Bioconjugate* **1**, 419
100. Drake, R.R., Slama, J.T., Wall, K.A., Abramova, M., D'Souza, C., Elbein, A.D., Crocker, P.J. and Watt, D.S. (1992). *Bioconjugate Chem.* **3**, 69
101. Pinney, K.C. and Katzenellenbogen, J.A. (1991). *J. Org. Chem.* **56**, 3125
102. Pinney, K.C., Carlson, K.E., Katzenellenbogen, S.B. and Katzenellenbogen, J.A. (1991). *Biochemistry.* **30**, 2421

103. Reed, M.W., Fraga, D., Schwartz, D.E., Scholler, J. and Hinrichsen, R.D. (1995). *Bioconjugate Chem.* **6**, 101
104. Kapfer, I., Jacques, P., Toubal, H. and Goeldner, M.P. (1995). *Bioconjugate Chem.* **6**, 109
105. Kym, P.R., Carlson, K.E. and Katzenellenbogen, J.A. (1993). *J. Med. Chem.* **36**, 1993
106. Kapfer, I., Hawkinson, J.E., Casida, J.E. and Goeldner, M.P.J. (1994). *Med. Chem.* **37**, 133
107. Poe, R., Schnapp, K., Young, M.J.T., Grayzar, J. and Platz, M.S. (1992). *J. Am. Chem. Soc.* **114**, 5054
108. Young, M.J.T. and Platz M.S. (1991). *J. Org. Chem.* **56**, 6403
109. Schnapp, K. and Platz, M.S. (1993). *Bioconjugate Chem.* **4**, 178
110. Schnapp, K., Poe, R., Leyva, E., Soundararajan, N. and Platz, M.S. (1993). *Bioconjugate Chem.* **4**, 172
111. Leyva, E. and Sagredo, R. (1998). *Tetrahedron* **54**, 7367
112. Reed, A.E., Weinstock, R.B. and Weinhold, F.A. (1985). *J. Chem. Phys.* **83**, 733
113. Anderson, K. (1995). *Theor. Chim. Acta* **91**, 31
114. Sung, K. (1999). *J. Chem. Soc. Perkin Trans.* 2, 1169
115. Leyva, E., Young, M.J.T. and Platz, M.S. (1986). *J. Am. Chem. Soc.* **108**, 8307
116. Marcinek, A., Platz, M.S., Chan, S.Y., Floresca, S., Rajagopalan, K., Golinski, M. and Watt, D. (1994). *J. Phys. Chem.* **98**, 412.
117. Michalak, J., Zhai, H.B. and Platz, M.S. (1996). *J. Phys. Chem.* **100**, 14028
118. Polshakov, D.A., Tsentalovich, Y.P. and Gritsan, N.P. (2001). *Kinetics and Catalysis* (Russ.). To be published
119. Kimura, Y., Yamamoto, M., Tobita, S. and Shizuka, H. (1997). *J. Phys. Chem. A.* **101**, 459
120. McClelland, R.A., Davids, P.A. and Hadzialic, G. (1995). *J. Am. Chem. Soc.* **117**, 4173
121. McClelland, R.A., Kahley, M.J., Davids, P.A. and Hadzialic, G. (1996). *J. Am. Chem. Soc.* **118**, 4794
122. Ren, D. and McClelland, R.A. (1998). *Can. J. Chem.* **76**, 78
123. Polshakov, D.A., Tsentalovich, Y.P. and Gritsan, N.P. (2000). *Russ. Chem. Bull.* **49**, 50
124. Marcinek, A., Leyva, E., Whitt, O. and Platz, M.S. (1993). *J. Am. Chem. Soc.* **115**, 8609
125. Reed, A.E., Weinhold, F.A. and Curtiss, L.A. (1988). *Chem. Rev.* **88**, 899
126. Smalley, R.K. and Suschitzky, H. (1964). *J. Chem. Soc.* 5922
127. Smirnov, V.A. and Brichkin, S.B. (1982). *Chem. Phys. Lett.* **87**, 548

Author Index

Numbers in italic refer to the pages on which references are listed at the end of each chapter.

Cumulative Index of Authors

Sandström, J., **25**, I
Savéant, J.-M., **26**, 1; **35**, 117
Savelli, G., **22**, 213
Schaleger, L.L., **1**, 1
Scheraga, H.A., 6, **103,** 334
Schleyer, P, von R., **14**, 1
Schmidt, S.P., **18**, 187
Schuster, G.B., **18**, 187; **22**, 311
Scorrano, G., **13**, 83
Shatenshtein, A.I., **1**, 156
Shine, H.J., **13**, I55
Shinkai, S., **17**, 435
Siehl, H.-U., **23**, 63
Silver, B.L., **3**, 123
Simonyi, M., **9**, 127
Sinnott, M.L., **24**, 113
Stock, L.M., **1**, 35
Sugawara, T., **32**, 219
Sustmann, R., **26**, 131
Symons, M.C.R., **1**, 284
Takashima, K., **21**, 197

Takasu, I., **32**, 219
Takeuchi, K., **30**, 173
Ta-Shma, R., **27**, 239
Tedder, J.M., **16**, 51
Tee, O.S., **29**, 1
Thatcher, G.R.J., **25**, 99
Thomas, A., **8**, 1
Thomas, J.M., **15**, 63
Tidwell, T.T., **36**, 1
Tonellato, U., **9**, 185
Toteva, M.M., **35**, 67
Toullec, J., **18**, 1
Tsuji, Y., **35**, 67
Tsuno, Y., **32**, 267
Tüdös, F., **9**, 127
Turner, D.W., **4**, 31
Turro, N.J., **20**, 1
Ugi, I., **9**, 25
Walton, J.C., **16**, 51
Ward, B., **8**, 1
Watt, C.I.F., **24**, 57
Wayner, D.D.M., **36**, 85

Wentworth, P., **31**, 249
Westaway, K.C., **31**, 143
Westheimer, F.H., **21**, 1
Whalley, E., **2**, 93
Williams, A., **27**, 1
Williams, D.L.H., **19**, 381
Williams, J.M., Jr., **6**, 63
Williams, J.O., **16**, 159
Williams, K.B., **35**, 67
Williams, R.V., **29**, 273
Williamson, D.G., **1**, 365
Wilson, H., l4, 133
Wolf, A.P., **2**, 201
Wolff, J.J., **32,** 121
Workentin, M.S., **36**, 85
Wortmann, R., **32**, 121
Wyatt, P.A.H., **12**, l31
Zimmt, M.B., **20**, 1
Zollinger, H., **2**, 163
Zuman, P., **5**, 1

Cumulative Index of Titles